GCSE AQA
Maths

Higher Level

Complete Revision
and Practice

For the new GCSE Mathematics AQA B (Modular) Course starting September 2010

Contents

Contents

Published by CGP

From original material by Richard Parsons

Editors: Katie Braid, Katherine Craig, Ben Fletcher, Ali Palin, Julie Wakeling

Contributors:
Pamela Chatley, Jane Chow, Mike Clarke, Sally Gill, Adrian Hall, Rosie Hanson, Philippa Holden, Manpreet Sambhi, Janet West, Jeanette Whiteman

Proofreading by: Dawn Wright, Janet Dickinson

ISBN: 978 1 84762 542 7

Website: www.cgpbooks.co.uk
Printed by Elanders Ltd, Newcastle upon Tyne.
Clipart source: CorelDRAW®

Photocopying – it's dull, grey and sometimes a bit naughty. Luckily, it's dead cheap, easy and quick to order more copies of this book from CGP – just call us on 0870 750 1242. Phew!

Calculating Tips

Welcome to GCSE Maths — not always fun, but stuff you have to learn. AQA Modular Maths is split into three Units, each with its own exam. Thankfully there are some nifty exam tricks you only have to learn once, which could get you marks in all three exams. Read on...

BODMAS
<u>B</u>rackets, <u>O</u>ther, <u>D</u>ivision, <u>M</u>ultiplication, <u>A</u>ddition, <u>S</u>ubtraction

<u>BODMAS</u> tells you the <u>ORDER</u> in which these operations should be done:
Work out <u>Brackets</u> first, then <u>Other</u> things like squaring, then <u>Divide</u> / <u>Multiply</u> groups of numbers before <u>Adding</u> or <u>Subtracting</u> them.
This set of rules works really well, so remember the word BODMAS.

EXAMPLE: An unknown quantity, T, is given by: $T = (P - 7)^2 + 4R/Q$
Find the value of T when P = 4, Q = -2 and R = 3

Write down the formula:	$T = (P - 7)^2 + 4R/Q$	
Put the numbers in:	$T = (4 - 7)^2 + 4 \times 3 / \text{-}2$	<u>Note BODMAS in operation</u>:
Then work it out <u>in stages</u> :	$= (-3)^2 + 4 \times 3 / \text{-}2$	<u>Brackets</u> worked out first,
	$= 9 + 4 \times 3 / \text{-}2$	then <u>squared</u>.
	$= 9 + \text{-}6$	<u>Multiplications</u> and <u>divisions</u> done
	$= 9 - 6 = \underline{3}$	<u>before</u> finally <u>adding</u> and <u>subtracting</u>.

Don't Be Scared of **Wordy Questions**

About <u>a quarter</u> of the marks on your exam are for answering <u>wordy</u>, <u>real-life</u> questions. For these you don't just have to do <u>the maths</u>, you've got to work out what the question's <u>asking you to do</u>. <u>Relax</u> and work through them <u>step by step</u>.

1) <u>READ</u> the question <u>carefully</u>. Work out <u>what bit of maths</u> you need to answer it.

2) <u>Underline the INFORMATION YOU NEED</u> to answer the question
— you might not have to use <u>all</u> the numbers they give you.

3) Write out the question <u>IN MATHS</u> and answer it, showing all your <u>working</u> clearly.

EXAMPLE:

a) The table shows rates of <u>depreciation</u> over a three year period for three different motorbikes. Helen bought a B260 for <u>£6300</u> three years ago. How much is the motorbike worth now?

Model	Depreciation over 3 years
A125	37%
B260	45%
F400	42%

1) The word "<u>depreciation</u>" tells you this is a <u>percentages</u> question.
2) You need the initial value of <u>£6300</u> and the B260 depreciation of <u>45%</u>. ⇐ *The rest of the table is irrelevant.*
3) "Depreciation" is a <u>percentage decrease</u>, so in maths:
$$£6300 \times (1 - 0.45) = \underline{£3465}$$ ⇐ *Don't forget to include any <u>units</u>.*

Percentage questions are covered on pages 12-13.

Calculating Tips

So far so good. You've read the question carefully and know what you have to do to answer it. You've done all your calculations accurately using BODMAS. But before you write down your answer — make sure you're not throwing marks away...

*Make Sure You Know What Your Answer **Means***

It's taken 2 minutes of frenzied button pressing
and finally your calculator screen looks like this.

Before you merrily jot down 3.6 as your answer, think about <u>what it means</u> — 3.6 what?
Pipers piping? It sounds silly, but it can lose you easy marks in the exam.

E.g. if you're answering a <u>money</u> question, 3.6 won't get you any marks
— you really need to write <u>£3.60</u>.
If it was a <u>percentages</u> question, then you need to write <u>3.6%</u>.

Or you might get something like this:

Think about <u>what you typed in</u> to get the answer in the first place
— 5⌐8 is actually the fraction 5/8.

*Make Sure You **Include the Right Units***

This is probably pretty obvious, but it's an easy thing to forget in the exam so...

ALWAYS CHECK YOU'VE USED THE RIGHT UNITS

The question might already say what units the answer needs to be in, or you might
need to work it out for yourself. This isn't too difficult.

For example, if it's a question about <u>area</u>, and the measurements
are given in <u>cm</u>, then your answer will need to be given as <u>cm</u>^{2}.

Or, if it's a question about <u>volume</u>, and the measurements are
given in <u>m</u>, then your answer will need to be given as <u>m</u>^{3}.

Think about what your answer means before you write it down

This might all seem like really boring, obvious stuff, but you'd be amazed how many people forget about these little things in the exam. So read over this page again, just to make sure you've got it all clear in your head. And in the exam, when the pressure's on — don't forget to stop and think...

Calculating Tips

The last step is to make sure the answer you're giving is <u>accurate</u>.
If you've got time at the end of the exam, always go back and <u>check your answers</u>.

Don't Do Any **Rounding** *Until the* **End of the Calculation**

The first few pages of this book are all about <u>rounding</u>.
But before you get all giddy and start rounding left, right and centre, a word of warning. <u>Don't</u>.

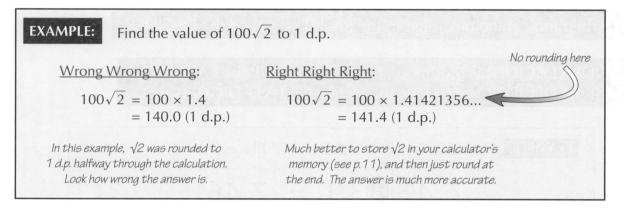

EXAMPLE: Find the value of $100\sqrt{2}$ to 1 d.p.

No rounding here

<u>Wrong Wrong Wrong</u>:

$100\sqrt{2} = 100 \times 1.4$
$= 140.0 \ (1 \ d.p.)$

*In this example, √2 was rounded to
1 d.p. halfway through the calculation.
Look how wrong the answer is.*

<u>Right Right Right</u>:

$100\sqrt{2} = 100 \times 1.41421356...$
$= 141.4 \ (1 \ d.p.)$

*Much better to store √2 in your calculator's
memory (see p.11), and then just round at
the end. The answer is much more accurate.*

If you're doing calculations with numbers that have <u>already been rounded</u> (e.g. measurements),
then all you can do is work out the maximum and minimum possible answers and know that the
real answer is somewhere in between (see p.6).

Always **Check** *Your Answer*

It's always a good idea to <u>check</u> your answers by working <u>backwards</u> through your calculations.
That way you can pick up any <u>silly mistakes</u> you might have made.

EXAMPLE: If $y = 2x^2 + 3$, find the value of y when x = 3.

<u>Answer</u>: $y = 2 \times (3)^2 + 3$
$= 2 \times 9 + 3$
$= 18 + 3$
$= \underline{21}$

<u>Check</u>: $21 - 3 = 18$
$18 \div 2 = 9$
$\sqrt{9} = 3$

*Perfect — you've got the same
number you started with.*

Algebra's covered on pages 64-70

An accurate answer is a good answer

Learn this stuff — it can really help you get marks whichever exam you're doing.
Now you've had the warm-up — on with the Maths...

Rounding Numbers

There are two different ways of specifying where a number should be rounded off.
They are: 'Decimal Places' and 'Significant Figures'.

Whichever way is used, the basic method is always the same and is shown below:

The Basic Method Has Three Steps

1) Identify the position of the LAST DIGIT.

2) Then look at the next digit to the RIGHT — called the DECIDER.

3) If the DECIDER is 5 or more, then ROUND-UP the LAST DIGIT.
   If the DECIDER is 4 or less, then leave the LAST DIGIT as it is.

EXAMPLE: "What is 7.45839 to 2 Decimal Places?"

$$7.45839 = 7.46$$

LAST DIGIT to be written
(2nd decimal place because
we're rounding to 2 d.p.)

DECIDER

The LAST DIGIT
rounds UP because the
DECIDER is 5 or more.

Decimal Places (D.P.)

This is pretty easy:

1) To round off to, say, 4 decimal places,
   the LAST DIGIT will be the 4th one after the decimal point.

2) There must be no more digits after the last digit (not even zeros).

EXAMPLE: Original number: 45.319461

Rounded to 5 decimal places (5 d.p.)	45.31946	(DECIDER was 1, so don't round up)
Rounded to 4 decimal places (4 d.p.)	45.3195	(DECIDER was 6, so do round up)
Rounded to 3 decimal places (3 d.p.)	45.319	(DECIDER was 4, so don't round up)
Rounded to 2 decimal places (2 d.p.)	45.32	(DECIDER was 9, so do round up)

You'll need to round off a lot of your answers in the exam

Rounding is a really important skill, and you'll be throwing easy marks away if you get it wrong.
Make sure you're completely happy with the basic method, then get plenty of practice.

Rounding Numbers

Obviously all numbers are significant, but when it comes to <u>rounding</u>,
some are more significant than others...

Significant Figures (S.F.)

The method for significant figures is <u>identical</u> to that for decimal places except that finding
the <u>position</u> of the <u>LAST DIGIT</u> is more difficult — <u>it wouldn't be so bad, but for the ZEROS</u>...

1) The <u>1st significant figure</u> of any number is
simply THE FIRST DIGIT WHICH ISN'T A ZERO.

2) The <u>2nd, 3rd, 4th, etc. significant figures</u> follow on immediately
after the 1st, REGARDLESS OF BEING ZEROS OR NOT ZEROS.

E.g.   0.002309   2.03070

<u>SIG FIGS</u>:   1st 2nd 3rd 4th   1st 2nd 3rd 4th
(If we're rounding to say, 3 s.f., then the LAST DIGIT is simply the 3rd sig. fig.)

3) After <u>Rounding Off</u> the LAST DIGIT, <u>end ZEROS</u> must be
filled in <u>up to, BUT NOT BEYOND, the decimal point</u>.

No <u>extra zeros</u> must ever be put in <u>after</u> the decimal point.

Examples	to 4 s.f.	to 3 s.f.	to 2 s.f.	to 1 s.f.
1) 54.7651	54.77	54.8	55	50
2) 17.0067	17.01	17.0	17	20
3) 0.0045902	0.004590	0.00459	0.0046	0.005
4) 30895.4	30900	30900	31000	30000

Appropriate Accuracy

To decide what is appropriate accuracy, you need only remember these <u>three rules</u>:

1) For fairly <u>CASUAL MEASUREMENTS</u>, <u>2 SIGNIFICANT FIGURES</u> is most appropriate.

E.g. <u>Cooking</u> — 250g (2 s.f.) of sugar, not 253g (3 s.f.), or 300g (1 s.f.)
<u>Distance</u> of a journey — 450 miles or 25 miles or 3500 miles (all 2 s.f.)
<u>Area</u> of a garden or floor — 330 m² or 15 m²

2) For more <u>IMPORTANT OR TECHNICAL THINGS</u>, <u>3 SIGNIFICANT FIGURES</u> is essential.

E.g. <u>A technical figure</u> like <u>34.2</u> miles per gallon, rather than 34 mpg
A length that is <u>cut to fit</u>, e.g. measure a shelf <u>25.6 cm</u> long not just 26 cm
Any <u>accurate</u> measurement with a ruler: <u>67.5 cm</u> not 70 cm or 67.54 cm

3) Only for <u>REALLY SCIENTIFIC WORK</u> would you have <u>more than 3 SIG FIG</u>.

Calculation Bounds

You need to be able to answer questions about <u>maximum</u> and <u>minimum</u> possible values for a given level of <u>accuracy</u>.

Upper and Lower Bounds of a Measurement

The simple rule is this: | The real value can be as much as HALF THE ROUNDED UNIT above and below the rounded-off value.

E.g. If a length is given as 2.4 m to the nearest 0.1 m, the rounded unit is 0.1 m so the real value could be anything up to <u>2.4 m ± 0.05 m</u> giving answers of <u>2.45 m and 2.35 m</u> for the <u>upper and lower bounds</u>.

Maximum and Minimum Values for Calculations

When a calculation is done using rounded-off values there will be a <u>DISCREPANCY</u> between the <u>CALCULATED VALUE</u> and the <u>ACTUAL VALUE</u>:

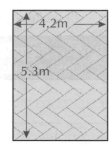

<u>EXAMPLE 1</u>: A floor is measured as being 5.3 m × 4.2 m to the nearest 10 cm. This gives an area of <u>22.26 m²</u>, but this is not the actual floor area because the real values could be anything from <u>5.25 m to 5.35 m</u> and <u>4.15 m to 4.25 m</u>,

∴ Maximum possible floor area = 5.35 × 4.25 = <u>22.7375 m²</u>,

∴ Minimum possible floor area = 5.25 × 4.15 = <u>21.7875 m²</u>.

<u>EXAMPLE 2</u>: A length, m, is given by the formula: $m = \dfrac{A}{h} - n$
A, h and n are measured to 2 d.p. as follows:
A = 50.13 m², h = 12.12 m, n = 3.46 m. Find the max. and min. possible values of m.

First of all, work out the <u>range of possible values</u> for each measurement:

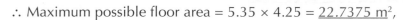

> – <u>A</u> could be anything from <u>50.125 to 50.135</u>.
> – <u>h</u> could be anything from <u>12.115 to 12.125</u>.
> – <u>n</u> could be anything from <u>3.455 to 3.465</u>.

Now you've got to work out which value of A, h and n to use. This is the <u>tricky bit</u>. Look at the <u>formula</u> and think what would happen to m as A, h or n gets bigger. You should be able to see that for a <u>maximum value of m</u> you need <u>A to be as big as possible</u>, but <u>h and n</u> to be as <u>small as possible</u>. And for the <u>minimum value of m</u>, you obviously need the exact opposite.

So...   Maximum possible value of m = 50.135 / 12.115 – 3.455 = 0.683 m (3 d.p.)

Minimum possible value of m = 50.125 / 12.125 – 3.465 = 0.669 m (3 d.p.)

This is all about how accurate your measurements are

It's all very well being able to round off your measurements, but you also need to know how accurate those rounded measurements are. There are two methods to learn — working out upper and lower bounds of a single measurement and working out maximum and minimum values of calculations.

Standard Index Form

Standard form (or 'standard index form') is only really useful for writing <u>VERY BIG</u> or <u>VERY SMALL</u> numbers in a more convenient way, e.g.

$56\,000\,000\,000$ would be 5.6×10^{10} in standard form.

$0.000\,000\,00\overline{3}\,45$ would be 3.45×10^{-9} in standard form.

But <u>ANY NUMBER</u> can be written in standard form and you need to know how to do it:

What it *Actually* *is*:

A number written in standard form must <u>ALWAYS</u> be in <u>EXACTLY</u> this form:

$$A \times 10^n$$

This <u>number</u> must <u>always</u> be <u>BETWEEN 1 AND 10</u>.
(The fancy way of saying this is: $1 \leq A < 10$ — they sometimes write that in exam questions. Don't let it put you off, just remember what it means.)

This number is just the <u>NUMBER OF PLACES</u> the <u>Decimal Point</u> moves.

Learn The Three Rules:

1) The <u>front number</u> must always be <u>BETWEEN 1 AND 10</u>.
2) The power of 10, n, is purely: <u>HOW FAR THE D.P. MOVES</u>.
3) n is <u>+ve</u> for BIG numbers, n is <u>−ve</u> for SMALL numbers.

(This is much better than rules based on which way the D.P. moves.)

Two Very Simple *Examples*:

You'd do well to learn this properly now. Standard form could rear its ugly head again on the Unit 2 exam, when you aren't armed with a calculator. And you wouldn't want to be unprepared would you?

1) "Express $35\,600$ in standard form."

METHOD:
1) Move the D.P. until $35\,600$ becomes 3.56 ('$1 \leq A < 10$')
2) The D.P. has moved 4 places so n = 4, giving: 10^4
3) $35\,600$ is a BIG number so n is +4, not −4

ANSWER:
3.5 6 0 0
$= 3.56 \times 10^4$

2) "Express 0.0000623 in standard form."

METHOD:
1) The D.P. must move <u>5 places to give 6.23</u> ('$1 \leq A < 10$')
2) So the power of 10 is 5
3) Since 0.0000623 is a <u>SMALL NUMBER</u> it must be 10^{-5} not 10^{+5}

ANSWER:
0.0 0 0 0 6 2 3
$= 6.23 \times 10^{-5}$

Remember, n tells you how far the decimal point moves

Standard form is just a way of writing down very big and small numbers without writing long rows of zeros. But in order to use it you have to learn the three rules or you'll be in a big mess.

Standard Index Form

Three *Very Important* Examples:

1) The Calculator's **Scientific Mode**

1) This mode <u>gives all numbers in standard form</u> to a specified number of significant figures.
2) A little SCI will be displayed somewhere when you're in this mode.
3) To get into this mode, press **MODE** and select SCI from one of the menus you get.
   (On other calculators look for a button with 'SCI' written above it as the 2nd or 3rd function.)

It'll ask you for the number of significant figures to display, something like this: `SCI 0-9?`

So if you choose 4, all numbers and answers will be displayed to 4 significant figures.

> <u>EXAMPLE</u>: $565 \div 3$ would give `188.3333333` in normal mode,
>
> ...or `1.883` ^{02} in 4 sig fig mode.

2) What is 146.3 Million in **Standard Form**?

The two favourite <u>wrong answers</u> for this are:

1) 146.3×10^6 — which is kind of right but it's not in <u>STANDARD FORM</u> because 146.3 is not between 1 and 10 (i.e. $1 \leq A < 10$ has not been done).

2) 1.463×10^6 — this one <u>is</u> in standard form but it's not big enough.

This is a very typical exam question, which <u>too many people get wrong</u>.
Just <u>take your time</u> and <u>do it IN TWO STAGES</u> like this:
<u>ANSWER</u>: 146.3 million = 146 300 000 = <u>1.463×10^8</u>

3) Remember, 10^5 **means** 1×10^5

So to enter 10^5 into the calculator you must remember it's actually 1×10^5 and press **1** **EXP** **5**

> <u>EXAMPLE</u>: "A nanometre is 10^{-9} m. How many nanometres are there in 0.35 m?"
> ANSWER: $0.35 \div (1 \times 10^{-9})$, so press **0.35** **÷** **1** **EXP** **(−)** **9** **=** = <u>3.5×10^8</u>.

Three top tips here for some easy marks

Practise entering and displaying numbers in standard form on your calculator. Notice in the middle section of this page there's a typical mistake made by people in the exam — so don't be one of them.

Warm-up and Worked Exam Questions

Without a good warm-up you're likely to strain a brain cell or two. So take the time to run through these simple questions and get the basic facts straight before plunging into the exam questions.

Warm-Up Questions

1) Round these numbers to the level of accuracy indicated:
   a) 40.218 to 2 d.p.   b) 39.888 to 3 sig. fig.   c) 27.91 to 2 sig. fig.
2) The moon is 250 000 miles away from Earth. Write this number in standard form.
3) The half-life of a chemical isotope is 0.0000027 seconds. Write this number in standard form.
4) An oxygen atom has a mass of 2.7×10^{-23} g. Write this as an ordinary number.
5) Work out $4 \times 10^3 \times 30\,000$, giving your answer in standard form.

Worked Exam Questions

With the answers written in, it's very easy to skim these worked examples and think you've understood. But that's not going to help you, so take the time to make sure you've really understood them.

1   A rug measures 1.5 m by 0.8 m (both measurements to the nearest 0.1 m).
    Calculate the upper and lower bounds of the rug's:

   (a) length .... *Upper bound = 1.55 m;*

   lower bound = 1.45 m.

   (b) width .... *Upper bound = 0.85 m;*

   lower bound = 0.75 m.

   (c) perimeter .... *Upper bound = 2 × (1.55 + 0.85) = 4.8 m;*   *perimeter of a rectangle*

   = 2 × (length + width)

   lower bound = 2 × (1.45 + 0.75) = 4.4 m.

   (6 marks)

2   The Sun is about 0.000016 light years from Earth.
    A light year, the distance travelled by light in one year = 9.46×10^{15} m.

   (a) How far is the Sun from the Earth in metres?
       Give your answer in standard form to 2 significant figures.

   $0.000016 \times 9.46 \times 10^{15} = 1.5136 \times 10^{11} = 1.5 \times 10^{11}$ m (2 s.f.)

   (2 marks)

   (b) Express the answer to (a) in km. Give your answer in standard form.

   To change metres into km divide by 1000

   1.5×10^{11} m ÷ 1000 = 150 000 000 km = 1.5×10^8 km

   (1 mark)

   If you get a question on standard form on your Unit 2 paper, you'll need to multiply or
   divide the number parts first, then the powers of 10 using the power rules on page 50.

Exam Questions

Some of these questions would have lots more space for answers in the real exam.
We've just squeezed them in here so you get more practice.

3   Ethan is buying carpet for a rectangular room.
The room is 4.1 m long and 3.6 m wide, each measured to the nearest 10 cm. How much carpet
(in full square metres) must Ethan buy to be sure he has enough for the room?

....

(2 marks)

4   If $a = 8$ and $b = 5$ (both rounded to the nearest whole number),
calculate the minimum value of:
(a) $a + b$

....

(2 marks)

(b) $a \div b$

....

(2 marks)

5   A cube measures 60 mm along each side, correct to the nearest millimetre.
Calculate the upper and lower bounds of the cube's volume.

....

(3 marks)

6   There is, on average, around 6 litres of blood in an adult man's body.
1 cubic millimetre of blood contains approximately 5×10^6 red blood cells.

(a)   Calculate how many red blood cells there are in an adult man's body.
Give your answer in standard form.
(1 litre = 1000 cubic cm, 1 cubic cm = 1000 cubic mm)

....

(2 marks)

(b)   Around $\frac{1}{120}$ of the total number of red blood cells are replaced every day.
How many is this in an adult man?
Give your answer in standard form.

....

(2 marks)

7   The Caspian Sea in Asia covers an area of 3.71×10^{11} m^2.
The Aral Sea in Asia covers 1.7×10^{10} m^2.

What is the total area covered by the two seas? Give your answer in standard form.

....

(2 marks)

Calculator Buttons

You can use a calculator for the Unit 1 and Unit 3 exams, so make sure you know how it can help you.

BODMAS and the Brackets Buttons (and)

1) This is really important when you want to work out even a simple thing like $\frac{23 + 45}{64 \times 3}$.

2) You can't just press `23` `+` `45` `÷` `64` `×` `3` `=` — it will be <u>completely wrong</u>.

3) The calculator follows BODMAS, so it'll think you mean $23 + \frac{45}{64} \times 3$. *For more on BODMAS, see p.1.*

4) The secret is to <u>OVERRIDE</u> the automatic <u>BODMAS</u> order of operations using the <u>BRACKETS BUTTONS</u>. Anything in brackets is worked out before anything else happens to it.

5) So all you have to do is write a couple of <u>pairs of brackets</u> into the expression like this: $\frac{(23 + 45)}{(64 \times 3)}$

6) Then just type it <u>as it's written</u>: `(` `23` `+` `45` `)` `÷` `(` `64` `×` `3` `)` `=`

It's OK to have brackets within other brackets too, <u>e.g. (4 + (5÷2))</u>. As a rule, you can't cause trouble by putting too many brackets in... <u>SO LONG AS THEY ALWAYS GO IN PAIRS</u>.

The Fraction Button: a^b_c

Use this <u>as much as possible</u>. It's very easy and really useful.

Some calculators might work differently. The important thing is to know how to do calculations with fractions on your calculator.

1) To enter $\frac{1}{4}$ press `1` `a^b_c` `4`

2) To enter $1\frac{3}{5}$ press `1` `a^b_c` `3` `a^b_c` `5`

3) To work out $\frac{1}{5} \times \frac{3}{4}$ press `1` `a^b_c` `5` `×` `3` `a^b_c` `4` `=`

Use this method to find a fraction of something. E.g. to find 2/3 of 8, just do the calculation 2/3 × 8. Simple.

4) To <u>reduce a fraction to its lowest terms</u> enter it and press `=`.
   E.g. $\frac{9}{12}$ — `9` `a^b_c` `12` `=` `3⌐4` $= \frac{3}{4}$

5) To convert between <u>mixed</u> and <u>top-heavy</u> fractions press `SHIFT` `a^b_c`.
   E.g. $2\frac{3}{8}$ — `2` `a^b_c` `3` `a^b_c` `8` `=` `SHIFT` `a^b_c` which gives $\frac{19}{8}$

The Memory Buttons (STO Store, RCL Recall)

These are really useful for keeping a number you've just calculated, so you can use it again afterwards.

E.g. Find $\frac{840}{15 + 12\sin40}$ — just work out the <u>bottom line</u> first and <u>stick it in the memory</u>.

So press `15` `+` `12` `SIN` `40` `=` and then `STO` `M` to keep the result of the bottom line in the memory.

The memory buttons might work a bit differently on your calculator. Note, if your calculator has an 'Ans' button, you can do the same thing — the Ans button gives you the result you got when you last pressed the '=' button.

Then you simply press `840` `÷` `RCL` `M` `=`, and the answer is <u>36.98</u>.

Percentages

You shouldn't have any trouble with most percentage questions, especially types 1 and 2.
Watch out for <u>type 3</u> questions and make sure you know the <u>proper method</u> for them.

Type 1

"Find x% of y" — e.g. Find 15% of £46 $\Rightarrow$ 0.15 × 46 = <u>£6.90</u>

You need to know how to convert between percentages, decimals and fractions — see page 58.

Type 2

"Express x as a percentage of y"
e.g. Give 40p as a percentage of £3.34 $\Rightarrow$ (40 ÷ 334) × 100 = <u>12%</u>

Type 3

— IDENTIFIED BY <u>NOT</u> GIVING THE "<u>ORIGINAL VALUE</u>"

These are the type most people get wrong — but only because they don't
recognise them as a type 3 and don't apply this simple method:

EXAMPLE:

A house increases in value by 20% to £72 000.
Find what it was worth <u>before</u> the rise.

METHOD:

$$\div 120 \begin{cases} £72\,000 &= 120\% \\ £600 &= 1\% \\ £60\,000 &= 100\% \end{cases} \times 100$$

So the original price was <u>**£60 000**</u>

An <u>INCREASE</u> of 20% means
that £72 000 represents <u>120%
of the original</u> value. If it was
a DROP of 20%, then we
would put '£72 000 = <u>80%</u>'
instead, and then divide by 80
on the LHS, instead of 120.

Always set them out <u>exactly like this example</u>. The trickiest bit is deciding the
top % figure on the RHS — the 2nd and 3rd rows are <u>always</u> 1% and 100%.

Percentage *Change*

It is common to give a <u>change in value</u> as a <u>percentage</u>.
This is the formula for doing so — <u>LEARN IT, AND USE IT</u>:

$$\text{PERCENTAGE 'CHANGE'} = \frac{\text{'CHANGE'}}{\text{ORIGINAL}} \times 100$$

By 'change', we could mean all sorts of things such as: 'profit', 'loss', 'appreciation',
'depreciation', 'increase', 'decrease', 'error', 'discount', etc. For example,

$$\text{percentage 'profit'} = \frac{\text{'profit'}}{\text{original}} \times 100$$

Note the great importance of using the
<u>ORIGINAL VALUE</u> in this formula.

Percentages are one of the most useful things you'll ever learn

Whenever you open a newspaper, see an advert, watch TV or do a maths exam paper you will see
percentages. So it's really important you get confident with using them — so practise.

Compound Growth and Decay

Compound growth is really useful for working out how much interest you'll get in your savings account.
Compound decay is kind of the opposite of that — and very useful for various science calculations.
This can also be called 'exponential' growth or decay (as the 'power number' is called the 'exponent').

The *Formula*

This topic is simple if you <u>LEARN THIS FORMULA</u>. If you don't, it's pretty well impossible:

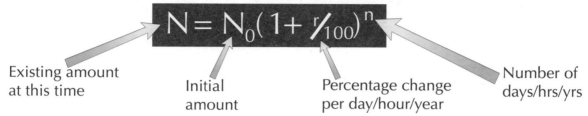

$$N = N_0\left(1 + \frac{r}{100}\right)^n$$

Existing amount
at this time

Initial
amount

Percentage change
per day/hour/year

Number of
days/hrs/yrs

Exam questions are often about money — where the compound growth is <u>interest</u> earned each year,
and the compound decay is <u>depreciation</u> in value each year. They are answered using the same formula.

Percentage *Increase* and *Decrease*

The $(1 + r/100)$ bit might look a bit confusing in the formula but in practice it's really easy:
E.g.   5% increase will be 1.05   5% decrease will be 0.95 $(= 1 - 0.05)$
       26% increase will be 1.26   26% decrease will be 0.74 $(= 1 - 0.26)$

3 Examples to show you how *Easy* it is:

1) "A man invests £1000 in a savings account which pays 8% per annum.
    How much will there be after 6 years?"

    <u>ANSWER:</u> Usual formula: Amount $= 1000(1.08)^6 = $ <u>£1586.87</u>

    Initial amount   8% increase   6 years

2) "The activity of a radioisotope falls by 12% every hour.
    If the initial activity is 800 counts per minute, what will it be after 7 hours?"

    <u>ANSWER:</u> Same old formula:
           Activity = Initial value$(1 - 12/100)^n$
           Activity $= 800(1 - 0.12)^7 = 800 \times (0.88)^7 = $ <u>327 cpm</u>

3) "In a sample of bacteria, there are initially 500 cells and they increase in number by 15% each day.
    Find the formula relating the number of cells, n, and the number of days, d."

    <u>ANSWER:</u> It's the same old easy-peasy compound growth formula <u>again</u>:
           $n = n_0(1 + 0.15)^d$ or finished off: <u>$n = 500 \times (1.15)^d$</u>

Compound growth and decay — percentages applied again and again

What this method does is to get the original value, change it by the percentage, then change that
amount by the percentage, then take that amount and change it by the percentage, then... get it?

Ratios

RATIOS get a lot easier when you do this:

| Turn RATIOS into FRACTIONS |

What the **Fraction** Form of the Ratio **Actually Means**

1) Suppose in a class there are <u>girls and boys</u> in the ratio **3 : 4**.
   This means there's $\frac{3}{4}$ as many girls as boys.

2) So if there were 20 boys, there would be $\frac{3}{4} \times 20 = 15$ girls.
   You've got to be careful though — it <u>doesn't mean</u> $\frac{3}{4}$ of the <u>people</u> in the class are girls.
   In fact, <u>three sevenths</u> of the class are girls.

*Have a look at page 60 on fractions —
you need to know how to cancel down fractions
and find fractions of numbers in Unit 1.*

Reducing **Ratios** to their **Simplest Form**

You reduce ratios just like you'd reduce fractions to their simplest form.

For the ratio 15 : 18, both numbers have a <u>factor</u> of 3, so <u>divide them by 3</u> — that gives 5 : 6. We can't reduce this any further. So the simplest form of 15 : 18 is <u>5 : 6</u>.

Treat them just like **fractions** — use your **calculator** if you can

Now this is really sneaky. If you stick in a fraction using the a^b_c button, your calculator automatically cancels it down when you press $=$.

So for the ratio 8 : 12, just press 8 a^b_c 12 $=$, and you'll get the reduced fraction $\frac{2}{3}$.
Now you just change it back to ratio form i.e. <u>2 : 3</u>.

The More **Awkward Cases**:

1) The a^b_c button will **only** accept **whole numbers**

So if the ratio is something like '2.4 : 3.6' or '1¼ : 3½' then you must...

| MULTIPLY BOTH SIDES by the SAME NUMBER until they are both WHOLE NUMBERS. |

E.g. for '1¼ : 3½', multiplying both sides by 4 gives '<u>5 : 14</u>' (Try a^b_c, but it won't cancel further.)

2) If the ratio is **mixed units**

| CONVERT BOTH SIDES into the SMALLER UNITS using the relevant CONVERSION FACTOR (p.170). |

E.g. '<u>24 mm : 7.2 cm</u>' (× 7.2 cm by 10) ⇒ 24 mm : 72 mm = <u>1 : 3</u> (using a^b_c)

3) To **reduce a ratio** to the form **1 : n** or **n : 1** (n can be any number)

| Simply DIVIDE BOTH SIDES BY THE SMALLEST SIDE. |

*This form is often the
<u>most useful</u>, since it shows
the ratio very clearly.*

E.g. take "<u>3 : 56</u>" — dividing both sides by 3 gives: <u>1 : 18.7</u> (56÷3) (i.e. 1 : n)

Ratios

There are lots of exam questions which at first sight seem completely different but in fact they can all be done using the GOLDEN RULE...

DIVIDE FOR ONE, THEN TIMES FOR ALL

Example:

"5 pints of milk cost £1.30. How much will 3 pints cost?"

The GOLDEN RULE says: **DIVIDE FOR ONE, THEN TIMES FOR ALL**

which means: Divide the price by 5 to find how much FOR ONE PINT, then multiply by 3 to find how much FOR THREE PINTS.

So... £1.30 ÷ 5 = 0.26 = <u>26p</u> (for 1 pint)
×3 = <u>78p</u> (for 3 pints)

The Best Buy — Learn a second Golden Rule

A favourite type of question they like to ask you in exams is comparing the 'value for money' of 2 or 3 similar items. Always follow the second GOLDEN RULE...

Divide by the PRICE in pence (to get the amount per penny)

Example:

The local 'Supplies 'n' Vittals' stocks three sizes of Jamaican Gooseberry Jam.

The question is: Which of these represents 'THE BEST VALUE FOR MONEY'?

500 g at £1.08   350 g at 80p   100 g at 42p

ANSWER: The GOLDEN RULE says:

DIVIDE BY THE PRICE IN PENCE TO GET THE AMOUNT PER PENNY

500 g ÷ 108p = <u>4.6 g PER PENNY</u>
350 g ÷ 80p = <u>4.4 g PER PENNY</u>
100 g ÷ 42p = <u>2.4 g PER PENNY</u>

So you can now see straight away that the 500 g jar is the best value for money because you get MORE JAM PER PENNY. (As you might guess, it being the big jar.)

With any question comparing 'value for money', DIVIDE BY THE PRICE (in pence) and it will always be the BIGGEST ANSWER is the BEST VALUE FOR MONEY.

Ratios — you're always trying to find the amount per part

For any question on ratio, you should immediately look for what you can divide by to get an amount per part. The 'part' depends on the question — for best buys, 1 part is usually 1 penny.

Warm-up and Worked Exam Questions

Warm-up questions first, then some worked examples — then you're on your own.
So make the most of this page by working through everything carefully.

Warm-Up Questions

1) Find 15% of £90.

2) What is 37 out of 50 as a percentage?

3) £3000 is invested at 3% compound interest (per year).
   Find the total investment at the end of 4 years.

4) Write these ratios in their simplest forms:
   a) 4 : 8   b) 1.2 : 5.4   c) 0.5 litres : 400 ml

5) A recipe uses flour and sugar in the ratio 3 : 2.
   How much flour do you need if you're using 300 g of sugar?

Worked Exam Questions

I've gone through these worked examples and written in answers just like you'll do in the exam.
It should really help with the questions which follow, so don't say I never do anything for you.

1   A pumpkin weighed 0.86 kg on June 1st, and 0.98 kg on June 15th.
    Calculate the percentage increase in weight over this time.

    0.98 − 0.86 = 0.12 kg increase

    (0.12 ÷ 0.86) × 100 = 13.95%

    (2 marks)

2   A TV has a label on it saying "Reduced by 15%. Now £340." What was its original price?

    Price now is 100% − 15% = 85% of the original price.

    1% of original price = £340 ÷ 85 = £4, so original price = £4 × 100 = £400

    (1 mark)

3   A motorbike depreciates in value by 5% every year. If the bike was bought for £1600,
    how much is it worth at the end of 3 years?

    5% decrease per year

    So worth after 3 years = £1600 × $\left(1 - \dfrac{5}{100}\right)^3$

    = 1600 × (0.95)^3

    = 1371.8 = £1371.80

    (3 marks)

Exam Questions

4 Alexander's gross salary is £2200 before deductions. He has worked out that 35% of his salary is deducted from his gross pay. How much is Alexander's take-home pay each month?

....

(2 marks)

5 Susan bought a camera for £95 and sold it a year later for £57.
What was her percentage loss?

....

(2 marks)

6 A hi-fi system costs £329, which includes VAT at 17.5%.
How much is the system worth before VAT is added?

....

(3 marks)

7 I invest £5000 in an account that pays 4% (compound) interest every year.
I leave the interest earned at the end of each year in the account to accumulate.
How much interest would I have earned at the end of 4 years?

....

(3 marks)

8 A car depreciates over the first five years at a regular rate of 8% each year.
The car was bought for £12 500. How much is it worth after 5 years?

....

(3 marks)

9 Carolyn opens a savings account with £6000. It pays 3.8% interest per year.
How many years will it take for her investment to be more than £7000?

....

(3 marks)

10 A cake recipe for 4 people uses 400 g of flour and 2 eggs.
How much flour and how many eggs are needed to make enough cake for 6 people?

....

(1 mark)

11 A supermarket sells 800 ml juice cartons.
It sells them in multi-packs of 4, costing £6.88, and in multi-packs of 6, which cost £9.90.
Which size of multi-pack is better value?

....

(3 marks)

Revision Summary for Unit 1 — 1

I know these questions seem difficult, but they are the very best revision you can do. The whole point of revision, remember, is to find out what you don't know and then learn it until you do. These searching questions test how much you know better than anything else ever can.

Keep learning the basic facts until you know them

1) What are the three steps for rounding off?

2) What are the three extra details concerning significant figure rounding?

3) Give three rules for deciding on appropriate accuracy.

4)* Jenny and two of her friends went out for dinner. The bill came to £51.98 and they decided to split it equally. How much, to two decimal places, should each of them pay?

5) How do you determine the upper and lower bounds of a rounded measurement?

6) How do you find the maximum and minimum possible values of a calculation?

7) What is the format of any number expressed in standard form?

8) What is scientific mode? Can you get in and out of it easily on your calculator?

9)* Anja is filling in some forms to show how much beer has been made at her brewery. The numbers must be entered in standard index form. Write Anja's numbers in standard form:
a) 970 000 cans   b) 6 830 000 bottles   c) 3 560 000 000 pints

10)* Paul needs to set his machine to cut metal sheeting to a thickness of 2.75×10^{-6} m. The machine won't accept standard index form. What number should Paul type in?

11) Use your calculator to reduce $\frac{12}{15}$ to its simplest form.

12) Give a good example of when the brackets buttons on your calculator should be used.

13) Give an example of when the memory buttons on your calculator should be used.

14) Do your own example to illustrate each of the three types of percentage question.

15)* Martin is trying to sell his car. He paid £5300 for it two years ago and is advised to sell it for 30% less than this original value. What price should he sell the car for?

16)* A DVD player costs £50 plus VAT. If VAT is 17.5%, how much does the DVD player cost.

17)* Carl has £35 to spend. He wants to use a 20%-off voucher to buy a top that should cost £45. Can he afford the top?

18)* Tim opens a savings account that pays 7% compound interest per annum. He puts £100 into the account. How much will he have after 5 years?

19)* Last week Rick ordered 5 pints of milk from the milkman. His bill was £2.35. This week he orders 3 pints of milk. How much will this week's bill be?

20)* Charley loves ham. Two different sized tins of Froggatt's Ham are on sale in his local shop. A 100 g tin costs 24p and a 250 g tin costs 52p. Which one is the 'Best Buy' for Charley?

* The answers to these questions can be found on page 218.

Collecting Data

Your data might be <u>quantitative</u> or <u>qualitative</u>...

Data can be *Quantitative* or *Qualitative*

QUANTITATIVE DATA measures <u>quantities</u>.	1) <u>Quantitative data</u> is anything that you can measure with a <u>number</u>.
	2) For example, <u>heights</u> of people, the <u>time taken</u> to complete a task or the <u>mass</u> of things.
	3) Quantitative data tends to be <u>easier to analyse</u> than qualitative data.

QUALITATIVE DATA is <u>descriptive</u>.	1) <u>Qualitative data</u> is data that uses <u>words</u> to <u>describe it</u> — it doesn't use any numbers.
	2) For example, <u>gender</u>, eye <u>colour</u> or <u>how nice</u> a curry is.
	3) This sort of data is usually <u>harder to analyse</u> than quantitative data.

Quantitative Data is Either *Discrete* or *Continuous*

DISCRETE DATA is data that can be recorded <u>exactly</u>.

1) If your data is something that's <u>countable</u> in whole numbers or can only take certain <u>individual values</u>, it's called <u>discrete data</u>.

2) Things like the <u>number of points</u> scored in a game, the <u>number of people</u> going into a shop on a Saturday and the <u>number of pages</u> in this revision guide are all examples of discrete data.

CONTINUOUS DATA is data that can take <u>any value</u> in an interval.

1) If your data is something that could <u>always</u> be <u>more accurately measured</u>, it's continuous data.

2) The <u>height</u> of <u>this page</u> is an example of continuous data. The height is 297 mm to the nearest mm, but you'd get a <u>more accurate</u> height if you measured to the nearest 0.1 mm or 0.01 mm or 0.001 mm or 0.0001 mm, etc... The actual height could take <u>any value</u> in the interval 296.5 mm to 297.5 mm.

3) Other things like the <u>weight</u> of a pumpkin, the <u>age</u> of a chicken and the <u>length</u> of a carrot are continuous data.

You can Split your Data into *Classes*

1) If you're collecting <u>lots of data</u>, or your data's <u>spread out</u> over a large range, you can make it more manageable by <u>grouping it</u> into different <u>classes</u>.

2) When you do this, it's important that you <u>define the classes well</u> so <u>none of them overlap</u> — this means that each bit of data can <u>only</u> be put into <u>one class</u>.

Age in completed years	0 – 19	20 – 39	40 – 59	60 – 79	80 – 99
Number of people	6	13	14	8	9

3) The <u>problem</u> with grouping data is that you <u>lose</u> some of the <u>accuracy</u> of it because you don't know what the <u>exact data values</u> are any more.

Qualitative — descriptive. Quantitative — numbers.

Nothing too complicated here, just a few more definitions to learn. Turn over and try to write them out.

Collecting Data

Questionnaires are a good way of collecting data — they're cheap and easy to distribute.

Design your Questionnaire Carefully

Bear these six points in mind when you design a questionnaire:

1) MAKE SURE YOUR QUESTIONS ARE RELEVANT

It's no good asking really fascinating questions if the answers aren't going to be useful.

2) QUESTIONS SHOULD BE CLEAR, BRIEF AND EASY TO UNDERSTAND

Your best bet is to assume that people will misunderstand a question if it's a bit unclear.

3) ALLOW FOR ALL POSSIBLE ANSWERS TO YOUR QUESTION

E.g. "What is your favourite subject: Maths, English or Science?" is difficult to answer truthfully if you like Art best — to help, you could add an "other" category.

4) QUESTIONS SHOULDN'T BE LEADING OR BIASED

Leading or biased questions are ones that suggest what answer is wanted.

For example: "Do you agree that thrash metal is really good music?"
The problem with this question is that it could make the interviewee feel pressurised into saying 'yes'.
A better question would be "What type of music do you prefer to listen to?"

5) QUESTIONS SHOULD BE UNAMBIGUOUS

Unambiguous questions aren't open to different interpretations.

For example: "How many hours do you play computer games per week?" is a better question than "Do you play computer games a lot?" which could be interpreted differently by different people. One person could answer yes, while another who plays the same amount could answer no.

6) PEOPLE MAY NOT ANSWER QUESTIONS TRUTHFULLY

This is often because they're embarrassed about the answer.

For example "What is your age?" might be a sensitive question for some people.
You can get round this by using groups so they don't have to answer with their exact age.

Some People Won't Respond to your Questionnaire

There could be many reasons for people not responding to your questionnaire but it's often because people can't be bothered. Here are some things you can do to improve the response:
- Use really clear questions that are simple and easy to answer.
- Follow up people who don't respond, e.g. go and collect their questionnaires in person.
- Provide an incentive for them to answer, e.g. enter them into a prize draw.

Take care with questionnaires

It's easy to ask daft questions, because you know what you mean — put yourself in the reader's shoes.

Sampling

The idea of <u>sampling</u> is to talk to <u>enough people</u> that you start to get a picture of what <u>everyone</u> thinks.

Sampling — Cheaper and Easier than Asking Everyone

1) For any statistical problem, you need to find out information about a group of people or things. This group is called the <u>POPULATION</u>. E.g. all the pupils in your school.

2) Usually, it would be too difficult, time-consuming and expensive to find out information about every person in a population, so you choose <u>only a few</u> members of the population and ask them instead — this is called <u>SAMPLING</u>.

3) You want to be able to draw <u>conclusions</u> about the whole population from your sample. This means your sample needs to be <u>REPRESENTATIVE</u> — it has to be <u>unbiased</u> and <u>big enough</u>.

There are lots of different sampling techniques. Here are two you should know about:

<u>SIMPLE RANDOM SAMPLING</u>

This makes sure that <u>every member</u> of a population has an <u>equal chance</u> of being chosen for the sample. Each member of the population is assigned a <u>number</u>. Then a <u>computer, calculator or random number table</u> is used to generate a list of <u>random</u> numbers which are <u>matched</u> to members of the population.

<u>STRATIFIED SAMPLING</u>

This gives different groups in the sample (e.g. people of a particular age) an amount of <u>representation</u> that's <u>proportional</u> to how big they are in the population — which means <u>big groups</u> get <u>more representation</u> and small groups get less. You still choose the right number from each group at <u>random</u>, to make your sample <u>unbiased</u>.

EXAMPLE: The table shows the distribution of students at a school by year group. Use <u>stratified</u> sampling to choose a <u>sample</u> of <u>50</u> students from the school.

Year 9	Year 10	Year 11
400	400	200

Find the proportion of <u>students</u> that are in <u>each year group</u> and multiply by the <u>sample size</u>.

$$\frac{\text{total in year}}{\text{total number of students}} \times \text{size of sample} = \begin{array}{c}\text{number of}\\ \text{students to be}\\ \text{picked}\end{array}$$

So... <u>Year 9</u> = (400 / 1000) × 50 = <u>20</u>
<u>Year 10</u> = (400 / 1000) × 50 = <u>20</u>
<u>Year 11</u> = (200 / 1000) × 50 = <u>10</u>

Spotting Problems With Sampling Methods

A <u>BIASED sample</u> is one that <u>doesn't fairly represent</u> the <u>whole population</u>. All sampling methods can be affected by <u>bias</u>. So, to make sure you can <u>spot a biased sample</u> a mile off, here's a lovely example...

EXAMPLE: In a telephone poll, 100 people were asked if they use the train regularly and 20% said yes. Does this mean 20% of the population regularly use the train?

<u>ANSWER</u>: <u>Probably not</u>. There are <u>several things wrong with this sampling technique</u>:
- <u>First and worst</u>: the sample is <u>far too small</u>. <u>At least 1000</u> would be more like it.
- What about people who don't have their own phone?
- What time of day was it done? When might regular train users be in or out?
- Which part or parts of the country were telephoned?
- If the results were to represent say, the whole country, then <u>stratified sampling</u> would be essential.

Warm-up and Exam Questions

Two lovely warm-up questions here on sampling. If you have any problems with these, flick back and have another look at the last few pages before trying the exam question.

Warm-up Questions

1) Dr Smith wants to survey a sample of 50 of his patients. In total he has 300 patients: 90 are children, 100 are men and 110 are women. He wants the sample to represent the proportion of each group. What type of sampling procedure should he use?

2) The following situation involves a population and a sample. Identify both and also identify the source of probable bias:

A flour company wants to know what proportion of Birmingham households bake some or all of their own bread. A sample of 600 residential addresses in Birmingham is taken and interviewers are sent to these addresses. The interviewers are employed during regular working hours on weekdays and interview only during these hours.

Now for a less lovely exam question. You'll have to do this one without any help.

Exam Question

1   A hamlet has a population of 720.
    The population is classified by age, as shown in the table below.

Age (years)	0-5	6-12	13-21	22-35	36-50	51+
No. of people	38	82	108	204	180	108

A survey of the residents of the hamlet is intended.
A sample of 80 residents will be selected using stratified sampling.

Calculate the approximate number that should be selected from each age group.

....

....

....

....

....
(3 marks)

Mean, Median, Mode and Range

If you don't manage to <u>learn these four basic definitions</u> then you'll be passing up on some of the easiest marks in the whole exam. It can't be that difficult can it?

> 1) <u>MODE</u> = <u>MOST</u> common
> 2) <u>MEDIAN</u> = <u>MIDDLE</u> value
> 3) <u>MEAN</u> = <u>TOTAL</u> of items ÷ <u>NUMBER</u> of items
> 4) <u>RANGE</u> = How far from the smallest to the biggest

<u>REMEMBER:</u>
<u>Mo</u>de = <u>mo</u>st (emphasise the 'o' in each when you say them)
<u>M*d</u>ian = <u>m*d</u> (emphasise the m*d in each when you say them)
<u>Mean</u> is just the <u>average</u>, but it's <u>mean</u> 'cos you have to work it out.

The *Golden* Rule

Mean, median and mode should be <u>easy marks</u> but even people who've gone to the incredible extent of learning them still manage to lose marks in the exam because they don't do <u>this one vital step</u>:

Always REARRANGE the data in ASCENDING ORDER

(and check you have the same number of entries)

Example

"Find the mean, median, mode and range of these numbers:"

2, 5, 3, 2, 6, -4, 0, 9, -3, 1, 6, 3, -2, 3   (14 numbers)

1) FIRST... rearrange them: -4, -3, -2, 0, 1, 2, 2, 3, 3, 3, 5, 6, 6, 9   (14) ✓

2) MEAN = $\frac{\text{total of items}}{\text{number of items}}$ = $\frac{-4-3-2+0+1+2+2+3+3+3+5+6+6+9}{14}$

= 31 ÷ 14 = <u>2.21</u>

3) MEDIAN = <u>the middle value</u> (only when they are <u>arranged in order of size</u>).

When there are two middle numbers as in this case, then the median is <u>HALFWAY BETWEEN THE TWO MIDDLE NUMBERS</u>.

-4, -3, -2, 0, 1, 2, 2, 3, 3, 3, 5, 6, 6, 9
← seven numbers this side ↑ seven numbers this side →
Median = 2.5

4) MODE = <u>most</u> common value, which is simply <u>3</u>. (Or you can say, "The <u>modal</u> value is 3.")

5) RANGE = distance from lowest to highest value, i.e. from -4 up to 9 = <u>13</u>

Mean, median, mode & range — easy marks for learning four words

The maths involved in working these out is so simple that you'd be mad not to learn the definitions. If you remember which is which and don't make careless arithmetic errors, there are marks to be had.

Quartiles and the Interquartile Range

Now we're getting to the good stuff. And by good stuff, I mean <u>quartiles</u> and <u>interquartile</u> range...

Finding the **Quartiles** is just like Finding the Median

1) <u>Quartiles</u> divide the data into <u>four equal groups</u>.
2) The quartiles are the <u>lower quartile Q_1</u>, the <u>median Q_2</u> and the <u>upper quartile Q_3</u>.
3) If you put the data in ascending order, the quartiles are 25% (¼), 50% (½) and 75% (¾) of the way through the list.

EXAMPLE Find the value of Q_1, Q_2 and Q_3 for this set of numbers: 7, 12, 5, 4, 3, 9, 5, 11, 6

This is discrete data (see p.19).

1) Put the data in <u>ASCENDING ORDER</u> — 3, 4, 5, 5, 6, 7, 9, 11, 12
2) Work out where the <u>QUARTILES</u> come in the list using the following <u>formulas</u>:

$$Q_1 \text{ position number} = (n + 1) \div 4$$
$$Q_2 \text{ position number} = 2(n + 1) \div 4$$
$$Q_3 \text{ position number} = 3(n + 1) \div 4$$

n is just the total number of values.

If you get "half values", like in this example, find the halfway point of the two numbers either side of this position. This is just like finding the median of an even number of values.

Step 1: n = 9 so
Q_1 position no. = $(9+1) \div 4 = 2.5$
Q_2 position no. = $2(9+1) \div 4 = 5$
Q_3 position no. = $3(9+1) \div 4 = 7.5$

Step 2:

| 3 | 4 | 5 | 5 | 6 | 7 | 9 | 11 | 12 |

position 1 — Q_1 $(4+5) \div 2 = 4.5$ — Q_2 — Q_3 $(9+11) \div 2 = 10$ — position 9

3) So, the lower quartile $Q_1 = 4.5$, the median $Q_2 = 6$ and the upper quartile $Q_3 = 10$.

Interquartile means "Between Quartiles"

The <u>interquartile range</u> is the <u>difference</u> between the <u>upper quartile</u> and the <u>lower quartile</u>.

EXAMPLE Find the <u>interquartile range</u> of the following set of numbers:

Put the data in ascending order: 3 4 ④ 5 5 6 7 7 ⑨ 11 12

Upper quartile = 9   Lower quartile = 4   Interquartile range = 9 – 4 = <u>5</u>

For non-grouped data that's all there is to it, but with grouped data it's a bit trickier. You can estimate the interquartile range using a cumulative frequency graph (see p.28-29).

Interquartile range — the spread of the middle 50% of the data

Another nice easy statistic to work out. The interquartile range is used to describe the spread of data, a bit like the range — but it's less affected by single values a long way from the rest of the data ("outliers"). If that doesn't make sense yet, there's more on the spread of data and outliers on p.33-34.

Frequency Tables

Frequency tables can either be done in <u>rows</u> or in <u>columns</u> of numbers and they can be quite confusing, <u>but not if you learn these eight key points</u>:

Eight **Key** Points

1) The word <u>FREQUENCY</u> just means <u>HOW MANY</u>, so a frequency table is nothing more than a '<u>How many in each group' table</u>.

2) The <u>FIRST ROW</u> (or column) just gives the <u>GROUP LABELS</u>.

3) The <u>SECOND ROW</u> (or column) gives the <u>ACTUAL DATA</u>.

4) You have to <u>WORK OUT A THIRD ROW</u> (or column) <u>yourself</u>.

5) The <u>MEAN</u> is always found using: <u>3rd Row Total ÷ 2nd Row Total</u>.

6) The <u>MEDIAN</u> is found from the <u>MIDDLE VALUE IN the 2nd row</u>.

7) The <u>INTERQUARTILE RANGE</u> is found from the values ¼ and ¾ of the way through the middle row.

8) The <u>RANGE</u> is found from <u>the extremes of the first row</u>.

Example

Here is a typical frequency table shown in both <u>ROW FORM</u> and <u>COLUMN FORM</u>:

No. of Sisters	0	1	2	3	4	5	6
Frequency	7	15	12	8	3	1	0

No. of Sisters	Frequency
0	7
1	15
2	12
3	8
4	3
5	1
6	0

Column Form

Row Form

There's no real difference between these two forms and you could get either one in your exam.

This is what the two types of table look like when they're completed:

No. of Sisters	Frequency	No. × Frequency
0	7	0
1	15	15
2	12	24
3	8	24
4	3	12
5	1	5
6	0	0
Totals	46	80

No. of Sisters	0	1	2	3	4	5	6	Totals
Frequency	7	15	12	8	3	1	0	46
No. × Frequency	0	15	24	24	12	5	0	80

(People asked) (Sisters)

"WHERE DOES THE THIRD ROW COME FROM?"

...I hear you cry!

<u>THE THIRD ROW</u> (or column) is <u>ALWAYS</u> obtained by <u>MULTIPLYING</u> the numbers from the <u>FIRST 2 ROWS</u> (or columns).

THIRD ROW = 1ST ROW × 2ND ROW

Once the table is complete, you can easily find the <u>MEAN, MEDIAN, MODE AND RANGE</u> (see next page) which is what they usually demand in the exam.

Frequency Tables and Averages

Mean, Median, Mode and Range:

This is easy enough <u>if you learn it</u>.

No. of Sisters	0	1	2	3	4	5	6	Totals
Frequency	7	15	12	8	3	1	0	46
No. × Frequency	0	15	24	24	12	5	0	80

Here's the table from the previous page (just to save you flicking back).

MEAN $= \dfrac{\text{3rd Row Total}}{\text{2nd Row Total}} = \dfrac{80}{46} = 1.74$

(sisters per person)

MEDIAN — imagine the original data <u>SET OUT IN ASCENDING ORDER</u>:

0000000 111111111111111 222222222222 33333333 444 5

and the median is just the middle number which is between the 23rd and 24th digits.

So for this data <u>THE MEDIAN IS 2</u>. (Of course, when you get slick at this you can easily find the position of the middle value straight from the table.)

The MODE is very easy — it's just the group with the most entries: i.e 1.

The RANGE is 5 – 0 = 5 The 2nd row tells us there are people with anything from 'no sisters' right up to 'five sisters' (but not 6 sisters). (Always give it as a <u>single number</u>.)

Averages and 'Spread'

1) AVERAGES can be used to <u>compare</u> sets of data. Take a look at this example:

EXAMPLE Below are the results of Steve's and Sachin's last 10 Physics tests. <u>Use these results to say who is better at Physics</u>.

<u>Steve</u>: Mean mark = 22.6   Median mark = 24   Modal mark = 16   Range = 18

<u>Sachin</u>: Mean mark = 34.4   Median mark = 33.5   Modal mark = 33   Range = 8

<u>ANSWER</u>: Sachin's mean, median and modal marks are all higher than Steve's, so "<u>the results suggest that Sachin is better at Physics</u>".

2) The <u>RANGE</u> is used to compare the <u>SPREADS</u> of data. So going back to the example — Steve's range of marks is a lot bigger than Sachin's, which means that his <u>spread of marks is greater</u>. In other words, <u>Sachin's marks are more consistent</u>.

Choosing the Best Average

The <u>mean</u>, <u>median</u> and <u>mode</u> all have their <u>advantages</u> and <u>disadvantages</u> — <u>LEARN THEM</u>:

Outliers are data points that don't fit the general pattern (see p.34).

	Advantages	Disadvantages
Mean	Uses all the data. Usually most representative.	Isn't always a data value. May be distorted by outliers.
Median	Easy to find in ordered data. Not distorted by outliers.	Isn't always a data value. Not always a good representation of the data.
Mode	Easy to find in tallied data. Always a data value.	Doesn't always exist or sometimes more than one. Not always a good representation of the data.

Frequency tables easily show the mean, median, mode and range

Exam questions will often ask you to get the mean, median, mode and range from a frequency table. As long as you have learnt the stuff on this page, you shouldn't have any trouble whatsoever.

Grouped Frequency Tables

These are a bit <u>trickier</u> than simple frequency tables.

The table below shows the distribution of weights of 60 school kids:

Weight (kg)	$30 \leq w < 40$	$40 \leq w < 50$	$50 \leq w < 60$	$60 \leq w < 70$	$70 \leq w < 80$
Frequency	8	16	18	12	6

What does $30 \leq w < 40$ mean?

Don't get confused by the notation used for the intervals.

1) The $\leq$ symbol means w can be <u>greater than or equal to 30</u>.

2) The $<$ symbol means w must be <u>less than 40</u> (but not equal to it).

So <u>a value of 30</u> will go in this class, but <u>a value of 40</u> will go in the next class up: $40 \leq w < 50$.

'Estimating' the Mean using Mid-Interval Values

Just like with ordinary frequency tables you have to <u>add extra rows and find totals</u> to be able to work anything out. Also notice <u>you can only 'ESTIMATE' the mean from grouped data tables</u> — you can't find it exactly unless you know all the original values.

> <u>Add a 3rd row</u> and enter **MID-INTERVAL VALUES** for each class.
> <u>Add a 4th row</u> and **multiply FREQUENCY × MID-INTERVAL VALUE** for each class.

Weight (kg)	$30 \leq w < 40$	$40 \leq w < 50$	$50 \leq w < 60$	$60 \leq w < 70$	$70 \leq w < 80$	Totals
Frequency	8	16	18	12	6	60
Mid-Interval Value	35	45	55	65	75	—
Frequency × Mid-Interval Value	280	720	990	780	450	3220

1) <u>ESTIMATING THE MEAN</u> is then the usual thing of <u>DIVIDING THE TOTALS</u>:

$$\text{Mean} = \frac{\text{Overall Total (4th Row)}}{\text{Frequency Total (2nd Row)}} = \frac{3220}{60} = 53.7$$

2) <u>THE MODE</u> is still nice'n'easy: the modal class is $50 \leq w < 60$ kg.

3) <u>THE MEDIAN</u> can't be found exactly but you can say <u>which class it's in</u>. If all the data were put in order, the 30th/31st entries would be in the $50 \leq w < 60$ kg class.

This time there are two rows to add

With frequency tables there was just one row to add. With grouped frequency tables there are two. It's still easy enough though as long as you remember what the rows are and how to find them.

Cumulative Frequency

Cumulative frequency tables and graphs keep a <u>running total</u> of the frequency.

Four Key Points

1) <u>CUMULATIVE FREQUENCY</u> just means <u>ADDING IT UP AS YOU GO ALONG</u>.

2) You have to <u>ADD A THIRD ROW</u> to the table — the <u>RUNNING TOTAL</u> of the 2nd row.

3) <u>When plotting the graph</u>, always plot points <u>using the HIGHEST VALUE in each group</u> (of row 1) with the value from <u>row 3</u>.

4) Cumulative Frequency is always plotted <u>up the side</u> of a graph, not across.

Three Vital Statistics

For a cumulative frequency curve there are <u>THREE VITAL STATISTICS</u> which you need to know how to find:

1) <u>MEDIAN</u>
   <u>Exactly halfway UP</u>, then across, then down and <u>read off the bottom scale</u>.

2) <u>LOWER AND UPPER QUARTILES</u>
   <u>Exactly ¼ and ¾ UP the side</u>, then across, then down and read off the <u>bottom scale</u>.

3) <u>INTERQUARTILE RANGE</u>
   The distance <u>on the bottom scale</u> between the lower and upper quartiles.

A Box Plot shows the Interquartile Range as a Box

To make a box plot you need to:

1) <u>Draw the scale</u> along the bottom.
2) <u>Draw a box</u> the length of the <u>interquartile range</u>.
3) <u>Draw a line</u> down the box to show the <u>median</u>.
4) <u>Draw 'whiskers'</u> up to the <u>maximum and minimum</u>.
   (They're sometimes called 'Box and Whisker diagrams'.)

Four key points, three vital statistics — and a box plot in a pear tree

Here's cumulative frequencies broken down into four points and three statistics — get it learnt. Then there's a big example on the next page to explain it a bit more and make sure you've got it all.

Cumulative Frequency

Cumulative Frequency Tables and Graphs — *Example*

Height (cm)	$140 \leq x < 150$	$150 \leq x < 160$	$160 \leq x < 170$	$170 \leq x < 180$	$180 \leq x < 190$	$190 \leq x < 200$	$200 \leq x < 210$
Frequency	4	9	20	33	36	15	3
Cumulative frequency	4 (at 150)	13 (at 160)	33 (at 170)	66 (at 180)	102 (at 190)	117 (at 200)	120 (at 210)

The graph is plotted from these pairs:
(150, 4) (160, 13) (170, 33) (180, 66) etc.

Note that the points are plotted using the HIGHEST VALUE in each group (of row 1) with the value from row 3, i.e. plot 13 at 160.

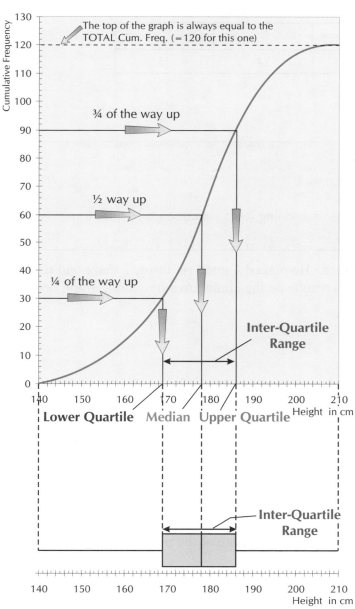

The top of the graph is always equal to the TOTAL Cum. Freq. (= 120 for this one)

¾ of the way up

½ way up

¼ of the way up

Inter-Quartile Range

Lower Quartile   Median   Upper Quartile   Height in cm

Inter-Quartile Range

See p.33 about the SHAPE of cumulative frequency curves.

So from the cumulative frequency curve for this data, we get these results:

MEDIAN = 178 cm

LOWER QUARTILE = 169 cm

UPPER QUARTILE = 186 cm

INTERQUARTILE RANGE = 17 cm
(186-169)

This example should leave you crystal clear on cumulative frequency

If some of these details are still hazy, go back over the previous page. It's tempting to nod your head and skip over it and think you've learnt it. But nodding and skipping won't get any marks in the exam.

Warm-up and Worked Exam Questions

By the time the big day comes you need to know all the methods on the previous pages like the back of your hand. It's not easy, but it's the only way to get good marks.

Warm-Up Questions

1) Write down the 4 basic definitions of the following: Mode, Median, Mean and Range.

2) The data shows the number of cars owned by 124 households in a survey. Find the:
   a) Mean; b) Median; c) Mode; d) Range.

Number of cars	0	1	2	3	4	5	6
Frequency	1	24	36	31	22	9	1

Probability is covered on p.41-45.

   e) Estimate the probability that a household chosen at random will have two cars.

3) The grouped frequency table below represents data from 79 random people.

Height (cm)	$145 \leq x < 155$	$155 \leq x < 165$	$165 \leq x < 175$	$175 \leq x < 185$
Frequency	18	22	24	15

   a) Estimate the mean.
   b) Which group contains the median?
   c) State the modal group.

Worked Exam Question

There's no better preparation for exam questions than doing, err... practice exam questions. Hang on, what's this I see...

1 Steve carried out an experiment many times. He placed a small rat inside a maze and timed how long it took to escape. He plotted his results on the cumulative frequency graph below.

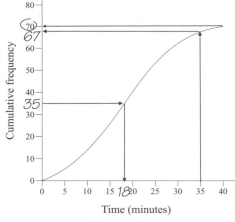

(a) How many times did Steve carry out the experiment?

...........*70 times.*...........

(1 mark)

(b) Use the cumulative frequency graph to find an estimate of the median time.

...........*70 ÷ 2 = 35. So read off the time at 35. That gives 18 minutes.*...........

(2 marks)

(c) Use the cumulative frequency graph to find what percentage of times were less than 35 minutes.

...........*67 ÷ 70 × 100 = 95.7 %.*...........

(3 marks)

Exam Questions

2   A survey was made of the time spent by each of 500 customers at the check-outs of a supermarket. The results were recorded in the frequency table below:

Time (t mins)	Frequency
$0 < t \leq 1$	77
$1 < t \leq 2$	142
$2 < t \leq 3$	143
$3 < t \leq 4$	60
$4 < t \leq 5$	49
$5 < t \leq 6$	29

(a)   Calculate the average time spent by each customer at the checkout (in minutes).

....
(4 marks)

(b)   Complete the cumulative frequency table.

Time ($\leq$ mins)	Cumulative Frequency
1	77
2	
3	
4	
5	
6	

(3 marks)

(c)   Draw the cumulative frequency curve on the axes below.

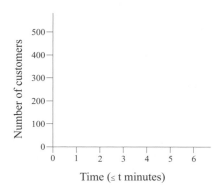

(4 marks)

(d)   Use the graph to estimate:
   (i)   The median time (in minutes).

....
(1 mark)

   (ii)   The interquartile range (in minutes).

....
(2 marks)

Histograms and Frequency Density

Histograms

A histogram is just a bar chart where the bars can be of DIFFERENT widths.

This changes them from nice easy-to-understand diagrams into seemingly incomprehensible monsters, and yes, you've guessed it, that makes them a firm favourite with the examiners.

In fact things aren't half as bad as that — but only if you LEARN THE THREE RULES:

1) It's NOT the height, but the AREA of each bar that matters.

2) Use the snip of information they give you to find how much is represented BY EACH AREA BLOCK.

3) Divide all the bars into THE SAME SIZED AREA BLOCKS and so work out the number for each bar (using AREAS).

EXAMPLE

The histogram below represents the age distribution of people arrested for antisocial behaviour in Chaddesden in 1995. Given that there were 36 people in the 55 to 65 age range, find the number of people arrested in all the other age ranges.

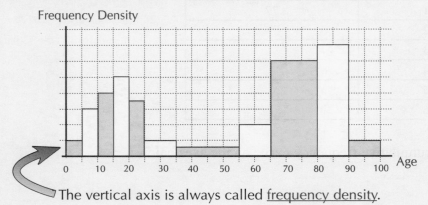

The vertical axis is always called frequency density.

ANSWER:

The 55-65 bar represents 36 people and contains 4 dotted squares, so each dotted square must represent 36 ÷ 4 = 9 people.

The rest is easy. E.g. the 80-90 group has 14 dotted squares so that represents 14 × 9 = 126 people.

> REMEMBER: ALWAYS COUNT AREA BLOCKS
> to find THE NUMBER IN EACH BAR

Frequency Density = Frequency ÷ Class Width

You don't need to worry too much about this, but you do need to learn the formula. If you're asked to draw a histogram, use this formula to work out the height of the bars.

With histograms it's area not height which matters

The histogram is an odd beast — like a bar chart with funny columns. However, all you need to do is work out how much is represented by each area block and then divide the bars into those blocks.

Spread of Data

This page is all about interpreting the shapes of histograms and cumulative frequency curves. Take a look back at pages 28-29 and 32 if you're not sure about these types of graph.

Shapes of *Histograms* and *'Spread'*

You can easily estimate the mean from the shape of a histogram — it's more or less <u>IN THE MIDDLE</u>.

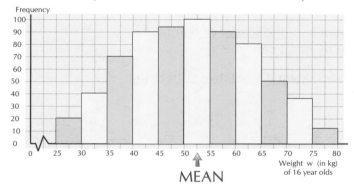

MEAN

Weight w (in kg) of 16 year olds

You must <u>LEARN the significance of the shapes</u> of these two histograms:

1) The first shows <u>high dispersion</u> (i.e. a <u>large spread</u> of results away from the mean).

   (i.e. the weights of a sample of 16 year olds will cover a very wide range)

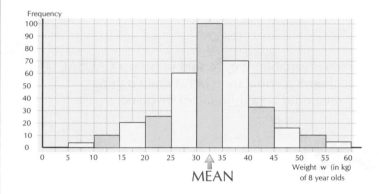

MEAN

Weight w (in kg) of 8 year olds

2) The second shows a '<u>tighter</u>' distribution of results where most values are within a <u>narrow range</u> either side of the mean.

   (i.e the weights of a sample of 8 year olds will show <u>very little</u> variation)

Cumulative Frequency *Curves* and *'Spread'*

The shape of a <u>CUMULATIVE FREQUENCY CURVE</u> also tells us <u>how spread out</u> the data values are.

The <u>blue</u> curve shows a <u>very tight distribution</u> around the <u>MEDIAN</u> and this also means the <u>interquartile range is small</u> as shown.

The <u>red</u> curve shows a more <u>widely spread</u> set of data and therefore a <u>larger interquartile range</u>.

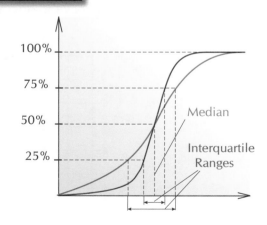

Median

Interquartile Ranges

'Tight' distribution represents <u>CONSISTENT</u> results.

E.g. the <u>lifetimes of batteries</u> would all be very close to the median, indicating a <u>good product</u>. The lifetimes of another product may show <u>wide variation</u>, which shows that the product is not as consistent.

They often ask about this 'shape significance' in <u>exams</u>.

More about two trickier types of graph

Learn how to estimate the mean from histograms and compare the spread of data from cumulative frequency curves. Don't forget questions about the significance of different shapes of graph and chart.

Scatter Graphs

Scatter Graphs — *Correlation* and the Line of Best Fit

A scatter graph tells you how closely two things are related — the fancy word for this is <u>CORRELATION</u>.

<u>Good</u> (or <u>strong</u>) <u>correlation</u> means the two things are <u>closely related</u> to each other.
<u>Poor</u> (or <u>weak</u>) <u>correlation</u> means there is <u>very little relationship</u>.

The <u>LINE OF BEST FIT</u> goes roughly <u>through the middle of the scatter of points</u>.
(It doesn't have to go through any of the points exactly but it can.)

If the line slopes <u>up</u> it's <u>positive correlation</u>, if it slopes <u>down</u> it's <u>negative correlation</u>.
<u>No correlation</u> means there's no <u>linear relationship</u>.

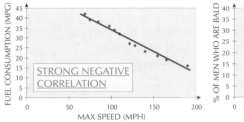 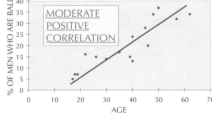 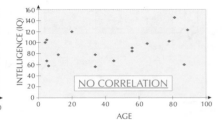

If a change in one variable <u>CAUSES</u> a change in the other variable, they're said to have a <u>CAUSAL LINK</u>. You have to be <u>VERY CAREFUL</u> though. Just because there's a correlation between two things, it <u>doesn't</u> necessarily mean there's a causal link — there could be a <u>third factor</u> involved.

Outliers don't fit the *General Pattern*

1) <u>Outliers</u> are data points that <u>don't fit</u> the <u>general pattern</u> (e.g. the 8-foot tall 15-year-old on this graph).

2) Outliers can show <u>possible errors</u> — but outliers aren't <u>necessarily</u> mistakes.

3) If you find one on a graph, <u>check</u> the <u>original data</u> to see whether it's been plotted correctly.

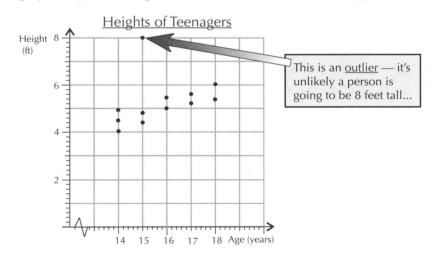

Don't forget, correlation doesn't necessarily mean cause and effect

Scatter graphs are a bit tricky because there are lots of terms to learn — correlation, strong and weak, positive and negative... Turn over and try to write it all out from memory to check you've learnt it.

Bar Charts and Stem and Leaf Diagrams

Dual Bar Charts Can be Used to Compare Data Sets

Dual bar charts show two sets of data at once so it's easy to compare them. Each category has two bars — one for each data set.

The dual bar chart on the right shows the favourite colours of a group of pupils, but it's split into two sets — boys and girls.

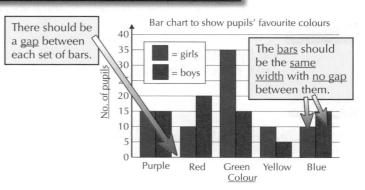

There should be a gap between each set of bars.

The bars should be the same width with no gap between them.

Bar chart to show pupils' favourite colours

Composite Bar Charts show Proportions

1) A composite bar chart has single bars, split into sections. The sections show frequencies for the different categories that make up the whole bar.

2) It's easy to read off total frequencies (the heights of the bars), as well as to compare different categories.

The data might be in percentages, with the height of the whole bar representing 100%.

The composite bar chart on the right shows the number of men, women and children visiting a county show.

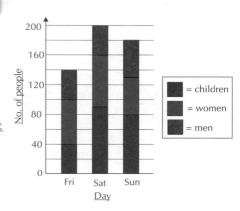

Stem and Leaf Diagrams Use Numbers instead of Bars

If you get one of these in the exam, you're laughing. It's the EASIEST THING IN THE WORLD.

7, 11, 12, 13, 16, 17, 20, 23, 24, 24, 25, 26, 26, 29, 29, 31, 32, 34

1) **Put the data in order.**
2) **Put it in groups and make a key.**
3) **Draw the diagram.**

This looks like it'll split nicely into tens:

Key: 2 | 3 = 23

Draw a line here.   Then put the second digits in rows like this.

Put the first digit of each group in a column.

```
0 | 7
1 | 1 2 3 6 7
2 | 0 3 4 4 5 6 6 9 9
3 | 1 2 4
```

This one means '26'.

To find the range from a stem and leaf diagram, just subtract the first from the last number, e.g. 34 – 7 = 27.

Three straightforward ways of showing data

Have a go at drawing your own dual bar charts and composite bar charts — it'll help you remember how to do them. For stem and leaf diagrams you just have to remember those three simple steps.

Other Graphs and Charts

Two-Way Tables

Two-way <u>tables</u> are a bit like frequency tables, but they show <u>two</u> things instead of just <u>one</u>.

EXAMPLE "Use this table to work out how many
a) <u>right-handed people</u> and
b) <u>left-handed women</u> there were in this survey."

	Women	Men	TOTAL
Left-handed		27	63
Right-handed	164	173	
TOTAL	200	200	400

ANSWER

a) 164 + 173 = <u>337 right-handed people</u> (or you could have done 400 − 63 = 337).
b) 200 − 164 = <u>36 left-handed women</u> (or you could have done 63 − 27 = 36). Easy.

Line Graphs and Frequency Polygons

A <u>line graph</u> is just a set of points joined with straight lines.

A <u>frequency polygon</u> looks similar and is used to show the information from a frequency table. The mid-interval values are used, e.g. the first point is (25, 12).

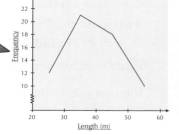

Length l (m)	Frequency
$20 \leq l < 30$	12
$30 \leq l < 40$	21
$40 \leq l < 50$	18
$50 \leq l < 60$	10

Pie Charts

Learn the <u>Golden Rule</u> for Pie Charts: **The TOTAL of Everything = 360°**

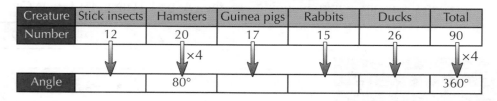

Creature	Stick insects	Hamsters	Guinea pigs	Rabbits	Ducks	Total
Number	12	20	17	15	26	90
Angle		80°				360°

×4

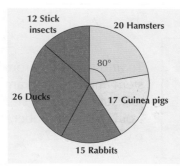

1) Add up all the numbers in each sector to get the <u>TOTAL</u> (90 for this one).

2) Then find the <u>MULTIPLIER</u> (or divider) that you need to <u>turn your total into 360°</u>:
For 90 → 360 as above, the <u>MULTIPLIER</u> is 4.

3) Now <u>MULTIPLY EVERY NUMBER BY 4</u> to get the angle for each sector.
E.g. the angle for hamsters will be 20 × 4 = <u>80°</u>.

Pie charts <u>only</u> tell you the <u>proportion</u> of the population that's in each category. You can't know the <u>actual number</u> of things in a category unless you're told the population size. This is especially important when you're <u>comparing</u> pie charts.

Two-way tables have row and column totals and a grand total

These tables and graphs aren't too complicated, just take your time and don't make any silly mistakes. Check that two-way table totals add up right, line graphs are labelled, and pie charts add up to 360°.

Warm-up Questions

There's a whole page of warm-up questions here covering all sorts of graphs and charts.
Now's the time to go back over any bits you're not sure of — in the exam it'll be too late.

Warm-Up Questions

1) Draw a stem and leaf diagram for this data:
   17, 12, 4, 19, 23, 29, 12, 25, 31, 2, 39, 9.

2) Decide what type of correlation best describes the two scatter graphs below.

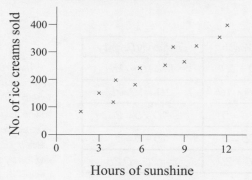

Graph 1 showing correlation between the amount of ice creams sold and hours of sunshine

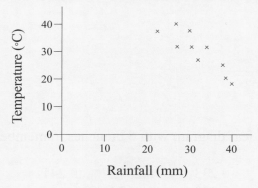

Graph 2 showing correlation between the average temperature and rainfall for ten weeks in a particular country

3) This frequency table shows how many of three types of fruit Jonathan eats in a week.

Fruit	Apples	Bananas	Oranges
Frequency	12	10	8

Construct a pie chart to show the information using a radius of 3 cm.

Worked Exam Questions

Worked Exam Questions

It's no good learning all the facts in the world if you go to pieces or just write nonsense in the exam. These worked examples show how to turn all those facts into good answers — and earn yourself marks.

1   Small mixed bags of sweets are sold in a convenience store.
45 bags were weighed and put into the table below.

Weight of sweets in grams (w)	$0 < w \le 10$	$10 < w \le 20$	$20 < w \le 25$	$25 < w \le 30$	$30 < w \le 50$
Frequency	5	10	10	15	5

Draw a histogram for this data.

w	Frequency	Class Width	Frequency Density
$0 < w \le 10$	5	$10 - 0 = 10$	$5 \div 10 = 0.5$
$10 < w \le 20$	10	$20 - 10 = 10$	$10 \div 10 = 1$
$20 < w \le 25$	10	$25 - 20 = 5$	$10 \div 5 = 2$
$25 < w \le 30$	15	$30 - 25 = 5$	$15 \div 5 = 3$
$30 < w \le 50$	5	$50 - 30 = 20$	$5 \div 20 = 0.25$

The first step is to calculate the frequency density values — these will be the heights of the bars. Remember — frequency density is the frequency divided by the class width.

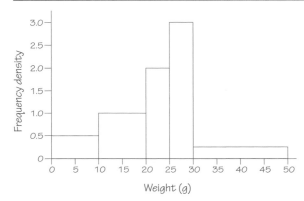

(3 marks)

2   Show the following numbers on a stem and leaf diagram with 6 branches, remembering to include the appropriate key.

0.212	0.223	0.226	0.230	0.233	0.237	0.241
0.242	0.248	0.253	0.253	0.259	0.262	

Key: 22 | 6 represents 0.226

```
21 | 2
22 | 3  6
23 | 0  3  7
24 | 1  2  8
25 | 3  3  9
26 | 2
```

(2 marks)

Exam Questions

3   The table below shows the number of blackcurrant juice cartons that were sold at a seaside supermarket and the number of hours of sunshine for 10 days in August last year.

Cartons of blackcurrant juice	410	340	350	610	1290	830	1070	1650	1560	1900
Sunshine (hours)	3	4	5	5	7	7.5	8	10.5	11	11

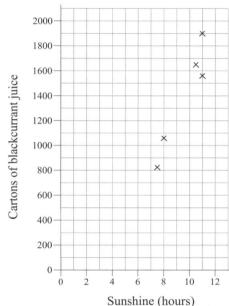

The last 5 results have been plotted on the scatter graph.

(a)   Complete the scatter graph by plotting the first 5 results.

(1 mark)

(b)   Describe, in a few words, the relationship between the hours of sunshine and the number of cartons sold.

....

(1 mark)

(c)   Draw a line of best fit on the scatter graph.

(1 mark)

(d)   By using your line of best fit, find estimates for the following:
   (i)   the number of hours of sunshine if 1000 cartons were sold.

   ....

(1 mark)

   (ii)   the number of cartons that would be sold if there were 9½ hours of sunshine.

   ....

(1 mark)

Exam Questions

4   The durations of sixty pop songs recorded by a certain band are outlined in the table below:

Song length in seconds (x)	No. of songs
$100 \leq x < 150$	1
$150 \leq x < 180$	9
$180 \leq x < 200$	15
$200 \leq x < 220$	17
$220 \leq x < 250$	12
$250 \leq x < 310$	6

(a)   Estimate the mean song length.

....
(2 marks)

(b)   Display the data in a histogram.

(2 marks)

5   Members of a cycling club meet up once a week. Each member picks one of three routes to ride. There's a Long Route, a Medium Route and a Short Route.

The table shows the number of cyclists doing each route for two weeks.
The composite bar chart below displays the data for Week 1.

Route	Long	Medium	Short
Number of Cyclists — week 1	15	3	2
Number of Cyclists — week 2	12	15	3

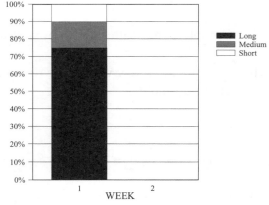

(a)   Show how the height of the 'Medium Route' bar was calculated.

....
(1 mark)

(b)   Complete the composite bar chart above by drawing the bar for Week 2.
      Show your working below.

....
(2 marks)

(c)   State one similarity between the data for both weeks.

....
(1 mark)

Probability

This is nobody's favourite subject for sure, I've never really spoken to anyone who's said they do like it (not for long anyway). Although it does seem a bit of a 'Black Art' to most people, it's not as bad as you might think, but <u>YOU MUST LEARN THE BASIC FACTS</u>.

All **Probabilities** are between **0 and 1**

A probability of <u>ZERO</u> means it will <u>NEVER HAPPEN</u>.
A probability of <u>ONE</u> means it <u>DEFINITELY WILL</u>.

<u>You can't have a probability bigger than 1.</u>

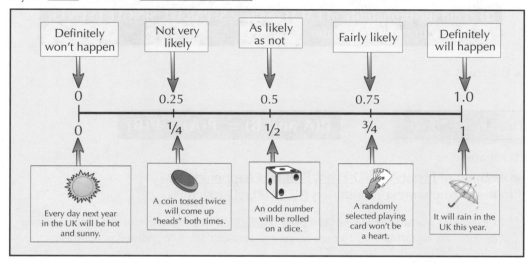

You should be able to put the probability of any event happening on this scale from 0 to 1.

Three **Important Details**

> 1) Probabilities should be given as either
>   a <u>FRACTION</u> (¼), or a <u>DECIMAL</u> (0.25) or a <u>PERCENTAGE</u> (25%)
> 2) The notation 'P(X) = ½' should be read as:
>   '<u>THE PROBABILITY OF EVENT X HAPPENING IS ½</u>'
> 3) Probabilities <u>ALWAYS ADD UP TO 1</u>. This is essential for finding the
>   probability of the other outcome. E.g. If P(pass) = ¼, then P(fail) = ¾

Listing **All Outcomes**: 2 Coins, Dice, Spinners

A simple question you might get is to list all the possible results from tossing two coins or spinning two spinners, or a dice and a spinner, etc. Whatever it is, it'll be very similar to these, so <u>LEARN THEM</u>:

The <u>possible outcomes</u> from <u>TOSSING TWO COINS</u> are:			
Head	Head	H	H
Head	Tail	H	T
Tail	Head	T	H
Tail	Tail	T	T

List the possible outcomes <u>METHODICALLY</u> to make sure you get them <u>ALL</u>.

1) A <u>SAMPLE SPACE DIAGRAM</u> is basically a posh name for a <u>table</u>. If you use one, you're less likely to <u>miss out</u> any outcomes.

2) This table shows all the outcomes from <u>TWO SPINNERS</u>, one with <u>3 colours</u> and the other with <u>numbers from 1 to 3</u>:

	Red	Blue	Green
1	1R	1B	1G
2	2R	2B	2G
3	3R	3B	3G

Probability

This is where most people start getting into trouble — and that's because they don't know the <u>three simple steps</u> and the <u>two rules</u> on this page.

Three Simple Steps

> 1) Always break down a complicated-looking probability question into A SEQUENCE of SEPARATE SINGLE EVENTS.
> 2) Find the probability of EACH of these SEPARATE SINGLE EVENTS.
> 3) Apply the AND/OR rule:

And now for the rules...

1) The **AND** Rule:

$$P(A \text{ and } B) = P(A) \times P(B)$$

Which means:

The probability of <u>Event A AND Event B BOTH happening</u> is equal to the two separate probabilities <u>MULTIPLIED together</u>.

> *(Strictly speaking, the two events have to be <u>INDEPENDENT</u>. All that means is that one event happening does not in any way affect the other one happening. Contrast this with mutually exclusive below.)*

2) The **OR** Rule:

$$P(A \text{ or } B) = P(A) + P(B)$$

Which means:

The probability of <u>EITHER Event A OR Event B happening</u> is equal to the two separate probabilities <u>ADDED together</u>.

> *(Strictly speaking, the two events have to be <u>MUTUALLY EXCLUSIVE</u> which means that if one event happens, the other one can't happen.)*

The way to remember this is that it's the <u>wrong way round</u> — i.e. you'd want the AND to go with the + but it doesn't: It's '<u>AND with ×</u>' and '<u>OR with +</u>'.

Example

"Find the probability of picking two kings from a pack of cards (assuming you don't replace the first card picked)."

1) <u>SPLIT</u> this into <u>TWO SEPARATE EVENTS</u> — i.e. picking the <u>first king</u> and then <u>picking the second king</u>.

2) <u>Find the SEPARATE probabilities</u> of these two <u>separate events</u>:
   P(1st king) = $\frac{4}{52}$ P(2nd king) = $\frac{3}{51}$ (— note the change from 52 to 51)

3) <u>Apply the AND/OR rule</u>: BOTH events must happen, so it's the <u>AND</u> rule: so <u>multiply</u> the two separate probabilities: $\frac{4}{52} \times \frac{3}{51} = \frac{1}{221}$

Three steps and two rules here

I repeat — you won't go far if you don't learn the AND/OR rules. You have been warned.

Probability — Relative Frequency

Relative frequency is nothing too difficult — it's just a way of working out <u>probabilities</u>.

Fair or Biased?

The probability of rolling a three on a dice is $\frac{1}{6}$ — you know that each
of the 6 numbers on a dice is <u>equally likely</u> to be rolled, and there's <u>only 1 three</u>.

BUT this only works if it's a <u>fair dice</u>. If the dice is a bit <u>wonky</u> (the technical term is 'biased') then each number <u>won't</u> have an equal chance of being rolled. That's where <u>relative frequency</u> comes in — you can use it to estimate probabilities when things might be wonky.

Do the Experiment Again and Again and Again and Again

You need to do an experiment <u>over and over again</u> and then do a quick calculation.
(Remember, an experiment could just mean rolling a dice.)
Usually the results of these experiments will be written in a <u>table</u>.

The Formula for Relative Frequency

$$\text{Probability of something happening} = \frac{\text{Number of times it has happened}}{\text{Number of times you tried}}$$

You can work out the relative frequency as a <u>fraction</u> but usually <u>decimals</u> are best for comparing relative frequencies.

The important thing to remember is:

The more times you <u>DO THE EXPERIMENT</u>, the <u>MORE ACCURATE</u> the probability will be.

Example

So, back to the wonky dice. <u>What is the probability of rolling a three?</u>

Number of Times the dice was rolled	10	20	50	100
Number of Threes rolled	2	5	11	23
Relative Frequency	$\frac{2}{10}=0.2$	$\frac{5}{20}=0.25$	$\frac{11}{50}=0.22$	$\frac{23}{100}=0.23$

We've got <u>4 possible answers</u>, but the best is the one worked out using the <u>highest number of dice rolls</u>. This makes the probability of rolling a three on this dice <u>0.23</u>. And since for a fair, unbiased dice, the probability of rolling a three is $\frac{1}{6}$ (about 0.17), then our dice is probably <u>biased</u>.

More experiments mean a more accurate probability estimate

It's bound to come up on the exam — so learn the formula for calculating relative frequency.
And remember, even with a fair dice you often won't get exactly the expected result, but the more experiments you do, the closer to the true probability you'll get.

Probability — Tree Diagrams

Tree diagrams are all pretty much the same, so it's a good idea to learn these basic details
(which apply to ALL tree diagrams) — ready for the one that's bound to be in the exam.

General Tree Diagram

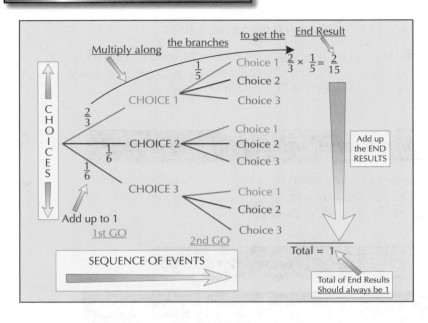

1) Always <u>MULTIPLY ALONG</u> the branches (as shown) to get the <u>END RESULTS</u>.

2) On any set of branches which all <u>meet at a point</u>, the numbers must always <u>ADD UP TO 1</u>.

3) <u>Check</u> that your diagram is correct by making sure the end results <u>ADD UP TO ONE</u>.

4) To answer any question, simply <u>ADD UP</u> the relevant <u>END RESULTS</u> (see below).

A Likely Tree Diagram Question

EXAMPLE "A box contains 5 red disks and 3 green disks. Two disks are taken at random <u>without replacement</u>. Draw a tree diagram and hence find the probability that both disks are the same colour."

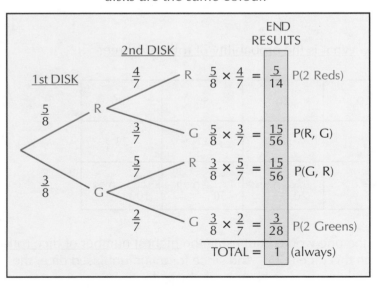

Once the tree diagram is drawn all you then need to do to answer the question is simply select the relevant <u>END RESULTS</u> and then <u>ADD THEM TOGETHER</u>:

> 2 REDS   (5/14)
> 2 GREENS (3/28)
>
> $$\frac{5}{14} + \frac{3}{28} = \frac{13}{28}$$

Remember, you can use a calculator for this.

The tree's the key

The tree diagram is the top toy when it comes to probability questions. Even if the question doesn't specifically ask for a tree diagram you should draw one straight away so you know what's going on.

Probability — Tree Diagrams

Four Extra Details for the Tree Diagram method:

1) Always break up the question into a sequence of separate events.

E.g. '3 coins are tossed together' — just split it into 3 separate events.
You need this sequence of events to be able to draw any sort of tree diagram.

2) Don't feel you have to draw complete tree diagrams.

Learn to adapt them to what is required. E.g. 'What is the chance of throwing
a dice 3 times and getting 2 sixes followed by an even number?'

This diagram is all you need to get the answer: $\frac{1}{6} \times \frac{1}{6} \times \frac{1}{2} = \frac{1}{72}$

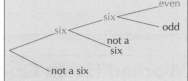

3) Watch out for conditional probabilities...

...where the fraction on each branch depends on what happened on the previous branch,
e.g. bags of sweets, packs of cards etc, where the bottom number of the fractions also changes
as items are removed. E.g. $\frac{11}{25}$ then $\frac{10}{24}$ etc.

4) With 'At Least' questions, it's always (1 – Prob of 'the other outcome'):

For example, 'Find the probability of having AT LEAST one girl in 4 children.'
There are in fact 15 different ways of having 'AT LEAST one girl in 4 children'
which would take a long time to work out, even with a tree diagram.

The clever trick you should know is this:
The prob of 'AT LEAST something or other' is just (1 – prob of 'the other outcome')
which in this case is (1 – prob of 'all 4 boys') = $(1 - \frac{1}{16}) = \frac{15}{16}$.

EXAMPLE   "Herbert and his two chums, along with five of Herbert's doting aunties, have to
squeeze onto the back seat of his father's Bentley, en route to Royal Ascot.
Given that Herbert does not sit at either end, and that the seating order is otherwise
random, find the probability of Herbert having his best chums either side of him."

The untrained probabilist wouldn't think of using a tree diagram here,
but see how easy it is when you do. This is the tree diagram you'd draw:

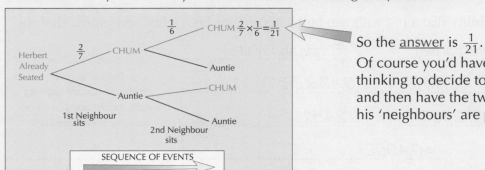

So the answer is $\frac{1}{21}$.
Of course you'd have to do a bit of
thinking to decide to place Herbert first
and then have the two events as each of
his 'neighbours' are placed beside him.

See how useful tree diagrams are

This example shows how a tree diagram once again saves the day. It takes a bit of thinking about to
decide how to do the diagram and which bits you need. Once you've done that it's plain sailing.

Warm-up and Worked Exam Questions

Probability is really not that difficult once you get the hang of it, but it's easy to throw away marks by being a little slap-dash with your calculations. It's important to get loads of practice. Try these questions.

Warm-Up Questions

1) What is the probability of rolling a six three times in a row with a six-sided dice?

2) A sweet is picked out of a bag containing 4 cola bottles and 3 toffees. It is then put back in and a sweet picked out again. What is the probability of getting a cola bottle both times?

3) A playing card is dropped 3 times.
   What is the probability of it landing face up all three times?

4) Three balls are picked randomly from a bag containing 3 blue and 4 red balls.
   What is the probability of getting a ball of each colour?

Worked Exam Question

Take a look at this worked exam question. It's not too hard but it should give you a good idea of what to write. You'll usually get at least one probability question in the exam.

1   Mr Jones is planting crocus bulbs which may produce white or purple flowers.
    The probability that each bulb produces purple flowers is 0.43.

   (a)   What is the probability that a bulb produces white flowers?

   1 – 0.43 = 0.57

   (1 mark)

   (b)   Complete the following tree diagram for two bulbs.

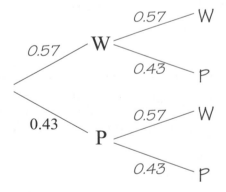

   (2 marks)

   (c)   Find the probability that a pot with two bulbs in contains both white and purple flowers.

   P (White and Purple)   +   P (Purple and White)

   (0.57 × 0.43)   +   (0.43 × 0.57)

   0.2451   +   0.2451

   = 0.4902

   Hint: You may assume that the two events (first bulb, second bulb) are independent and therefore multiply the probabilities.

   (3 marks)

   (d)   Find the probability that neither of the two bulbs produces white flowers.

   0.43 × 0.43 = 0.1849   This is really saying: "what is the probability of getting two purple-flowered bulbs?"

   (2 marks)

Exam Questions

2   Katie has 24 socks in her drawer. 12 of them are grey, 8 of them are black and
     4 of them are red. Katie takes two socks at random, without replacement, from the drawer.
     Calculate the probability that she takes two socks that are the same colour.

     ....
                                                                                                    (5 marks)

3   A school canteen offers a choice of main course and sweet.
     For each course, one of two choices must be selected. The probabilities are shown below.
     Complete the tree diagram:

     (a)

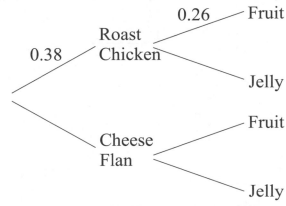

                                                                                                    (1 mark)

     (b)   Work out the probability that a pupil chooses roast chicken and jelly.

     ....
                                                                                                    (2 marks)

4   There are 9 balls in a box. 8 of the balls are yellow and 1 ball is red. Simon selects balls
     at random, without replacement, from the box until he obtains the red ball.
     When he obtains the red ball, he stops selecting.
     By extending the tree diagram shown below, or otherwise, calculate the probability that Simon
     selects the red ball on one of his first three selections.

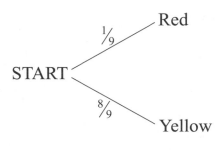

     ....
                                                                                                    (3 marks)

Revision Summary for Unit 1 — 2

Here's the really fun page. The inevitable list of straight-down-the-middle questions to test how much you know. Remember, these questions will sort out (quicker than anything else can) exactly what you <u>know</u> and what you <u>don't</u>. And that's exactly what revision is all about, don't forget: <u>find out what you DON'T know</u> and then learn it <u>until you do</u>. Enjoy.

Keep learning the basic facts until you know them

1) What is sampling all about? When is it needed?

2) Comment on the sampling used in the following statistical investigation: "A survey of motorists carried out in London found that 85% of British people drive Black Cabs."

3)* Steven works in a shoe shop. His boss wants to know which is the most common size of shoe they've sold this month, and how many pairs of that size they've sold on average per week.
   a) Which two values does Steven need to work out: Mean, Median, Mode or Range?
   b) Work out these two values using the information in the table.

Week Size of shoe	1	2	3	4
5	29	11	17	12
6	21	35	7	16
7	2	17	10	2
8	15	6	2	2

4) Write down eight important details about frequency tables.

5)* Jessica's science class are collecting their results in a grouped frequency table. Jessica's result is 5 g. Into which group in the table should her data go?

Mass (g)	$1 < m \leq 5$	$5 < m \leq 10$	$10 < m \leq 15$
Frequency	6	23	5

6)* Calum is writing an article on the Skelly Crag half-marathon for the local paper. He wants to include the mean time taken. Estimate the mean time from the table below.

Time (min)	$60 < t \leq 90$	$90 < t \leq 120$	$120 < t \leq 150$	$150 < t \leq 180$	$180 < t \leq 210$	$210 < t \leq 240$
Frequency	15	60	351	285	206	83

7) Why is it not possible to find the exact value of the mean from a grouped frequency table?

8) Write down four key points about cumulative frequency.

9)* Sean goes for a checkup at the doctors. The doctor measures his height and checks it on a cumulative frequency curve to see how he compares with other 15 year old males.
   a) What's the median height for a 15 year old male?
   b) Sean is 180 cm tall. What percentage of 15 year old boys are taller than Sean?

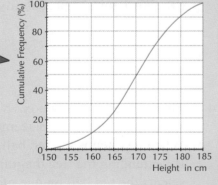

10) What is a histogram?

11) What are the three steps of the method for tackling all histograms?

12) Write down the formula for frequency density.

13) How do you estimate the mean from looking at a histogram?

14)* A newspaper has claimed that a study shows a strong positive correlation between eating cheese and having nightmares. The results of the study are shown here.
   a) What does strong positive correlation mean?
   b) Do you agree with the newspaper claim?

15) What are the AND and OR rules of probability?

16)* Jackie is preparing a game for the school fair. She wants the players to have a less than 10% chance of winning to make sure the school doesn't lose much money. In Jackie's game you roll two dice. If you roll two sixes you win £20. Is the chance of winning less than 10%?

17) What's the formula for relative frequency?

18) Write down four important facts about tree diagrams.

19) Draw a general tree diagram and put all the features on it.

* The answers to these questions can be found on page 220.

Types of Number

A nice easy start to the unit. I can't promise things won't get harder later on, so enjoy it while you can.

1) *Square* Numbers:

(1x1) (2x2) (3x3) (4x4) (5x5)   (6x6) (7x7) (8x8) (9x9) (10x10) (11x11) (12x12)(13x13) (14x14) (15x15)

| 1 | 4 | 9 | 16 | 25 | 36 | 49 | 64 | 81 | 100 | 121 | 144 | 169 | 196 | 225... |

3   5   7   9   11   13   15   17   19   21   23   25   27   29

Note that the <u>DIFFERENCES</u> between the <u>square numbers</u> are all the ODD numbers.

A nifty bit of notation: $3 \times 3 = 3^2$ — "three squared"
$5 \times 5 = 5^2$ — "five squared"

You need to <u>LEARN</u> the first 15 square numbers and make sure you know their <u>SQUARE ROOTS</u> too (see page 51). You'll be expected to use them in the exam <u>without a calculator</u>.

2) *Cube* Numbers:

They're called <u>CUBE NUMBERS</u> because they're like the volumes of this pattern of cubes.

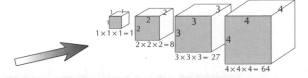

$1 \times 1 \times 1 = 1$
$2 \times 2 \times 2 = 8$
$3 \times 3 \times 3 = 27$
$4 \times 4 \times 4 = 64$

| 1 | 8 | 27 | 64 | 125 | 216 | 343 | 512 | 729 | 1000... |

Another nifty bit of notation: $2 \times 2 \times 2 = 2^3$ — "two cubed"
$7 \times 7 \times 7 = 7^3$ — "seven cubed"

You need to know some of the cube numbers off by heart too — <u>LEARN</u> the cubes of <u>2, 3, 4, 5 and 10</u>.

3) *Powers*:

Powers are 'numbers <u>multiplied by themselves</u> so many times'.
'<u>Two to the power four</u>' = $2^4 = 2 \times 2 \times 2 \times 2 = 16$

Here's the first few <u>POWERS OF 2</u>:

| 2 | 4 | 8 | 16 | 32... |

$2^1=2$ $2^2=4$ $2^3=8$ $2^4=16$ etc...

— there's more on using powers on the next page.

... and the first <u>POWERS OF 10</u> (even easier):

| 10 | 100 | 1000 | 10 000 | 100 000... |

$10^1=10$ $10^2=100$ $10^3=1000$ etc...

Knowing your powers of 10 comes in handy when you're faced with numbers in standard index form (see pages 7 & 8). You need to be able to deal with numbers in standard form in this unit as well, so make sure you understand them.

4) *Prime* Numbers:

Prime numbers only divide by <u>themselves</u> and <u>1</u> (note that 1 is NOT a prime number)

| 2 | 3 | 5 | 7 | 11 | 13 | 17 | 19 | 23 | 29 | 31 | 37 | 41 | 43... |

— see page 55 for all the details on how to find prime numbers.

All these types of number just need learning

You should be able to spot these different types of numbers from a mile away and the only way to do that is to keep writing them down and learning them.

Powers and Roots

Powers are a very useful shorthand:
$$2 \times 2 \times 2 \times 2 \times 2 \times 2 \times 2 = 2^7$$
('two to the power 7')

That bit is easy to remember. Unfortunately, there are <u>ten special rules</u> for powers —
seven easy ones (on this page) and three trickier ones (on the next page).
They are not tremendously exciting, but you do need to know them for the exam:

The **Seven** Easy Rules:

1) When <u>MULTIPLYING</u>, you <u>ADD THE POWERS</u>.

   e.g. $3^4 \times 3^6 = 3^{4+6} = 3^{10}$

2) When <u>DIVIDING</u>, you <u>SUBTRACT THE POWERS</u>.

   e.g. $5^4 \div 5^2 = 5^{4-2} = 5^2$

   The first two only work for
   powers of the same number.

3) When <u>RAISING</u> one power to another, you <u>MULTIPLY THEM</u>.

   e.g. $(3^2)^4 = 3^{2 \times 4} = 3^8$

4) $X^1 = X$, <u>ANYTHING</u> to the <u>POWER 1</u> is just <u>ITSELF</u>.

   e.g. $3^1 = 3, \; 6 \times 6^3 = 6^4$

5) $X^0 = 1$, <u>ANYTHING</u> to the <u>POWER 0</u> is just <u>ONE</u>.

   e.g. $5^0 = 1 \quad 67^0 = 1$

6) $1^x = 1$, <u>1 TO ANY POWER</u> is <u>STILL JUST 1</u>.

   e.g. $1^{23} = 1 \quad 1^{89} = 1 \quad 1^2 = 1$

7) <u>FRACTIONS</u> — Apply power to <u>both TOP and BOTTOM</u>.

   e.g. $\left(1\frac{3}{5}\right)^3 = \left(\frac{8}{5}\right)^3 = \frac{8^3}{5^3} = \frac{512}{125}$

These seven rules are the key to all power questions
If you can add, subtract and multiply, there's nothing here you can't do — as long as you
learn the rules. Try copying them over and over until you can do it with your eyes closed.

Powers and Roots

The *Three* Tricky Rules:

8) <u>NEGATIVE Powers — Turn it Upside-Down</u>

People do have quite a bit of difficulty remembering this.

Whenever you see a negative power you're supposed to immediately think:

> **"That means turn it the other way up and make the power positive"**

Like this: e.g. $7^{-2} = \dfrac{1}{7^2} = \dfrac{1}{49}$
$\qquad \left(\dfrac{3}{5}\right)^{-2} = \left(\dfrac{5}{3}\right)^{+2} = \dfrac{5^2}{3^2} = \dfrac{25}{9}$

9) <u>FRACTIONAL POWERS</u>

The power $\frac{1}{2}$ means <u>Square Root</u>,
$\qquad$ e.g. $25^{\frac{1}{2}} = \sqrt{25} = 5$

The power $\frac{1}{3}$ means <u>Cube Root</u>,
$\qquad\qquad$ $64^{\frac{1}{3}} = \sqrt[3]{64} = 4$ (as 4^3 is 64)

The power $\frac{1}{4}$ means <u>Fourth Root</u> etc.
$\qquad\qquad$ $81^{\frac{1}{4}} = \sqrt[4]{81} = 3$ (as 3^4 is 81) etc.

The one to really watch is when you get a <u>negative fraction</u> like $49^{-\frac{1}{2}}$ — people get mixed up and think that the minus is the square root, and forget to turn it upside down as well.

10) <u>TWO-STAGE FRACTIONAL POWERS</u>

They really like putting these in exam questions so learn the method:
With fractional powers like $64^{\frac{5}{6}}$ always <u>split the fraction</u> into a <u>root</u> and a <u>power</u>, and do them in that order: <u>root</u> first, then <u>power</u>: $(64)^{\frac{1}{6} \times 5} = (64^{\frac{1}{6}})^5 = (2)^5 = 32$

Square Roots can be Positive or *Negative*

Whenever you take the square root of a number, the answer can be <u>positive</u> or <u>negative</u>...

E.g. $\boxed{x^2 = 4 \text{ gives } x = \pm\sqrt{4} = + 2 \text{ or } - 2}$ $\qquad$ *You always get a +ve and −ve version of the <u>same number</u>.*

The reason for it becomes clear when you work backwards by squaring the answers:

$2^2 = 2 \times 2 = 4$ but also $(-2)^2 = (-2) \times (-2) = 4$

These three rules might be a bit trickier — but they are essential

Because these are things which people often get muddled, examiners love to sneak them into the exam — so scribble these rules down and learn them. Then in the exam you'll have the last laugh.

Manipulating Surds and Use of π

RATIONAL NUMBERS Most numbers you deal with are rational. They can always be written as <u>fractions</u>. You'll come across them in 3 different forms:

1) A <u>whole number</u> (either positive (+ve), or negative (–ve)), e.g. 4 $(=\frac{4}{1})$, -5 $(=\frac{-5}{1})$, -12 $(=\frac{-12}{1})$

2) A <u>fraction</u> p/q, where p and q are whole numbers (+ve or –ve), e.g. $\frac{1}{4}$, $-\frac{1}{2}$, $\frac{3}{4}$

3) A <u>terminating or recurring decimal</u>, e.g. 0.125 $(=\frac{1}{8})$, 0.3333333333... $(=\frac{1}{3})$, 0.143143143... $(=\frac{143}{999})$

See p.59 for more on terminating and recurring decimals.

IRRATIONAL NUMBERS are messy! They <u>can't</u> be written as fractions.

1) They are always <u>never-ending non-repeating decimals</u>. π is irrational.

2) <u>Square roots</u> and <u>cube roots</u> are good sources of irrational numbers.

Manipulating Surds — 7 Rules to Learn

Surds are expressions with irrational square roots in them. You <u>MUST USE THEM</u> if they ask you for an <u>EXACT</u> answer. There are 7 rules you need to learn...

1) $\sqrt{a} \times \sqrt{b} = \sqrt{a \times b}$ e.g. $\sqrt{2} \times \sqrt{3} = \sqrt{2 \times 3} = \sqrt{6}$ — also $(\sqrt{b})^2 = b$, fairly obviously

2) $\frac{\sqrt{a}}{\sqrt{b}} = \sqrt{\frac{a}{b}}$ e.g. $\frac{\sqrt{8}}{\sqrt{2}} = \sqrt{\frac{8}{2}} = \sqrt{4} = 2$

3) $\sqrt{a} + \sqrt{b}$ — <u>**DO NOTHING**</u> ... (in other words it is DEFINITELY NOT $\sqrt{a+b}$)

4) $(a + \sqrt{b})^2 = (a + \sqrt{b})(a + \sqrt{b}) = a^2 + 2a\sqrt{b} + b$ (NOT just $a^2 + (\sqrt{b})^2$) *See p.66 for more on multiplying out brackets.*

5) $(a + \sqrt{b})(a - \sqrt{b}) = a^2 + a\sqrt{b} - a\sqrt{b} - (\sqrt{b})^2 = a^2 - b$

6) Express $\frac{3}{\sqrt{5}}$ in the form $\frac{a\sqrt{5}}{b}$ where a and b are whole numbers.

To do this you must '<u>RATIONALISE the denominator</u>', which just means multiplying top and bottom by $\sqrt{5}$: $\frac{3\sqrt{5}}{\sqrt{5}\sqrt{5}} = \frac{3\sqrt{5}}{5}$ so a = 3 and b = 5

7) If you want an <u>exact</u> answer, <u>LEAVE THE SURDS IN</u>.

Even if you got a question like this in a calculator-allowed paper, you shouldn't use a calculator to work it out. You'd get a <u>big fat rounding error</u> — and you'd get the answer <u>WRONG</u>.

Exact calculations using π — Leave π in the answer

π is an <u>irrational</u> number that often comes up in calculations, e.g. in finding the area of a circle. In a calculator-allowed unit you could use the π button on your calculator, unless you're asked for an exact answer. To calculate with π in Unit 2 questions, or to give an <u>exact</u> answer, just <u>leave</u> the π symbol in the calculation.

Example: The formula for the area of a circle is $A = \pi r^2$.
Find the exact area of a circle with radius 4 cm.
Answer:

$A = \pi \times 4^2 = 16\pi$ cm².

Once you get used to them, surds are quite easy

They do seem a bit fiddly with all those square roots everywhere, but with a bit of practice surds can become your best friend. Just learn these simple rules, then practise, practise and practise some more.

Warm-up and Worked Exam Questions

Take a deep breath and go through these warm-up questions one by one.
If you don't know the basic facts there's no way you'll cope with the exam questions.

Warm-Up Questions

1) Choose from the numbers 1, 2, 3, 4, 5, 6, 7, 8, 9, 10:
   Which numbers are (a) square? (b) cube?
   (c) powers of 2? (d) prime?

2) Repeat Question 1 using the numbers 30-40 inclusive.

3) Simplify: a) $4^5 \times 4^{-2}$ b) $6^5 / 6^2$ c) $(3^2)^4$

4) Evaluate: a) $2^1 \times 1^{23} \times 9^0$ b) $(1\frac{2}{7})^2$ c) $27^{2/3}$

5) Work out $\sqrt{5} \times \sqrt{6}$, leaving your answer as a surd.

6) Work out $\sqrt{12} \times \sqrt{3}$, giving your answer as a normal number.

Worked Exam Questions

Exam questions are the best way to practise what you've learnt. After all, they're exactly what you'll have to do on the big day — so work through these worked examples very carefully.

1 Simplify the following expressions, writing your answers in the form x^k.

(a) $\dfrac{x^7}{x^4}$

$\dfrac{x^7}{x^4} = x^{7-4} = x^3$ *You just need to remember the power laws — for dividing, you subtract the powers...*

(1 mark)

(b) $\sqrt[4]{x^9}$

$\sqrt[4]{x^9} = x^{\frac{9}{4}}$ *...for fractional powers, the denominator is a root, i.e. $x^{\frac{1}{a}} = \sqrt[a]{x}$*

(1 mark)

(c) $\sqrt[3]{x^9 x^2}$

$\sqrt[3]{x^9 x^2} = \sqrt[3]{x^{9+2}}$ *First, sort out the powers inside the root — for multiplying, you just add the powers...*

...then use the root / power rule that you used in part b). $= \sqrt[3]{x^{11}} = x^{\frac{11}{3}}$

(2 marks)

2 In a right-angled triangle, the square of the length of the longest side is equal to the sum of the squares of the shorter sides. This is Pythagoras' Theorem.

Use Pythagoras' Theorem to find lengths a and b, leaving your answers in surd form:

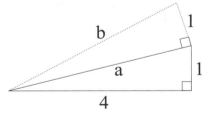

$a^2 = 4^2 + 1^2 = 16 + 1$

$a^2 = 17$ *Leaving "a" in surd form means your answer for "b" will be accurate.*

so $a = \sqrt{17}$

$b^2 = a^2 + 1^2 = (\sqrt{17})^2 + 1^2$

$b^2 = 17 + 1 = 18$

$b = \sqrt{18}$

(3 marks)

Exam Questions

Non-calculator Exam Questions:

Some of these questions would have lots more space for answers in the real exam. We've just squeezed them in here so you get more practice.

3 What is the 15th number in this sequence?

$$1, 4, 9, 16, 25, 36, \ldots$$

....

(1 mark)

4 Simplify these expressions, and say whether each answer is rational or irrational:

(a) $\sqrt{8} \times \sqrt{2}$ ....

(1 mark)

(b) $\sqrt{20} \div \sqrt{8}$ ....

(1 mark)

5 Simplify:

(a) $p^4 \times p^3$

....

(1 mark)

(b) $14t^5 / 7t^2$

....

(1 mark)

(c) $(6a^3d^2)^2$

....

(1 mark)

(d) $a(3^2 + 4^0)$

....

(1 mark)

6 Express $\dfrac{16}{\sqrt[5]{81}}$ in the form $2^m 3^n$.

....

(3 marks)

7 Rationalise the denominator in the expression $\dfrac{2}{\sqrt{7}}$.

....

(2 marks)

Prime Numbers

1) Basically, **PRIME** Numbers **don't divide** by anything...

...and that's the best way to think of them. (Strictly, they divide by themselves and 1).
So prime numbers are all the numbers that <u>don't</u> come up in times tables:

| 2 | 3 | 5 | 7 | 11 | 13 | 17 | 19 | 23 | 29 | 31 | 37... |

For example:

<u>The only numbers</u> that multiply to give 7 are 1 × 7
<u>The only numbers</u> that multiply to give 31 are 1 × 31

In fact the <u>only way</u> to get <u>ANY PRIME NUMBER</u> is <u>1 × ITSELF</u>

2) They **End** in **1**, **3**, **7** or **9**

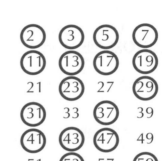

1) <u>1</u> is <u>NOT</u> a prime number.

2) The first four prime numbers are <u>2, 3, 5 and 7</u>.

3) <u>Prime numbers</u> end in <u>1, 3, 7 or 9</u> (2 and 5 are the only exceptions to this rule).

4) But <u>NOT ALL</u> numbers ending in <u>1, 3, 7 or 9</u> are primes, as shown here:
(Only the <u>circled ones</u> are <u>primes</u>)

3) How to **FIND** Prime Numbers — *a very simple method*

1) <u>Since all primes</u> (above 5) <u>end in 1, 3, 7, or 9</u>, then to find a prime number between say, 70 and 80, <u>the only possibilities</u> are: <u>71, 73, 77 and 79</u>.

2) Now, to find which of them <u>ACTUALLY ARE</u> primes you only need to <u>divide each one by 3 and 7</u>. If it doesn't divide exactly by either 3 or 7 then it's a prime.
(This simple rule <u>using just 3 and 7</u> is true for checking primes <u>up to 120</u>.)

So, to find the primes between 70 and 80, just try dividing <u>71, 73, 77 and 79</u> by <u>3 and 7</u>:

71 ÷ 3 = 23 remainder 2   71 ÷ 7 = 10 remainder 1   so <u>71 IS a prime number</u>
                                                                 (because it ends in 1, 3, 7 or 9 and it <u>doesn't divide by 3 or 7</u>)

73 ÷ 3 = 24 remainder 1   73 ÷ 7 = 10 remainder 3   so <u>73 IS a prime number</u>

79 ÷ 3 = 26 remainder 1   79 ÷ 7 = 11 remainder 2   so <u>79 IS a prime number</u>

77 ÷ 3 = 25 remainder 2   <u>BUT</u>: 77 ÷ 7 = <u>11</u> — 11 is a <u>whole number</u> (or 'integer'),
                                                 so <u>77 is NOT a prime</u>, because it <u>divides by 7</u>.

Remember — prime numbers don't come up in times tables

You have to be able to recognise prime numbers. The first few are easy enough to remember by heart, but when it comes to bigger numbers the only way is to use the prime number test.

Multiples, Factors and Prime Factors

Multiples

The <u>MULTIPLES</u> of a number are simply its <u>TIMES TABLE</u>:

So the <u>multiples of 13</u> are... 13 26 39 52 65 78 91 104 ...

Factors

The <u>FACTORS</u> of a number are all the numbers that <u>DIVIDE INTO IT</u>.

There's a special method which guarantees you find them <u>ALL</u>...

EXAMPLE 1: "Find all the factors of 24."

1) Start off with 1 × the number itself, then try 2 ×, then 3 × and so on, listing the pairs in rows like this.
2) Try each one in turn, putting a dash if it doesn't divide exactly.
3) Eventually, when you get a number <u>REPEATED</u>, you <u>STOP</u>.
4) So the <u>FACTORS OF 24</u> are <u>1, 2, 3, 4, 6, 8, 12, 24</u>.

Increasing by 1 each time

1 × 24
2 × 12
3 × 8
4 × 6
5 × –
6 × 4

EXAMPLE 2: "Find all the factors of 64."

1) <u>Check each one in turn</u>, to see if it divides or not.
2) So the <u>FACTORS of 64</u> are <u>1, 2, 4, 8, 16, 32, 64</u>.

1 × 64
2 × 32
3 × –
4 × 16
5 × –
6 × –
7 × –
8 × 8

The 8 has <u>repeated</u> so <u>stop here</u>.

Finding **Prime Factors** — The **Factor Tree**

1) <u>Any number</u> can be broken down into a string of prime numbers all multiplied together — this is called 'Expressing it as a product of prime factors', and it's not difficult so long as you know the method below.

2) The '<u>Factor Tree</u>' method is best. You start at the top and split your number up into factors as shown.

3) Each time you get a prime you <u>ring it</u> and you finally end up with all the prime factors, which you can then arrange in order.

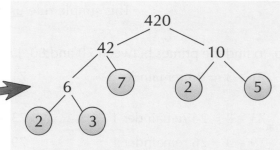

So, 'as a product of prime factors',
420 = 2 × 2 × 3 × 5 × 7

Factors and multiples are easy marks

Factor and multiple questions are simple multiplication and division so there's no reason to lose marks. Practise doing them quickly and accurately and make sure you know what all the words mean.

LCM and HCF

Two big fancy names but don't be put off — they're not complicated.

LCM — 'Lowest Common Multiple'

LCM stands for 'Lowest Common Multiple' — all it means is this:

The SMALLEST number that will DIVIDE BY ALL the numbers in question.

METHOD:
1) LIST the MULTIPLES of ALL the numbers.
2) Find the SMALLEST one that's in ALL the lists.
3) That's the LCM.

It's sometimes called the 'Least Common Multiple'

EXAMPLE: Find the lowest common multiple (LCM) of 6 and 7.

Multiples of 6 are: 6, 12, 18, 24, 30, 36, 42, 48, 54, 60, 66, ...
Multiples of 7 are: 7, 14, 21, 28, 35, 42, 49, 56, 63, 70, 77, ...

So the lowest common multiple (LCM) of 6 and 7 is 42.

HCF — 'Highest Common Factor'

'Highest Common Factor' — all it means is this:

The BIGGEST number that will DIVIDE INTO ALL the numbers in question.

METHOD:
1) LIST the FACTORS of ALL the numbers.
2) Find the BIGGEST one that's in ALL the lists.
3) That's the HCF.

EXAMPLE: Find the highest common factor (HCF) of 36 and 54.

Factors of 36 are: 1, 2, 3, 4, 6, 9, 12, 18, 36
Factors of 54 are: 1, 2, 3, 6, 9, 18, 27, 54

So the highest common factor (HCF) of 36 and 54 is 18.

Another way to work out the HCF is using prime factors (see previous page):
- Write out both numbers as products of their prime factors.
- Multiply together all the numbers that appear in both lists (if the same number appears in both lists more than once, include it more than once.) That's the HCF.
  E.g. $36 = 2 \times 2 \times 3 \times 3$ $54 = 2 \times 3 \times 3 \times 3$
  So the HCF of 36 and 54 is $2 \times 3 \times 3 = 18$.

Don't be put off by the fancy names

Lowest common multiple and highest common factor questions can be a bit intimidating in the exam — but they're easy enough if you take them step by step. It's just multiplication and division again.

Fractions, Decimals and Percentages

The one word that could describe all these three is <u>PROPORTION</u>.

Fractions, decimals and percentages are simply <u>three different ways</u> of expressing a <u>proportion</u> of something — and it's pretty important you should see them as <u>closely related</u> <u>and completely interchangeable</u> with each other. This table shows the really common conversions which you should know straight off without having to work them out:

Fraction	Decimal	Percentage
$\frac{1}{2}$	0.5	50%
$\frac{1}{4}$	0.25	25%
$\frac{3}{4}$	0.75	75%
$\frac{1}{3}$	0.333333...	33.333...%
$\frac{2}{3}$	0.666666...	66.666...%
$\frac{1}{10}$	0.1	10%
$\frac{2}{10}$	0.2	20%
$\frac{X}{10}$	0.X	X0%
$\frac{1}{5}$	0.2	20%
$\frac{2}{5}$	0.4	40%

Check out page 12 for more on dealing with percentages. But remember, you can't use your calculator in the Unit 2 exam.

The more of those conversions you learn, the better — but for those that you <u>don't know</u>, you must <u>also learn</u> how to <u>convert</u> between the three types. These are the methods:

$$\text{Fraction} \xrightarrow{\text{Divide}} \text{Decimal} \xrightarrow{\times \text{ by 100}} \text{Percentage}$$

e.g. $\frac{1}{2}$ is $1 \div 2$ = 0.5   e.g. 0.5×100 = 50%

$$\text{Fraction} \xleftarrow[\text{The awkward one}]{} \text{Decimal} \xleftarrow[\div \text{ by 100}]{} \text{Percentage}$$

<u>Converting decimals to fractions</u> is fairly easy to do when you have <u>exact</u> (terminating) decimals. It's best illustrated by examples — you should be able to work out the rule...

$0.6 = \frac{6}{10}$ $0.3 = \frac{3}{10}$ $0.7 = \frac{7}{10}$ $0.x = \frac{x}{10}$ etc.

$0.12 = \frac{12}{100}$ $0.78 = \frac{78}{100}$ $0.45 = \frac{45}{100}$ $0.05 = \frac{5}{100}$ etc.

$0.345 = \frac{345}{1000}$ $0.908 = \frac{908}{1000}$ $0.024 = \frac{24}{1000}$ $0.xyz = \frac{xyz}{1000}$ etc.

Some of these can then be <u>cancelled</u> <u>down</u> — see p.60

<u>Recurring</u> decimals like 0.3333333 are actually just <u>exact fractions</u> in disguise. There is a simple method for converting them into fractions — see the next page...

Fractions, decimals and percentages are interchangeable

It's important you remember that a fraction, decimal or percentage can be converted into either of the other two forms. And it's even more important that you learn how to do it.

Fractions and Recurring Decimals

Recurring and terminating decimals can always be written as fractions.

Recurring or Terminating...

1) Recurring decimals have a pattern of numbers which repeats forever, e.g. $\frac{1}{3}$ is the decimal 0.333333...
Note, it doesn't have to be a single digit that repeats. You could have, for instance: 0.143143143....

2) Terminating decimals are finite, e.g $\frac{1}{20}$ is the decimal 0.05.

The denominator (bottom number) of a fraction, tells you if it'll be a recurring or terminating decimal when you convert it. Fractions where the denominator has prime factors of only 2 or 5 will give terminating decimals. All other fractions will give recurring decimals.

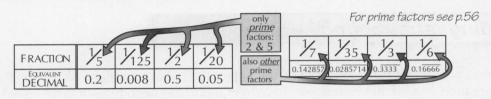

For prime factors see p.56

| FRACTION | $\frac{1}{5}$ | $\frac{1}{125}$ | $\frac{1}{2}$ | $\frac{1}{20}$ | only *prime* factors: 2 & 5 | $\frac{1}{7}$ | $\frac{1}{35}$ | $\frac{1}{3}$ | $\frac{1}{6}$ |
| EQUIVALENT DECIMAL | 0.2 | 0.008 | 0.5 | 0.05 | also *other* prime factors | 0.142857 | 0.0285714 | 0.3333 | 0.16666 |

You should have worked out from the previous page the easy method for converting terminating decimals into fractions — you just divide by a power of 10 depending on the number of digits after the decimal point. Converting recurring decimals isn't much harder once you've learnt the method...

Recurring Decimals into Fractions

There's two ways to do it: 1) by UNDERSTANDING   2) by just LEARNING THE RESULT.

The Understanding Method:

1) Find the length of the repeating sequence and multiply by 10, 100, 1000, 10 000 or whatever to move it all up past the decimal point by one full repeated lump:
   E.g. 0.234234234... × 1000 = 234.234234...

2) Subtract the original number, r, from the new one (which in this case is 1000r)
   i.e. 1000r − r = 234.234234... − 0.234234... giving: 999r = 234

3) Then just DIVIDE to leave r: $r = \frac{234}{999}$, and cancel if possible: $r = \frac{26}{111}$

The 'Just Learning The Result' Method:

The fraction always has the repeating unit on the top and the same number of nines on the bottom — easy as that. Look at these and marvel at the elegant simplicity of it.

$$0.4444444... = \frac{4}{9} \qquad 0.34343434... = \frac{34}{99}$$

$$0.124124124... = \frac{124}{999} \qquad 0.14561456... = \frac{1456}{9999}$$

Always check if it will CANCEL DOWN of course, e.g. $0.363636... = \frac{36}{99} = \frac{4}{11}$.

Understanding or just learning, the choice is yours

It doesn't matter if you decide to understand turning recurring decimals into fractions or just learn the pattern — remember how to do it and practise it and there are some easy marks to be had.

Fractions

This page shows you how to cope with fraction calculations without your calculator.

1) Multiplying — easy

Multiply top and bottom separately:
$$\frac{3}{5} \times \frac{4}{7} = \frac{3 \times 4}{5 \times 7} = \frac{12}{35}$$

2) Dividing — quite easy

Turn the 2nd fraction UPSIDE DOWN and then multiply:
$$\frac{3}{4} \div \frac{1}{3} = \frac{3}{4} \times \frac{3}{1} = \frac{3 \times 3}{4 \times 1} = \frac{9}{4}$$

3) Adding, subtracting — more difficult

Add or subtract TOP LINES ONLY but only if the bottom numbers (denominators) are the same. If they're not, you have to equalise the denominator first — see below.
$$\frac{5}{7} - \frac{3}{7} = \frac{2}{7}$$
$$\frac{2}{6} + \frac{1}{6} = \frac{3}{6}$$

4) Cancelling down — easy

Divide top and bottom by the same number, till they won't go any further:
$$\frac{18}{24} = \frac{6}{8} = \frac{3}{4}$$
(÷3, ÷2)

5) Finding a fraction of something — just multiply

Multiply the 'something' by the TOP of the fraction, then divide it by the BOTTOM:
$$\frac{9}{20} \text{ of } £360 = (9 \times £360) \div 20 = \frac{£3240}{20} = £162$$

6) Equalising the Denominator

This comes in handy for ordering fractions by size, and for adding or subtracting fractions. You need to find a common multiple of all the denominators:

Example: Put these fractions in ascending order of size: $\frac{8}{3}, \frac{6}{4}, \frac{12}{5}$

Lowest common multiple of 3, 4 and 5 is 60 so put all the fractions over 60...
$$\frac{8}{3} = \frac{8}{3} \times \frac{20}{20} = \frac{160}{60}$$
$$\frac{6}{4} = \frac{6}{4} \times \frac{15}{15} = \frac{90}{60}$$
$$\frac{12}{5} = \frac{12}{5} \times \frac{12}{12} = \frac{144}{60}$$

So the correct order is $\frac{90}{60}, \frac{144}{60}, \frac{160}{60}$ i.e. $\frac{6}{4}, \frac{12}{5}, \frac{8}{3}$

Ratios

You've already done some ratios stuff in Unit 1, but you need some more details for Unit 2...

Using The **Formula Triangle** in **Ratio** Questions

EXAMPLE: "Mortar is made from sand and cement in the ratio 7 : 2.
If 9 buckets of sand are used, how much cement is needed?"

This is a fairly common type of exam question and it can seem pretty tricky
— but once you start using the formula triangle method below, it's a bit of a breeze...

*See p.172-173
for more on
formula triangles*

This is the basic <u>FORMULA TRIANGLE</u> for ratios, <u>but NOTE</u>:

1) <u>THE RATIO MUST BE THE RIGHT WAY ROUND</u>, with the <u>FIRST NUMBER IN THE RATIO</u> relating to the item <u>ON TOP</u> in the triangle.

2) You'll always need to <u>CONVERT THE RATIO</u> into its <u>EQUIVALENT FRACTION or DECIMAL</u> to work out the answer.

1) Here's the formula triangle for the mortar question...
2) The trick is to replace the ratio 7 : 2 by its
   <u>EQUIVALENT FRACTION</u> — 7/2, or 3.5 as a decimal (7 ÷ 2).

So <u>covering up cement in the triangle</u> gives us
   'cement = sand / (7 : 2)'
   i.e. '9 ÷ $\frac{7}{2}$' = 9 × $\frac{2}{7}$ = $\frac{18}{7}$ or about <u>2½ buckets of cement</u>.

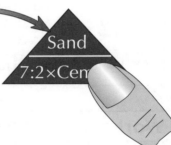

Proportional **Division**

In a <u>proportional division</u> question a <u>TOTAL AMOUNT</u> is to be <u>split in a certain ratio</u>.

EXAMPLE: "£9100 is to be split in the ratio 2 : 4 : 7. Find the 3 amounts."

The key word here is <u>PARTS</u> — concentrate on 'parts' and it becomes quite painless:

1) <u>ADD UP THE PARTS:</u>
   The ratio 2 : 4 : 7 means there will be a total of 13 <u>parts</u>, i.e. 2 + 4 + 7 = <u>13 PARTS</u>

2) <u>FIND THE AMOUNT FOR ONE "PART"</u>
   Just divide the <u>total amount</u> by the number of <u>parts</u>:
   £9100 ÷ 13 = <u>£700</u> (= 1 PART)

3) <u>HENCE FIND THE THREE AMOUNTS:</u>
   2 parts = 2 × 700 = <u>£1400</u>,   4 parts = 4 × 700 = <u>£2800</u>,   7 parts = <u>£4900</u>

Ratios — remember to turn them into fractions

The only time you don't turn ratios into fractions is with proportional division questions.
Then it's the amount per "part" that matters. Once you've got that, working out the rest is easy.

Warm-up and Worked Exam Questions

This stuff is pretty straightforward, but that doesn't mean you can get away without learning the facts and practising the questions. You should have learnt the facts already — try these and we'll see.

Warm-Up Questions

1) Explain why 231 is not a prime number.

2) Find all the factors of 40.

3) Write 40 as a product of its prime factors.

4) What percentage is the same as $\frac{2}{5}$?

5) What percentage is the same as $\frac{2}{3}$?

6) a) What fraction is the same as 0.4?
   b) What fraction is the same as 0.444444...?
   c) What fraction is the same as 0.45454545...?

7) a) What decimal is the same as $\frac{7}{10}$?   b) What decimal is the same as $\frac{7}{9}$?

8) Work these out, then simplify your answers:
   a) $\frac{2}{5} \times \frac{2}{3}$ b) $\frac{2}{5} \div \frac{2}{3}$ c) $\frac{2}{5} + \frac{2}{3}$ d) $\frac{2}{3} - \frac{2}{5}$

9) Divide 180 in the ratio 3 : 4 : 5.

Worked Exam Question

Take a look at this worked exam question. It's not too hard, but it should give you a good idea of what to write. Make the most of the handy hints now — they won't be there in the exam.

1   By writing 240 and 150 as a product of their prime factors,
    find the Highest Common Factor (HCF) of 240 and 150.

Start by drawing a factor tree for each number.

240

24   10

12 ②   ② ⑤

150

15   10

③ ⑤   ② ⑤

12

6 ·②

② ③

So 240 = 2 × 2 × 2 × 2 × 3 × 5

and 150 = 2 × 3 × 5 × 5

The Highest Common Factor is the highest number which divides into both 240 and 150. To find it, we need to look at which numbers are in both lists of prime factors and multiply them together.

The numbers in both lists are 2, 3 and 5, so HCF = 2 × 3 × 5 = 30

(3 marks)

Exam Questions

Non-calculator Exam Questions:

2   (a)   Express 168 as a product of prime factors.

....
(1 mark)

(b)   What is the highest common factor (HCF) of 168 and 210?

....
(2 marks)

3   Calculate   (a) $5\frac{2}{7} - 2\frac{3}{5}$

....
(2 marks)

(b) $2\frac{2}{3} \times 3\frac{3}{4}$

....
(2 marks)

4   Natalie works part time. Each week, she gives $\frac{1}{10}$ of her wages to charity,
she puts $\frac{1}{3}$ of her wages into a savings account, and spends the rest.
In one week, Natalie earnt £60. How much did she have to spend that week?

....
(3 marks)

5   Express $0.\dot{2}\dot{7}$ as a fraction in its lowest terms.   *$0.\dot{2}\dot{7}$ just means 0.272727...*

....
(2 marks)

6   Three families, the Andersons, the Brents and the Campbells go out for dinner together.
At the end of the meal, they work out that the Brents owe three times as much as the
Campbells, and the Andersons owe half as much as the Brents.

a)   In what ratio is the bill divided between the three families?
Write your answer in its simplest form.

....
(2 marks)

b)   The total bill is £187. How much does each family owe?

....

Andersons: £ _____, Brents £ _____, Campbells £ _____
(3 marks)

Algebra — Basics

Negative numbers crop up everywhere so you need to learn this rule for dealing with them:

+	+	makes	+
+	−	makes	−
−	+	makes	−
−	−	makes	+

Only to be used when:

1) <u>Multiplying or dividing</u>:   e.g. $-2 \times 3 = \underline{-6}$ $-8 \div -2 = \underline{+4}$ $-4p \times -2 = \underline{+8p}$

2) <u>Two signs are together</u>:   e.g. $5 - -4 = 5 + 4 = \underline{9}$ $4 + -6 - -7 = 4 - 6 + 7 = \underline{5}$

Letters *Multiplied* Together

Watch out for these combinations of letters in algebra that regularly catch people out:

1) abc means a×b×c. The ×s are often left out to make it clearer.

2) gn^2 means g×n×n. Note that only the n is squared, not the g as well, e.g. πr^2.

3) $(gn)^2$ means g×g×n×n. The brackets mean that <u>BOTH</u> letters are squared.

4) $p(q - r)^3$ means $p \times (q - r) \times (q - r) \times (q - r)$. Only the brackets get cubed.

5) -3^2 is a bit ambiguous. It should either be written $(-3)^2 = 9$, or $-(3^2) = -9$.

EXAMPLE   Substitute -5 in place of x in the expression $3x^2 + 4$

ANSWER $3x^2 + 4 = (3 \times x \times x) + 4 = (3 \times -5 \times -5) + 4 = (3 \times 25) + 4 = 75 + 4 = \underline{79}$

Terms, Expressions, Equations, Formulas and Identities

You need to know the difference between these five things, and be able to spot them all.

1) <u>TERM</u>: A term is a collection of letters, numbers and brackets all multiplied/divided together.
   E.g. 8, -9a, $x(y^2 + 4)$. See the next page for more on terms.

2) <u>EXPRESSION</u>: This is just a bunch of terms added or subtracted together. (Or it could just be one
   term on its own.) E.g. y^2, 2 + 6, mx + 2, $3y^3 - 2n$.

3) <u>EQUATION</u>: This is <u>two expressions</u> joined with an <u>equals sign</u>. It says that the two expressions
   either side of the equals sign have the same value. E.g. $2x^2 = 3x + 2$.

4) <u>FORMULA</u>: This is a <u>relationship</u> or <u>rule</u> for working something out, written in symbols.
   E.g. A = ½bh (formula for the area of a triangle, p.121) or s = d ÷ t (formula for speed, p.173).

5) <u>IDENTITY</u>: This is an equation that's true for <u>all values of the variables</u>. E.g. a + b = b + a.
   It doesn't matter what 'a' and 'b' are — this is always true.

Identities are sometimes written with a ≡ instead of an = sign — you read it as 'is equivalent to'.

Algebra — Simplifying

The next four pages have some really important algebra rules. You'll find yourself using these quite a lot, so it's a good idea to learn them now rather than struggling later on...

1) Terms

1) **A TERM IS A COLLECTION OF NUMBERS, LETTERS AND BRACKETS, all multiplied/divided together.**

2) Terms are separated by <u>+ and − signs</u>. E.g. $4x^2 - 3py - 5 + 3p$

3) Terms always have a + or − attached to the <u>front of them</u>. E.g.

$$(-4xy) \quad (+\ 5x^2) \quad (-\ 2y) \quad (+\ 6y^2) \quad (+\ 4)$$

Invisible + sign   'xy' term   'x²' term   'y' term   'y²' term   'number' term

2) Simplifying or 'Collecting Like Terms'

EXAMPLE   Simplify $2x - 4 + 5x + 6$

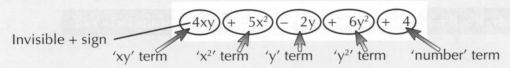

Invisible + sign

number terms

x-terms

$$(2x)(-4)(+5x)(+6) \quad = \quad (+2x)(+5x)(-4)(+6)$$
$$= \quad 7x \qquad +2 \qquad = \underline{7x + 2}$$

1) Put <u>bubbles</u> round each term — be sure you capture the <u>+/− sign</u> in front of each.

2) Then you can move the bubbles into the <u>best order</u> so that <u>like terms</u> are together.

3) "<u>Like terms</u>" have exactly the same combination of letters, e.g. x-terms or xy-terms.

4) <u>Combine like terms</u>.

You need to know what terms are — and how to collect like ones

Terms are a collection of numbers and letters separated by + and − signs. When you collect like terms together, you combine x terms, or y terms, or xy terms, or x^2 terms or y^2 terms or...

Algebra — Brackets

3) *Multiplying* out Brackets

1) The thing <u>outside</u> the brackets multiplies <u>each separate term</u> inside the brackets.

$$3(2x + 5) = \underline{6x + 15}$$

2) When letters are multiplied together, they are just written next to each other, pq.

$$4p(3r - 2t) = \underline{12pr - 8pt}$$

3) Remember, $R \times R = R^2$, and TY^2 means $T \times Y \times Y$, whilst $(TY)^2$ means $T \times T \times Y \times Y$.

4) Remember a minus outside the bracket <u>REVERSES ALL THE SIGNS</u> when you multiply.

$$-4(3p^2 - 7q^3) = -12p^2 + 28q^3 \quad \text{(note both signs have been reversed)}$$

5) <u>DOUBLE BRACKETS</u> — you get <u>4 terms</u>, and usually 2 of them combine to leave <u>3 terms</u>.

$$
\begin{aligned}
(2P - 4)(3P + 1) \quad &= (2P \times 3P) + (2P \times 1) + (-4 \times 3P) + (-4 \times 1) \\
&= \quad 6P^2 \quad + \quad 2P \quad -12P \quad -4 \\
&= \quad \underline{6P^2 - 10P - 4} \qquad \text{(these 2 combine together)}
\end{aligned}
$$

6) <u>SQUARED BRACKETS</u> — always write these out as <u>TWO BRACKETS</u>:

E.g. $(3d + 5)^2$ should be written out as $(3d + 5)(3d + 5)$ and then worked out as above.
YOU SHOULD ALWAYS GET <u>FOUR</u> TERMS from a pair of brackets.
The usual <u>WRONG ANSWER</u> is $(3d + 5)^2 = 9d^2 + 25$ (eeek)
It should be: $(3d + 5)^2 = (3d + 5)(3d + 5) = 9d^2 + 15d + 15d + 25 = \underline{9d^2 + 30d + 25}$

People often make mistakes multiplying out brackets

Remember the usual wrong answer for $(3d + 5)^2$. You should get four terms. As long as you write it out in full as $(3d + 5)(3d + 5)$ and do it like any other double brackets, then you won't go wrong.

Algebra — Factorising

4) Factorising — putting brackets in

This is the <u>exact reverse</u> of multiplying out brackets. Here's the method to follow:

1) Take out the <u>biggest number</u> that goes into all the terms.

2) <u>Take each letter in turn</u> and take out the <u>highest power</u> (e.g. x, x^2 etc) that will go into EVERY term.

3) Open the brackets and fill in all the bits needed to <u>reproduce each term</u>.

EXAMPLE   Factorise $15x^4y + 20x^2y^3z - 35x^3yz^2$

<u>Answer:</u> $5x^2y(3x^2 + 4y^2z - 7xz^2)$

Biggest number that'll divide into 15, 20 and 35.

Highest powers of x and y that will go into all three terms.

z was not in ALL terms so it can't come out as a <u>common factor</u>.

> <u>REMEMBER:</u>   The bits <u>taken out</u> and put at the front are the <u>common factors</u>.
> The bits <u>inside the brackets</u> are what's needed to get back to the <u>original terms</u> if you multiply the brackets out again.

D.O.T.S. — The Difference Of Two Squares:

$$a^2 - b^2 = (a + b)(a - b)$$

The 'difference of two squares' (D.O.T.S. for short) is where you have 'one thing squared' take away 'another thing squared'. Too many people have more trouble than they should with this, probably because they don't make enough effort to learn it as a separate item in its own right. Better learn it now, before it's too late.

1) Factorise $9P^2 - 16Q^2$.

> Answer: $9P^2 - 16Q^2 = (3P + 4Q)(3P - 4Q)$

2) Factorise $1 - T^4$.

> Answer: $1 - T^4 = (1 + T^2)(1 - T^2)$

3) Factorise $3K^2 - 75H^2$.

> Answer: $3K^2 - 75H^2 = 3(K^2 - 25H^2) = 3(K + 5H)(K - 5H)$

D.O.T.S. is straightforward as long as you recognise the pattern

Once you've seen one D.O.T.S. question you've seen them all because they all follow the same basic pattern. The third example is the trickiest one because it doesn't look like a D.O.T.S. However if you're on your guard you'll see that taking out the factor of three makes everything look d.o.t. ier.

Algebra — Algebraic Fractions

5) Algebraic **Fractions**

The basic rules are exactly the same as for ordinary fractions.

1) *Multiplying* (easy)

Multiply top and bottom separately and cancel if possible:

$$\text{e.g.} \quad \frac{st}{10w^3} \times \frac{35s^2tw}{6}$$

$$= \frac{35s^3t^2w}{60w^3} = \frac{7s^3t^2}{12w^2}$$

2) *Dividing* (easy)

Turn the second one upside down, then multiply and cancel if possible:

$$\text{e.g.} \quad \frac{12}{p+4} \div \frac{4(p-3)}{3(p+4)}$$

$$= \frac{\cancel{12}^{3}}{\cancel{p+4}} \times \frac{3\cancel{(p+4)}}{\cancel{4}(p-3)} = \frac{9}{p-3}$$

3) *Adding/subtracting* (not so easy)

Always get a common denominator, i.e. same bottom line
(by cross-multiplying) and then <u>ADD TOP LINES ONLY</u>:

$$\frac{t-2p}{3t-p} - \frac{1}{3} = \frac{3(t-2p)}{3(3t-p)} - \frac{1(3t-p)}{3(3t-p)}$$

$$= \frac{3t-6p-3t+p}{3(3t-p)} = \frac{-5p}{3(3t-p)}$$

It's exactly the same as normal fractions

This stuff should be second nature now because the rules are the same as those for normal fractions.
OK, it might look a bit harder with all those letters instead of numbers, but that's algebra for you.

Solving Equations

<u>Solving equations</u> means finding the value of x from something like: $3x + 5 = 4 - 5x$.
Now, not a lot of people know this, but <u>exactly the same method applies</u> to both <u>solving equations</u> and <u>rearranging formulas</u>, as illustrated over the next two pages.

> **1) EXACTLY THE SAME METHOD APPLIES TO BOTH FORMULAS AND EQUATIONS.**
> **2) THE SAME SEQUENCE OF STEPS APPLIES EVERY TIME.**

To illustrate the sequence of steps we'll use this equation:
$$\sqrt{2 - \frac{x + 4}{2x + 5}} = 3$$

The *Six Steps* Applied to *Equations*

1) Get rid of any square root signs by <u>squaring both sides</u>: $2 - \dfrac{x + 4}{2x + 5} = 9$

2) Get everything off the bottom by <u>cross-multiplying</u> up to <u>EVERY OTHER TERM</u>:

$$②\;\frac{x + 4}{2x + 5}\;⑨ \;\Rightarrow\; 2(2x + 5) - (x + 4) = 9(2x + 5)$$

3) <u>Multiply out</u> any brackets: $\qquad\qquad 4x + 10 - x - 4 = 18x + 45$

4) Collect all <u>subject terms</u> on one side of the '=' and all <u>non-subject terms</u> on the other. Remember to reverse the +/– sign of any term that crosses the '='

+18x moves across the '=' and becomes –18x
+10 moves across the '=' and becomes –10
–4 moves across the '=' and becomes +4

$$4x + 10 - x - 4 = 18x + 45$$
$$4x - x - 18x = 45 - 10 + 4$$

5) <u>Combine together like terms</u> on each side of the equation, and reduce it to the form '<u>Ax = B</u>', where A and B are just numbers (or bunches of letters, in the case of formulas):

$-15x = 39$
('Ax = B':
  A = -15, B = 39, x is the subject)

6) Finally <u>slide the A underneath the B</u> to give ' $x = \dfrac{B}{A}$ ', divide, and that's your answer.

$$x = \frac{39}{-15} = -2.6$$

So <u>x = –2.6</u>

The *Seventh Step* (if You Need It)

If the term you're trying to find is squared, don't panic.

Follow steps 1) to 6) like normal, but solve it for x^2 instead of x:

7) <u>Take the square root</u> of both sides and stick a ± sign in front of the expression on the right:

$x^2 = 9$
$x = \pm 3$

Don't forget the ± sign...
(see p.51 if you don't know what I mean).

Rearranging Formulas

Rearranging formulas means making one letter the subject, e.g. getting 'y = ' from '2x + z = 3(y + 2p)'.

We'll illustrate this by making 'y' the subject of this formula: $\quad M = \sqrt{2K - \dfrac{K^2}{2y + 1}}$

The **Six Steps** Applied to **Formulas**

1) Get rid of any square root signs by <u>squaring both sides</u>: $\qquad M^2 = 2K - \dfrac{K^2}{2y + 1}$

2) Get everything off the bottom by <u>cross-multiplying</u> up to <u>EVERY OTHER TERM</u>:

$$M^2 = 2K - \frac{K^2}{2y + 1} \Rightarrow M^2(2y + 1) = 2K(2y + 1) - K^2$$

3) <u>Multiply out</u> any brackets: $\qquad\qquad 2yM^2 + M^2 = 4Ky + 2K - K^2$

4) Collect all <u>subject terms</u> on one side of the '=' and all <u>non-subject terms</u> on the other. Remember to reverse the +/– sign of any term that crosses the '='.

+4Ky moves across the '=' and becomes –4Ky
+M² moves across the '=' and becomes –M²

$$2yM^2 + M^2 = 4Ky + 2K - K^2$$
$$2yM^2 - 4Ky = -M^2 + 2K - K^2$$

5) <u>Combine together like terms</u> on each side of the equation, and reduce it to the form '<u>Ax = B</u>', where A and B are just bunches of letters which <u>DON'T</u> include the subject (y). Note that the LHS has to be <u>FACTORISED</u>:

$$(2M^2 - 4K)y = 2K - K^2 - M^2$$

('Ax = B' i.e. A = (2M² – 4K), B = 2K – K² – M², y is the subject)

6) Finally <u>slide the A underneath the B</u> to give 'x = $\dfrac{B}{A}$', (cancel if possible) and that's your answer. $\qquad$ So $\quad y = \dfrac{2K - K^2 - M^2}{(2M^2 - 4K)}$

The **Seventh Step** (if You Need It)

If the term you're trying to make the subject of the equation is squared, this is what you do:

$\qquad M = \sqrt{2K - \dfrac{K^2}{2y^2 + 1}}$

Follow steps 1) to 6), $\quad y^2 = \dfrac{2K - K^2 - M^2}{(2M^2 - 4K)}$ and then...

(I've skipped steps 1) - 6) because they're exactly the same as the first example — but with y² instead of y.)

7) <u>Take the square root</u> of both sides and stick a ± sign in front of the expression on the right:

$$y = \pm\sqrt{\frac{2K - K^2 - M^2}{(2M^2 - 4K)}}$$

Remember — square roots can be +ve or –ve. See p.51.

Warm-up and Worked Exam Questions

It's easy to think you've learnt everything in the section until you try the warm-up questions. Don't panic if there are bits you've forgotten. Just go back over them until they're firmly fixed in your brain.

Warm-Up Questions

1) Make sure you know and can apply the rules of signs. Here's a quick test for you:
   a) $-1 + 3$ b) $-1 - -3$ c) $4 - -2$ d) $4 + -2$
   e) -1×-3 f) $-1 \div -3$ g) 4×-2 h) $4 \div -2$.

2) Simplify: a) $4a + c - 2a - 6c$ b) $3r^2 - 2r + 4r^2 - 1 - 3r$.

3) Multiply out:
   a) $4(2p + 7)$ b) $(4x - 2)(2x + 1)$ c) $a(5a - 3)$.

4) Factorise:
   a) $6p - 12q + 4$ b) $4cd^2 - 2cd + 10c^2d^3$.

5) Factorise $x^2 - 4y^2$.   *HINT: Remember D.O.T.S.*

6) Express as single fractions: *Algebraic fractions work like number fractions.*
   a) $\dfrac{x}{2} + \dfrac{3x}{5}$ b) $\dfrac{abc}{d} \div \dfrac{b^2}{dc}$

7) Solve these equations to find the value of x:
   a) $8x - 5 = 19$ b) $3(2x + 7) = 3$ c) $4x - 9 = x + 6$.

8) Identify the subject in each of these formulas:
   a) $p = \sqrt{\dfrac{ml^2}{h}}$ b) $t = px - y^3$.

Worked Exam Questions

These worked examples are exactly like you'll get in the real exam,
except here they've got the answers written in for you already — pretty handy.

1   (a)   Simplify $4(3x + 4) - 3(x - 2)$.

Be careful — this is -3 × -2 = +6

$$4(3x + 4) - 3(x - 2) = 12x + 16 - 3x + 6 = 9x + 22$$

(2 marks)

(b)   Factorise $36p^2 - 25q^2$.

$$36p^2 - 25q^2 = (6p + 5q)(6p - 5q)$$

It's a squared thing minus another squared thing which means it's the difference of 2 squares.

(2 marks)

(c)   Expand and simplify $(3c + 4)(2c - 1)$.

$$(3c + 4)(2c - 1) = 6c^2 - 3c + 8c - 4 = 6c^2 + 5c - 4$$

(2 marks)

Worked Exam Questions

2   (a)   Simplify $8p^2q - 3pq + 2pq^2 - 4p^2q - 7pq$.

pq² is a different term from p²q so keep them separate

$8p^2q - 3pq + 2pq^2 - 4p^2q - 7pq = 4p^2q - 10pq + 2pq^2$

(2 marks)

(b)   Factorise fully $16a^2b - 4ab^2 + 8abc$.

$16a^2b - 4ab^2 + 8abc = 4ab(4a - b + 2c)$

(2 marks)

(c)   Expand and simplify $(5s - 2)^2$.

$(5s - 2)^2 = (5s - 2)(5s - 2)$

$= 25s^2 - 10s - 10s + 4 = 25s^2 - 20s + 4$

(2 marks)

3   Solve for p:

(a) $\dfrac{500}{p} = 16$

$\dfrac{500}{p} = 16$ so $\dfrac{500}{16} = p$ so $p = \dfrac{125}{4} = 31\frac{1}{4}$

(2 marks)

(b) $10 - \dfrac{p + 3}{2} = \dfrac{(2p + 1)}{3}$

To get rid of the fractions, multiply all three terms by 6 (the LCM of 2 and 3).

$10 - \dfrac{(p + 3)}{2} = \dfrac{(2p + 1)}{3} \Rightarrow 60 - 3(p + 3) = 2(2p + 1)$

$\Rightarrow 60 - 3p - 9 = 4p + 2$

$\Rightarrow 49 = 7p$

$\Rightarrow p = 7$

(3 marks)

4   (a)   Expand $(3x + p)^2$.

$(3x + p)^2 = (3x + p)(3x + p) = 9x^2 + 6px + p^2$

(2 marks)

(b)   Find the positive values of p and q that would make $(3x + p)^2 = 9x^2 + qx + 16$.

$9x^2 + 6px + p^2 = 9x^2 + qx + 16 \Rightarrow p^2 = 16$, so $p = 4$ *(positive value)*

and $6p = q$, so $q = 24$

(2 marks)

Exam Questions

Non-calculator Exam Questions:

5   Simplify these expressions:

(a) $3x^2y - 2xy^2 + x^2y - 4y^2x$.

....

(2 marks)

(b) $4(k + 2r) - 3k - 2(r + k)$.

....

(2 marks)

6   Multiply out the brackets and simplify if possible:

(a) $4(2x - 3) - 3(4 + 3x)$.

....

(2 marks)

(b) $(3c - 1)(2c + 6)$.

....

(2 marks)

7   Express as a single fraction:

(a) $\dfrac{8}{3x} + 2$.

....

(1 mark)

(b) $\dfrac{x^2y}{z} + \dfrac{xy^3}{3z}$.

....

(2 marks)

8   (a)   Factorise $12c^2d^3 + 18cd^2 - 30c^3d^4$.

....

(2 marks)

(b)   (i)   Simplify $-2bc \times -4b^2d$.

....

(2 marks)

(ii)   Simplify $t - t(t - 1)$.

....

(2 marks)

Exam Questions

9   Factorise:

(a) $2cx + xy + 2ac + ay$.

....
(3 marks)

(b) $16x^2 - 4p^2$.

....
(2 marks)

10 Solve these equations to find the value of x:

(a) $7x - 3(x + 1) = 7$.

....
(2 marks)

(b) $\dfrac{3x - 1}{5} = \dfrac{x}{4} + \dfrac{1}{2}$.

....
(3 marks)

11 (a) Expand $(x - 3)^2$.

....
(2 marks)

(b) Simplify $(x - 3)^2 - x(x - 4)$.

....
(2 marks)

(c) Solve the equation $(x - 3)^2 - x(x - 4) = 7x + 18$.

....
(2 marks)

12 The cost of a blank CD is 33p and the admin charge for copying a CD is 5p.
Postage of p pence per CD is added.

(a) Write a formula for the cost (£c) of buying, copying and posting n CDs.

....
(2 marks)

(b) What will be the total cost of sending out 150 CDs, each using one second-class
stamp of 32p?

....
(2 marks)

Revision Summary for Unit 2 — 1

I'm sure you know what you need to do with these by now. Try them all, and if there are any you struggle with, go back and revise the pages again. I know it's not much fun, but it's the only way to make sure you know all this stuff.

Keep learning the basic facts until you know them

1) What are square numbers, cube numbers and prime numbers?

2) List the first ten of each from memory.

3) Write down the first 5 powers of 2 and the first 5 powers of 10.

4)* Christine works in a laboratory with a type of bacteria that double in number every 20 minutes.
She has 2^{10} bacteria in some liquid in a test tube.
She splits the liquid equally into 2 new test tubes.
a) Approximately how many bacteria will there be in each test tube now?
b) Approximately how many bacteria will there be in each test tube after 1 hour?

5) What are the two possible square roots of 9?

6) Name three different forms that a rational number can take, and give examples.

7) Explain the difference between rational and irrational numbers.

8) Write down all you know about manipulating surds.

9) What are the steps of the method for determining if a number is prime?

10) Express these as a product of prime factors: a) 210 b) 1050

11) Find the HCF of 42 and 28 and the LCM of 8 and 10.

12) Demonstrate the 2 methods for converting recurring decimals to fractions.

13) Describe in words the methods for doing fractions by hand.

14)* Sarah is in charge of ordering new stock for a clothes shop. The shop usually sells red scarves and blue scarves in the ratio 5:8. Sarah orders 150 red scarves. How many blue scarves should she order?

15) What are the three steps of the method of proportional division?

16)* Jill, Heather and Susie spent Saturday helping out in their mum's cafe. Jill worked for 3 hours, Heather worked the next 2.5 hours and Susie worked for the final 1.5 hours of the day. They were given £42 to split between them for the work they'd done. How much should each of them receive?

17) What are 'terms'?

18) What is the method for multiplying out brackets such as $3(2x + 4)$?

19) What is the method for multiplying pairs of brackets? What about squared brackets?

20) What does 'D.O.T.S.' stand for? Give two examples of it.

21) What are the three steps for factorising expressions such as $12x^2y^3z + 15x^3yz^2$?

22) Give details of the three techniques for doing algebraic fractions, with examples.

23) What are the six steps for solving equations or rearranging formulas? What's the 7th step?

* The answers to these questions can be found on page 222.

Factorising Quadratics

Quadratic equations have a squared term in (e.g. x^2) but no larger powers (e.g. x^3, y^4).
There are a few ways of solving a quadratic equation. You need to know all the methods on these pages.

Factorising a Quadratic

'Factorising a quadratic' means 'putting it into 2 brackets'.
(There are several different methods for doing this, so stick with the one you're happiest with.
If you have no preference then learn the one below.)

The standard format for quadratic equations is: $ax^2 + bx + c = 0$
Most exam questions have a = 1, making them much easier.
     E.g. $x^2 + 3x + 2 = 0$ (See next page for when a is not 1)

Factorising Method When a = 1

1) ALWAYS rearrange into the STANDARD FORMAT: $ax^2 + bx + c = 0$

2) Write down the TWO BRACKETS with the x's in: (x   )(x   ) = 0

3) Then find 2 numbers that MULTIPLY to give 'c' (the end number) but also ADD/SUBTRACT to give 'b' (the coefficient of x)

4) Put them in and check that the +/− signs work out properly.

EXAMPLE "Solve $x^2 − x = 12$ by factorising."

ANSWER:

1) First rearrange it (into the standard format): $x^2 − x − 12 = 0$

2) a = 1, so the initial brackets are (as ever): (x   )(x   ) = 0

3) We now want to look at all pairs of numbers that multiply to give c (= 12), but which also add or subtract to give the value of b:
     1 × 12 Add/subtract to give: 13 or 11
     2 × 6   Add/subtract to give: 8 or 4
     3 × 4   Add/subtract to give: 7 or ① ← *this is what we're after (=±b)*

4) So 3 and 4 will give b = ±1, so put them in: (x   3)(x   4) = 0

5) Now fill in the +/− signs so that the 3 and 4 add/subtract to give -1 (=b).
     Clearly it must be +3 and −4 so we'll have: (x + 3)(x − 4) = 0

6) As an ESSENTIAL check, EXPAND the brackets out again to make sure they give the original equation:
     $(x + 3)(x − 4) = x^2 + 3x − 4x − 12 = x^2 − x − 12$

We're not finished yet mind, because (x + 3)(x − 4) = 0 is only the factorised form of the equation — we have yet to give the actual SOLUTIONS. This is very easy:

7) THE SOLUTIONS are simply the two numbers in the brackets, but with OPPOSITE +/− SIGNS: i.e. x = -3 or +4

Make sure you remember that last step. It's the difference between SOLVING THE EQUATION and merely factorising it.

Factorising quadratics is not easy — but it is important

The difficult bit is finding which numbers combine to give the right multiples and addition/subtraction.

Factorising Quadratics

When 'a' is not **1**   E.g. $3x^2 + 5x + 2 = 0$

The basic method is still the same but it's <u>a lot messier</u>.
Chances are, the exam question will be with a = 1,
so <u>make sure you can do that type easily</u>.
Only then should you try to get to grips with these harder ones.

An Example   "Solve $3x^2 + 7x = 6$ by factorising."

1) <u>First rearrange it</u> (into the standard format): $3x^2 + 7x - 6 = 0$

2) Now because a = 3, the two x-terms in the brackets will have to multiply to give $3x^2$
   so the initial brackets will have to be: $(3x\quad)(x\quad) = 0$

   (i.e. <u>you put in the x-terms first</u>, with coefficients that will multiply to give 'a')

3) We now want to look at <u>all pairs of numbers</u> that <u>multiply with each other to give 'c'</u>
   (=6, ignoring the minus sign for now): i.e. 1×6 and 2×3

4) <u>Now the difficult bit</u>: to find the combination which does this:

   > multiply with the 3x and x terms in the brackets and then
   > add or subtract to give the value of b (=7)

   The best way to do this is by trying out all the possibilities in the
   brackets until you find the combination that works. Don't forget
   that <u>EACH PAIR</u> of numbers can be tried in <u>TWO</u> different positions:

   $(3x\quad 1)(x\quad 6)$ <u>multiplies</u> to give <u>18x and 1x</u> which <u>add/subtract</u> to give <u>19x or 17x</u>
   $(3x\quad 6)(x\quad 1)$ <u>multiplies</u> to give <u>3x and 6x</u> which <u>add/subtract</u> to give <u>9x or 3x</u>
   $(3x\quad 3)(x\quad 2)$ <u>multiplies</u> to give <u>6x and 3x</u> which <u>add/subtract</u> to give <u>9x or 3x</u>
   $(3x\quad 2)(x\quad 3)$ <u>multiplies</u> to give <u>9x and 2x</u> which <u>add/subtract</u> to give <u>11x or 7x</u>

   So $(3x\quad 2)(x\quad 3)$ is the combination that gives b = 7, (give or take a +/–).

5) <u>Now fill in the +/– signs</u> so that the combination will add/subtract to give +7 (=b).
   Clearly it must be +3 and –2 which gives rise to +9x and -2x.
   So the final brackets are: $(3x - 2)(x + 3)$

6) <u>As an ESSENTIAL check, EXPAND the brackets</u> out again to make sure they give the original equation:
   $(3x - 2)(x + 3) = 3x^2 + 9x - 2x - 6 = 3x^2 + 7x - 6$

   7) The last step is to get <u>THE SOLUTIONS TO THE EQUATION</u>: $(3x - 2)(x + 3) = 0$
      which you do <u>by separately putting each bracket = 0</u>
      i.e. $(3x - 2) = 0 \Rightarrow x = 2/3$ $(x + 3) = 0 \Rightarrow x = -3$
      Don't forget that last step. <u>Again, it's the difference</u> between
      <u>SOLVING THE EQUATION</u> and merely <u>factorising it</u>.

Factorising quadratics when a is not 1 is quite a bit harder

The problem is it's a lot harder to work out the right combination of numbers to go in the brackets.
Don't get stressed out, just take your time and work through the possibilities as you did on the last page.

Completing the Square

$$x^2 + 12x - 5 = (x + 6)^2 - 41$$

The SQUARE... ...COMPLETED

Solving Quadratics by 'Completing The Square'

This is quite a clever way of solving quadratics, but it's perhaps a bit confusing at first. The name 'Completing the Square' doesn't help — it's called that because you basically:

1) Write down a <u>SQUARED</u> bracket, and then
2) Stick a number on the end to '<u>COMPLETE</u>' it.

It's quite easy if you learn all the steps — some of them aren't all that obvious.

Method:

1) As always, <u>REARRANGE THE QUADRATIC INTO THE STANDARD FORMAT</u>:
   $$ax^2 + bx + c = 0$$

2) <u>If 'a' is not 1 then divide the whole equation by 'a'</u> to make sure it is

3) Now <u>WRITE OUT THE INITIAL BRACKET</u>: $(x + b/2)^2$
   NB: <u>THE NUMBER IN THE BRACKET</u> is always <u>HALF THE (NEW) VALUE OF 'b'</u>

4) <u>MULTIPLY OUT THE BRACKETS</u> and <u>COMPARE TO THE ORIGINAL</u>
   to find what extra is needed, and add or subtract the adjusting amount.

Example:

"<u>Express $x^2 - 6x - 7 = 0$ as a completed square, and hence solve it.</u>"

The equation is already in the standard form and 'a' = 1, so:

1) The coefficient of x is -6, so the squared brackets must be:

   $(x - 3)^2$

2) <u>Square out the brackets</u>: $x^2 - 6x + 9$, <u>and compare</u> to the original: $x^2 - 6x - 7$.
   To make it like the original equation it needs -16 on the end, hence we get:

   $(x - 3)^2 - 16 = 0$ as the alternative version of $x^2 - 6x - 7 = 0$

   Don't forget though, we wish to <u>SOLVE</u> this equation, which entails these 3 special steps:

   1) <u>Take the 16 over</u> to get: $(x - 3)^2 = 16$

   2) Then <u>SQUARE ROOT BOTH SIDES</u>: $(x - 3) = \pm 4$ <u>AND DON'T FORGET THE</u> $\pm$

   3) <u>Take the 3 over</u> to get: $x = \pm 4 + 3$ <u>so x = 7 or -1</u> (don't forget the $\pm$)

Make a SQUARE (bracket) and COMPLETE it (add or take away)

Completing the square basically means working out a squared bracket which is almost the same as your equation and then deciding what has to be added or subtracted to make it right.

Warm-up and Worked Exam Questions

This algebra stuff isn't everyone's cup of tea. But once you get the knack of it, through lots of practice, you'll find the questions are all really similar. Which is nice.

Warm-Up Questions

1) Which is the correct factorisation for $x^2 + 4x - 12$?
   a) $(x + 6)(x + 2)$ b) $(x + 6)(x - 2)$ c) $(x - 6)(x + 2)$.

2) Which is the correct factorisation of $3x^2 - 5x - 2$?
   a) $(3x - 2)(x + 1)$ b) $(3x + 1)(x - 2)$ c) $(3x - 1)(x + 2)$.

3) Factorise:
   a) $x^2 + 11x + 28$ b) $x^2 + 16x + 28$ c) $x^2 + 12x - 28$.

4) Solve by factorisation:
   a) $x^2 + 8x + 15 = 0$ b) $x^2 + 5x - 14 = 0$ c) $x^2 - 7x + 7 = -5$.

5) Complete the square for the expression $x^2 + 8x + 20$.

6) Express $x^2 - 10x + 9$ as a completed square, and hence solve $x^2 - 10x + 9 = 0$.

Worked Exam Questions

Now, the exam questions — the good news is, if you've got the hang of the warm-up questions, you'll find the exam questions pretty much the same.

1 Solve $x^2 - x = 30$ by factorising.

The first thing you need to do is get all the terms on the same side — otherwise you'll be stuck from the outset.

Rearrange to give $x^2 - x - 30 = 0$;

Factorise to give $(x + 5)(x - 6) = 0$;

Once you've factorised, put each bracket equal to 0 to get the values for x.

If $x + 5 = 0$, $x = -5$.   If $x - 6 = 0$, $x = 6$.

So $x = -5$ or $x = 6$.

(2 marks)

2 Solve $2x^2 + 6x = 20$ by factorisation.

Rearrange to give $2x^2 + 6x - 20 = 0$;

To get $2x^2$, you'll need to start with $(2x\ \ )(x\ \ )$. Then find numbers which multiply to 20. Just keep trying different pairs until you find the one that works...

Factorise to give $(2x - 4)(x + 5) = 0$;

Hence $(2x - 4) = 0$ or $(x + 5) = 0$;

Solve to give $x = 2$ or $x = -5$.

(3 marks)

Exam Questions

Non-calculator Exam Questions:

3   (a)   Factorise $x^2 - x - 20$.

....
(1 mark)

(b)   Factorise $6x^2 + x - 12$.

....
(2 marks)

4   Factorise $2x^2 - 6x - 8$ and hence solve $2x^2 - 6x - 8 = 0$.

....

....

....
(3 marks)

5   Solve by factorisation $x^2 - 7x = -12$.

....

....

....
(3 marks)

6   Solve $x^2 + 9x + 9 = -9$.

....

....

....
(3 marks)

7   Complete the square for the expression $x^2 + 10x + 10$.

....
(2 marks)

8   Express $x^2 - 6x - 40 = 0$ as a completed square, and hence solve.

....

....

....
(3 marks)

Simultaneous Equations

The rules for solving simultaneous equations are really quite simple, but <u>you must follow ALL the steps, in the right order, and treat them as a strict method</u>.

There are two types of simultaneous equations you could get
— EASY ONES (where both equations are linear) and TRICKY ONES (where one's quadratic).

1 $2x = 6 - 4y$ and $-3 - 3y = 4x$

2 $7x + y = 1$ and $2x^2 - y = 3$

1 Six Steps For *Easy Simultaneous Equations*

We'll use these two equations for our example: $2x = 6 - 4y$ and $-3 - 3y = 4x$

1) <u>Rearrange both equations</u> into the form <u>$ax + by = c$</u> where a, b, c are numbers, (which can be negative). Also label the two equations — ① and — ②.

$$2x + 4y = 6 \quad —①$$
$$-4x - 3y = 3 \quad —②$$

2) You need to <u>match up the numbers in front</u> (the 'coefficients') of either the x's or y's in both equations. To do this you may need to multiply one or both equations by a suitable number. You should then relabel them: — ③ and — ④

$$①\times2 : 4x + 8y = 12 \quad —③$$
$$-4x - 3y = 3 \quad —④$$

3) <u>Add or subtract the two equations</u> to eliminate the terms with the same coefficient.
   If the <u>coefficients are the same</u> (both +ve or both –ve) then <u>SUBTRACT</u>.
   If the <u>coefficients are opposite</u> (one +ve and one –ve) then <u>ADD</u>.

$$③+④ \quad 0x + 5y = 15$$

4) Solve the resulting equation to find whichever letter is left in it.

$$5y = 15 \quad \Rightarrow \quad \underline{y = 3}$$

5) Substitute this value back into equation ① and solve it to find the other quantity.

Sub in ① : $2x + 4\times3 = 6 \Rightarrow 2x + 12 = 6 \Rightarrow 2x = -6 \Rightarrow \underline{x = -3}$

6) Then substitute both these values into equation ② to make sure it works.
   If it doesn't then you've done something wrong and you'll have to do it all again.

Sub x and y in ② : $-4\times-3 - 3\times3 = 12 - 9 = \underline{3}$, which is right, so it's worked.
So the solutions are: $\underline{x = -3}$, $\underline{y = 3}$

And these are the easy simultaneous equations

It might just be me, but I think simultaneous equations are quite fun... well maybe not fun... but quite satisfying... Anyway it doesn't matter whether you like them or not — you must learn how to do them.

Simultaneous Equations

2) Seven Steps For *Tricky Simultaneous Equations*

Example: Solve these two equations simultaneously: $7x + y = 1$ and $2x^2 - y = 3$

1) <u>Rearrange the quadratic equation</u> so that you have the <u>non-quadratic unknown on its own</u>. Label the equations ① and ②.

$$7x + y = 1 \quad — ①$$
$$y = 2x^2 - 3 \quad — ②$$

2) <u>Substitute the quadratic expression</u> into the <u>other equation</u>. You'll get another equation — label it ③.

$$7x + y = 1 — ①$$
$$y = 2x^2 - 3 — ②$$
$$7x + (2x^2 - 3) = 1 \quad — ③$$

In this example you just shove the expression for y into equation ①, in place of y.

3) <u>Rearrange</u> to get a <u>quadratic equation</u>. And guess what... You've got to <u>solve it</u>.

$$2x^2 + 7x - 4 = 0$$
That factorises into:
$$(2x - 1)(x + 4) = 0$$
So, $2x - 1 = 0$ OR $x + 4 = 0$
In other words, <u>$x = 0.5$</u> OR <u>$x = -4$</u>

Check this step by multiplying out again:
$(2x - 1)(x + 4) = 2x^2 - x + 8x - 4 = 2x^2 + 7x - 4$ ☺

Remember — if it won't factorise, you can complete the square. Have a look at p.78 for more details.

4) Stick the <u>first value back in</u> one of the <u>original equations</u> (pick the easy one).

① $7x + y = 1$ <u>Substitute in $x = 0.5$</u>: $3.5 + y = 1$, so <u>$y = 1 - 3.5 = -2.5$</u>

5) Stick the <u>second value back in</u> the same <u>original equation</u> (the easy one again).

① $7x + y = 1$ <u>Substitute in $x = -4$</u>: $-28 + y = 1$, so <u>$y = 1 + 28 = 29$</u>

6) <u>Substitute</u> both pairs of answers back into the other <u>original equation</u> to <u>check</u> they work.

② $y = 2x^2 - 3$
<u>Substitute in $x = 0.5$ and $y = -2.5$</u>: $-2.5 = (2 \times 0.25) - 3 = -2.5$ — jolly good.
<u>Substitute in $x = -4$ and $y = 29$</u>: $29 = (2 \times 16) - 3 = 29$ — smashing.

7) <u>Write the pairs of answers out again</u>, <u>CLEARLY</u>, at the bottom of your working.

The two pairs of answers are: <u>$x = 0.5$ and $y = -2.5$</u> or <u>$x = -4$ and $y = 29$</u>

(Do this even if you think it's <u>pointless and stupid</u>. If there's even the <u>remotest chance</u> of the examiner getting the pairs mixed up, it's worth a <u>tiny bit of extra effort</u>, don't you think.)

Remember to write the two pairs out clearly

You are basically combining the two equations to make one quadratic equation. Solve that equation and stick the solutions back in to get the other two corresponding answers. What could be easier?*

*Inventive answers on a postcard to "Entertain the editor", CGP, Cumbria. Examples of inventive answers do not include "falling off a log" or "pie".

Number Sequences

There are different types of <u>number sequence</u> you could get in the exam.

They're not difficult — <u>AS LONG AS YOU WRITE WHAT'S HAPPENING IN EACH GAP.</u>

*"State the Rule for **Extending** the **Pattern**"*

This is what a lot of <u>exam questions</u> end up asking for and it's easy enough, just remember:

ALWAYS say what you do to the <u>PREVIOUS TERMS</u> to get the next term.

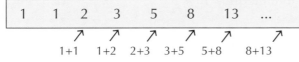

| 1 | 1 | 2 | 3 | 5 | 8 | 13 | ... |

1+1 1+2 2+3 3+5 5+8 8+13

The <u>RULE</u>:
"Add the previous two terms"

| 53 | 43 | 34 | 26 | 19 | ... |

-10   -9   -8   -7   -6

The <u>RULE</u>:
"Subtract from the <u>previous term</u> the difference between <u>the previous two terms</u> less one."

Once you know the <u>rule</u>, you can find the <u>next few terms</u> in the sequence <u>really easily</u>.

Finding the nth term: 'dn + (a – d)'

"<u>The nth term</u>" is a formula with "n" in it which gives you <u>every term in a sequence</u> when you put different values for n in.

For any sequence such as 3, 7, 11, 15, where there is a <u>COMMON DIFFERENCE</u>,
                                 4   4   4

you can always find 'the nth term' using the formula:

'nth term = dn + (a – d)'

1) 'a' is simply the value of <u>THE FIRST TERM</u> in the sequence.

2) 'd' is simply the value of <u>THE COMMON DIFFERENCE</u> between the terms.

3) To get the <u>nth term</u>, you just find the values of '<u>a</u>' and '<u>d</u>' from the sequence and <u>stick them in the formula</u>. You don't replace n though — that wants to stay as n.

4) Of course <u>YOU HAVE TO LEARN THE FORMULA</u>, but life is like that.

Example: "Find the nth term of this sequence: 5, 8, 11, 14 ...."

1) The formula is dn + (a – d)

2) The <u>first term</u> is 5, so <u>a = 5</u>. The <u>common difference</u> is 3 so <u>d = 3</u>.

3) Putting these in the formula gives: 3n + (5 – 3) so the <u>nth term = 3n + 2</u>.

4) Now you can use the nth term to find any term in the sequence:

12th term: 3(12) + 2 = 38

50th term: 3(50) + 2 = 152

Millionth term: 3(1 000 000) + 2 = 3 000 002

Learn the formula and you're halfway there

"Common difference" sequences are the easiest type to spot — you only need to do a couple of subtractions and you're there. So when you get into the exam, try that first.

Warm-up and Worked Exam Questions

Time for some questions on simultaneous equations and sequences.
Neither topic is hard once you've learnt the methods, so if you're struggling
all you need is more practice.

Warm-Up Questions

1) Solve the simultaneous equations $2x + 3y = 19$ and $2x + y = 9$.

2) Solve the simultaneous equations $3x + 2y = 20$ and $x - 2y = -4$.

3) a) Find the first 6 terms of the sequence whose nth term is $5n + 3$.
   b) Find the first 6 terms of the sequence whose nth term is $3n + 5$.

4) Find the nth term of the following sequences:
   a) 5, 10, 15, 20, 25, ...   b) 7, 10, 13, 16, 19, ...

5) How many crosses are in the nth pattern?

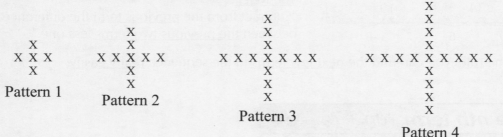

Pattern 1   Pattern 2   Pattern 3   Pattern 4

Worked Exam Question

Have a read through this worked example and make sure you understand it...

1   Solve these simultaneous equations:
$$3x + 3y = 21$$
$$5x - 2y = 14$$

$3x + 3y = 21 \ (1) \quad 5x - 2y = 14 \ (2)$

Equation (1) $\times$ 2: $6x + 6y = 42$ —— (3) ◄—— *You need to multiply both equations to make the coefficient of either x or y the same. It's probably easier to go for y.*

Equation (2) $\times$ 3: $15x - 6y = 42$ —— (4)

(3) + (4): $21x = 84$, so $x = 4$.

Now, substitute $x = 4$ into equation (1): ◄—— *Once you've found x, just put it into one of the other equations to find y.*

$3x + 3y = 21 \Rightarrow 12 + 3y = 21 \Rightarrow 3y = 9 \Rightarrow y = 3$.

So $x = 4$, $y = 3$

(4 marks)

It's a good idea to substitute both the x and y values into the other equation as a check.

Exam Questions

Non-calculator Exam Questions:

2   Solve simultaneously $5x + 4y = 75$ and $2x + 4y = 54$.

....

(3 marks)

3   Solve the simultaneous equations $3x - 2y = 7$ and $4x - 4y = 8$.

....

(3 marks)

4   Solve the simultaneous equations $x = 4y + 3$ and $3x^2 = y + 1$.

....

(5 marks)

5   (a)   Sketch the next pattern in this sequence:

(1 mark)

     (b)   Complete this table:

Pattern number:	1	2	3	4	5
Number of crosses:	4	7			

(1 mark)

     (c)   How many crosses would be in the 20th pattern?

....

(1 mark)

     (d)   How many crosses would be in the nth pattern?

....

(2 marks)

6   (a)   Sketch the fifth pattern:

Pattern 1   Pattern 2   Pattern 3   Pattern 4

(1 mark)

     (b)   How many dots will there be in the nth pattern?

....

(1 mark)

     (c)   How many crosses will there be in the nth pattern?

....

(1 mark)

X and Y Coordinates

To start off with, here's some basic stuff about coordinates.
Get stuck into it — it'll get you off to a running start.

The Four **Quadrants**

A graph has <u>four different quadrants</u> (regions) where
the x- and y- coordinates are either <u>positive</u> or <u>negative</u>.

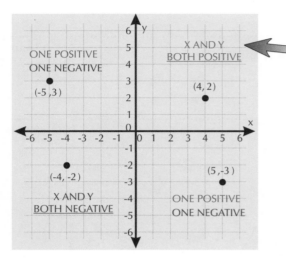

This is the easiest region by far because
here <u>all the coordinates are positive</u>.

You have to be careful in the <u>other regions</u> though,
because the x- and y- coordinates could be <u>negative</u>,
and that always makes life much more difficult.

Coordinates are always written in brackets
like this: (x, y) — remember x is <u>across</u>, and y is <u>up</u>.

Finding the **Midpoint** of a Line Segment

This regularly comes up in exams and is fairly straightforward.

> **Find the <u>average</u> of the <u>two x-coordinates</u>,
> then do the same for the <u>y-coordinates</u>.
> <u>These will be the coordinates of the midpoint</u>.**

EXAMPLE "Point P has coordinates (8, 3) and point Q has coordinates (-4, 8).
Find the midpoint of the line PQ."

SOLUTION

Average of <u>x-coordinates</u> = (8 + -4)/2 = 2
Average of <u>y-coordinates</u> = (8 + 3)/2 = 5.5
So, coordinates of midpoint = (2, 5.5)

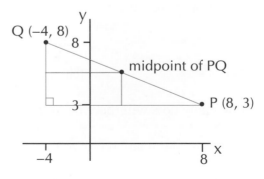

Midpoint of a line — just find two averages

Learn how to find the midpoint of a line segment and how to use coordinates in all four quadrants.
You'll need to be really confident with this simple stuff for the rest of the unit.

Straight Line Graphs

You ought to know these simple graphs straight off with no hesitation:

Horizontal and *Vertical* lines: 'x = a' and 'y = a'

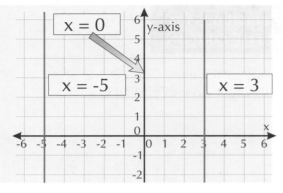

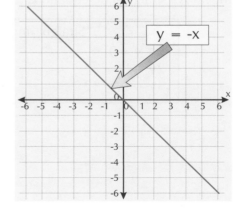

x = a is a <u>vertical line</u> <u>through 'a'</u> on the x-axis

Don't forget: <u>the y-axis is also the line x = 0</u>

y = a is a <u>horizontal line</u> <u>through 'a'</u> on the y-axis

Don't forget: <u>the x-axis is also the line y = 0</u>

The *Main Diagonals*: 'y = x' and 'y = –x'

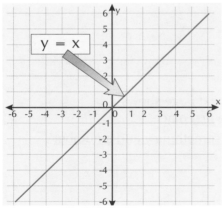

'<u>y = x</u>' is the <u>main diagonal</u> that goes <u>UPHILL</u> from left to right.

'<u>y = -x</u>' is the <u>main diagonal</u> that goes <u>DOWNHILL</u> from left to right.

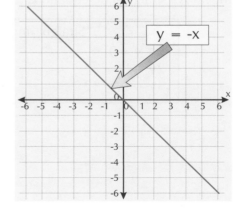

Simple lines you have to learn — it'll only take a second

Vertical line: x = a, horizontal line: y = a, main diagonals: y = x and y = –x.
Say no more...

Straight Line Graphs

Here are some more of the basic straight line graphs that you really need to know:

Other **Sloping Lines** Through the Origin: 'y = ax' and 'y = –ax'

y = ax and **y = -ax** are the equations for
A SLOPING LINE THROUGH THE ORIGIN.

The value of '**a**' (known as the <u>gradient</u>) tells you the steepness of the line.
The bigger '**a**' is, the steeper the slope. A <u>MINUS SIGN</u> tells you it slopes <u>DOWNHILL</u>.

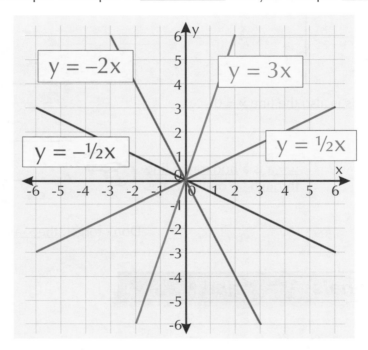

All Other **Straight** Lines

Other straight-line equations are a little more complicated. The next page shows
you how to draw them, but the first step is identifying them in the first place.

Remember: All straight-line equations just contain '<u>something x, something y and a number</u>'.

<u>Straight lines</u>:

$x - y = 0$ $y = 2 + 3x$
$2y - 4x = 7$ $4x - 3 = 5y$
$3y + 3x = 12$ $6y - x - 7 = 0$

<u>NOT straight lines</u>:

$y = x^3 + 3$ $2y - 1/x = 7$
$1/y + 1/x = 2$ $x(3 - 2y) = 3$
$x^2 = 4 - y$ $xy + 3 = 0$

Get it straight — which lines are straight (and which aren't)

The graphs $y = ax$ and $y = -ax$ are diagonals just like $y = x$ and $y = -x$ on the last page.
They're steeper or flatter depending on the value of 'a'.

Plotting Straight Line Graphs

Some people wouldn't know a straight-line equation if it ran up and bit them, but they're pretty easy to spot — they just have <u>two letters</u> and <u>a few numbers</u>, but <u>nothing fancy</u> like squared or cubed.

In the exam you'll be expected to be able to draw the graphs of straight-line equations. "y = mx + c" is one way of doing it (see pages 91-92), but here are <u>two other nice easy methods</u>:

The 'Table of 3 Values' Method

You can <u>easily</u> draw the graph of <u>any equation</u> using this <u>easy</u> method:

1) Choose <u>3 values of x</u> and <u>draw up a table</u>.
2) <u>Work out the y-values</u>.
3) <u>Plot the coordinates</u>, and <u>draw the line</u>.

If it's a <u>straight-line equation</u>, the 3 points will be in a <u>dead straight line</u> with each other, which is the usual check you do when you've drawn it — <u>if they aren't</u>, then it could be a <u>curve</u> and you'll need to add <u>more values to your table</u> to find out what's going on.

EXAMPLE: "Draw the graph of y = 2x – 3"

1) <u>Draw up a table</u> with some suitable values of x. Choosing x = 0, 2, 4 is usually OK:

X	0	2	4
Y			

2) <u>Find the y-values</u> by putting each x-value into the equation:

X	0	2	4
Y	–3	1	5

(e.g. When <u>x = 4</u>, y = 2x – 3 = 2 × 4 – 3 = <u>5</u>)

3) <u>Plot the points</u> and <u>draw the line</u>.

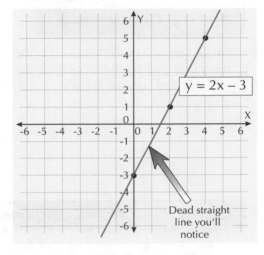

y = 2x – 3

Dead straight line you'll notice

The 'x = 0', 'y = 0' Method

1) <u>Set x = 0</u> in the equation and <u>find y</u> — this is where it <u>crosses the y-axis</u>.
2) <u>Set y = 0</u> in the equation and <u>find x</u> — this is where it <u>crosses the x-axis</u>.
3) <u>Plot these two points</u> and <u>join them up with a straight line</u> — and just hope it should be a straight line, since with only two points you can't really tell.

EXAMPLE: "Draw the graph of 5x + 3y = 15"

Putting <u>x = 0</u> gives "3y = 15" ⇒ <u>y = 5</u>
Putting <u>y = 0</u> gives "5x = 15" ⇒ <u>x = 3</u>

So plot <u>(0, 5)</u> and <u>(3, 0)</u> on the graph and join them up with a straight line.

Only doing two points is risky unless you're sure the equation is definitely a straight line.

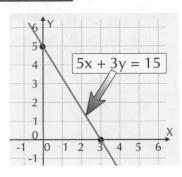

5x + 3y = 15

Plotting these graphs is straightforward with these simple methods

This gives you two simple methods for drawing straight line graphs. It's a very popular question with examiners. If you learn the methods it'll be very popular with you too.

Finding the Gradient

Time to work out some gradients. I'm afraid "quite steep" won't do.

Finding the **Gradient**

Find **Two Accurate Points** and **Complete the Triangle**

Both points should be in the <u>upper right quadrant</u> if possible (to keep all the numbers positive).

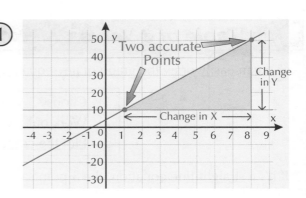

① Two accurate Points
Change in Y
Change in X

Find the **Change in Y** and the **Change in X**

Make sure you subtract the x coordinates.
the <u>same way round</u> as you do the y coordinates.
E.g. y coordinate of point A – y coordinate of point B
<u>and</u> x coordinate of point A – x coordinate of point B

② <u>Change in y</u> = 50 – 10 = <u>40</u>
<u>Change in x</u> = 8 – 1 = <u>7</u>

Learn this formula, and use it:

$$\text{GRADIENT} = \frac{\text{CHANGE IN Y}}{\text{CHANGE IN X}}$$

③ <u>Gradient</u> = $\frac{40}{7}$ = <u>5.7</u>

Check the **Sign's** right.

If it slopes <u>UPHILL</u> left → right ( ) <u>then it's positive</u>
If it slopes <u>DOWNHILL</u> left → right () <u>then it's negative</u>

④ As the graph goes <u>UPHILL</u>, the gradient is positive.
So <u>5.7 is correct</u>, not -5.7

If you subtracted the coordinates the right way round, the sign should be correct. If it's not, go back and check what you've done.

Gradients are incredibly useful

It might seem unlikely but gradients are one of maths' most useful tools. The more maths you do, the more you come across. But even if you plan to do no maths after GCSE, you need them for the exam.

y = mx + c

Using 'y = mx + c' is perhaps the 'proper' way of dealing with straight-line equations, and it's a nice trick if you can do it. The first thing you have to do though is <u>rearrange</u> the equation into the standard format like this:

Straight line:		Rearranged into 'y = mx +c'	
y = 2 + 3x	→	y = 3x + 2	(m = 3, c = 2)
2y − 4x = 7	→	y = 2x + 3½	(m = 2, c = 3½)
x − y = 0	→	y = x + 0	(m = 1, c = 0)
4x − 3 = 5y	→	y = 0.8x − 0.6	(m = 0.8, c = -0.6)
3y + 3x = 12	→	y = -x + 4	(m = -1, c = 4)

<u>REMEMBER</u>:   '<u>m</u>' equals the <u>gradient</u> of the line.
                       '<u>c</u>' is the '<u>y-intercept</u>' (where the graph hits the y-axis).

<u>BUT WATCH OUT</u>: people mix up 'm' and 'c' when they get something like y = 5 + 2x.
Remember, 'm' is the number <u>in front of the 'x'</u> and 'c' is the number <u>on its own</u>.

Sketching a **Straight Line** using y = mx + c

1)   Get the equation into the form '<u>y = mx + c</u>'.

2)   <u>Put a dot on the y-axis</u> at the value of c.

3)   Then go <u>along one unit</u> and <u>up or down by the value of m</u> and make another dot.

4)   <u>Repeat</u> the same 'step' in <u>both directions</u>.

5)   Finally check that the gradient <u>looks right</u>.

The graph shows the process for the equation 'y = 2x + 1':

1) 'c' = 1, so put a first dot at y = 1 on the y-axis.

2) Go along 1 unit → and then up by 2 because 'm' = +2.

3) Repeat the same step, 1→ 2↑ in both directions.

4) CHECK: a gradient of <u>+2</u> should be <u>quite steep</u> and <u>uphill</u> left to right which it is, so it looks OK.

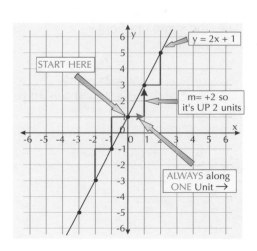

m is the gradient and c is the y-intercept

The key thing to remember is that m is the number in front of the x, and c is the number on its own.
If you remember that, then y = mx + c is a very easy way of sketching or identifying straight lines.

y = mx + c

Another <u>popular exam question</u> is asking you to find the equation for a given line.
If you get a question like this you just need to use the process on the last page <u>in reverse</u>...

Finding the **Equation** Of a Straight Line **Graph**

This is the reverse of the process on the last page and is <u>EASIER</u>.

> 1) From the axes, <u>identify the two variables</u> (e.g. 'x and y' or 'h and t').
>
> 2) <u>Find the values</u> of '<u>m</u>' (gradient) and '<u>c</u>' (y-intercept) from the graph.
>
> 3) Using these values from the graph, <u>write down the equation</u> with the standard format 'y = mx + c'.

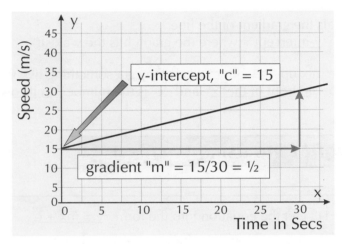

For the example above: '<u>S = ½t + 15</u>'

Parallel Lines have the **Same Gradient**

Parallel lines have the <u>same value of m</u>,
i.e. the <u>same gradient</u>.
So the lines:

$$y = 2x + 3,$$
$$y = 2x, \text{ and}$$
$$y = 2x - 4 \text{ are all parallel.}$$

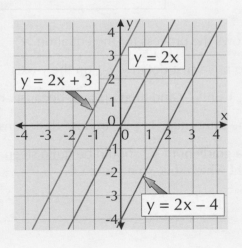

Find m and c — and write down the equation

Either you have an equation and have to sketch the graph, or you have the graph and have to find the equation. Both ways round are popular in the exam. For both, all you need is y = mx + c.

D/T Graphs and V/T Graphs

Distance-time (D/T graphs) and velocity-time (V/T graphs) are so common in exams that they deserve a page all to themselves — just to make sure you know all the vital details about them. The best thing about them is that they don't vary much, and they're always easy.

Distance-Time Graphs

Just remember these 3 important points:

1) At any point, GRADIENT = SPEED, but watch out for the UNITS.

2) The STEEPER the graph, the FASTER it's going.

3) FLAT SECTIONS are where it is STOPPED.

EXAMPLE "What is the speed of the return section on the graph shown?"

ANSWER Speed = gradient = 1000 m ÷ 30 mins
= 33.33 m/min.

But m/min are naff units, so it's better to do it like this: 1 km ÷ 0.5 hrs = 2 km/h

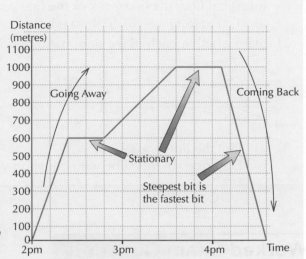

Velocity-Time Graphs

A velocity-time graph can look just the same as a distance-time graph but it means something completely different. The graph shown here is exactly the same shape as the one above, but the actual motions are completely different.

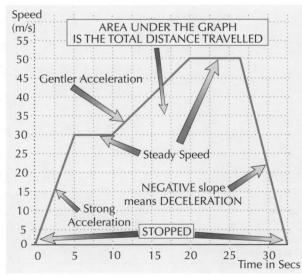

Remember these 4 important points:

1) At any point, GRADIENT = ACCELERATION, (The UNITS are m/s² don't forget).

2) NEGATIVE SLOPE is DECELERATION.

3) FLAT SECTIONS are STEADY SPEED.

4) AREA UNDER GRAPH = DISTANCE TRAVELLED.

The D/T graph shows something moving away and then back again with steady speeds and long stops, rather like a donkey on Blackpool Beach. The V/T graph on the other hand shows something that sets off from rest, accelerates strongly, holds its speed, then accelerates again up to a maximum speed which it holds for a while and then comes to a dramatic halt at the end. More like a Ferrari than a donkey...

Gradients just mean something per something

You can see why gradients are so useful. Remember, on distance-time graphs the gradients represent distance per time (speed), and on velocity-time graphs they represent speed per time (acceleration).

Warm-up and Worked Exam Questions

On the day of the exam you'll have to know straight-line graphs like the back of your hand. If you struggle with any of the warm-up questions, go back over the section again before you go any further.

Warm-Up Questions

1) Without drawing, state whether the lines joining the following points form a horizontal line, a vertical line, the line y = x or the line y = -x.
   a) (1,1) to (5,5)   b) (0,4) to (-3,4)   c) (-1,3) to (-1,7)   d) (4,-4) to (-3,3).

2) State whether each of the lines has a positive gradient, a negative gradient or a gradient of zero.

3) a) Plot the line y = 3x – 4.
   b) Describe where a line with equation y = 3x + 2 lies in relation to y = 3x – 4.

Worked Exam Question

You know the routine by now — work carefully through this example and make sure you understand it. Then it's on to the real test of doing some exam questions for yourself.

1   Find the equation of the straight line which passes through the points (3, 1) and (-1, 3).

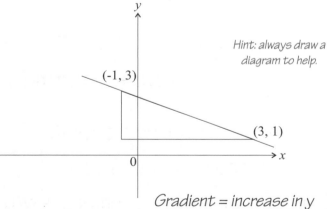

Hint: always draw a diagram to help.

$$\text{Gradient} = \frac{\text{increase in } y}{\text{increase in } x} = \frac{2}{-4} = \frac{1}{-2}$$

So equation of line: $y = mx + c$ $y = -½x + c$

Substitute x = 3, y = 1 (because we know this point is on the line)

$1 = (-½ \times 3) + c$ $1 = -1½ + c$ $c = 2½$

The equation is $y = -½x + 2½$.

(3 marks)

Exam Questions

Non-calculator Exam Questions:

2

A	B	C	D	E
$y = 3x - 2$	$y = 7 - 2x$	$7y = 10x$	$2y = 6x + 9$	$x + y = 14$

(a) Which two lines are parallel? ....
(1 mark)

(b) Which two lines have negative gradients? ....
(1 mark)

(c) Which two lines go through the point (4,10)? ....
(1 mark)

3 Complete this table and hence draw the graph of $y = 2.5x - 2.5$ for values of x between -3 and 3.

x	-3	-1	1	3
y	-10			

(2 marks)

4 Dominic cycled to visit his Gran who lives 24 km away. His journey is shown on the graph below. Letters A - G represent different stages of the journey.

(a) After cycling for 20 minutes,
Dominic realised he'd forgotten his wallet
and had to go back.
How far had he cycled by this time?

....
(1 mark)

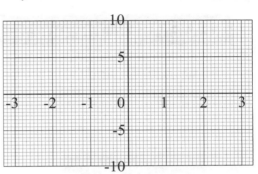

(b) Dominic stopped for two breaks on the way.
Which letters on the diagram represent
these breaks?

....
(2 marks)

(c) Work out Dominic's speed during the fastest leg of his journey.

....
(3 marks)

(d) Work out Dominic's average speed for the total journey (after picking up his wallet).

....
(3 marks)

Inequalities

Inequalities aren't <u>half as difficult as they look</u>.
Once you've learned the tricks involved, most of the algebra for them is <u>identical to ordinary equations</u>.

The *Inequality* Symbols:

$>$ means 'Greater than'

$\geq$ means 'Greater than or equal to'

$<$ means 'Less than'

$\leq$ means 'Less than or equal to'

<u>REMEMBER</u>, the one at the <u>BIG</u> end is <u>BIGGEST</u>

so $x > 4$ and $4 < x$ both say: '<u>x is greater than 4</u>'

Algebra With *Inequalities*

$5x < x + 2$
$5x = x + 2$

The thing to remember here is that
<u>inequalities are just like regular equations</u> in the sense that

<u>all the normal rules of algebra apply</u>

<u>WITH ONE BIG EXCEPTION:</u>

Whenever you MULTIPLY OR DIVIDE BY A <u>NEGATIVE NUMBER</u>, you must <u>FLIP THE INEQUALITY SIGN.</u>

Treat inequalities like equations — but remember the exception

Two things to remember here — "the one at the big end is the biggest" and "flip the inequality sign when you multiply or divide by a negative number". Otherwise it's more of the same old algebra.

Inequalities

Three *Important* Examples

1) Solve $5x < 6x + 2$

The equivalent equation is $5x = 6x + 2$, which is easy — as is the inequality:

First subtract 6x from both sides: $5x - 6x < 2$ which gives $-x < 2$
Then divide both sides by -1: $\underline{x > -2}$ (i.e. x is greater than -2)

(NOTE: The < has flipped around into a >, because we divided by a negative number)

2) Find all integer values of x where $-4 \leq x < 1$

This type of expression is <u>very common</u> — <u>you must learn them in this way</u>:

'x is between -4 and +1, possibly equal to -4 but never equal to +1'.
     (Obviously the answers are <u>-4, -3, -2, -1, 0</u>   (but not 1))

3) Find the range of values of x where $x^2 \leq 25$

The trick here is: <u>Don't forget the negative values</u>.
Square-rooting both sides gives $x \leq 5$. However, this is <u>only half the story</u>,
because $-5 \leq x$ is also true. There is little alternative but to simply learn this:

> $x^2 \leq 25$ **gives the solution** $-5 \leq x \leq 5$,
>   (x is between -5 and 5, possibly equal to either).
> $x^2 \geq 36$ **gives the solution** $x \leq -6$ **or** $6 \leq x$
>   (x is 'less than or equal to -6' or 'greater than or equal to +6').

You Can Show Inequalities on *Number Lines*

EXAMPLE   "Show the solution to $x^2 \leq 25$ on a number line."

You draw it like this:

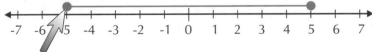

The <u>filled circles</u> mean the solution <u>includes</u> the numbers 5 and -5.

If your inequality had a < or > instead of a ≤ or ≥, you'd draw an <u>open circle</u> (O).

This stuff is straightforward as long as you learnt the last page

These three examples give you a really clear idea of what you need to do in the exam. The biggest stumbling block is forgetting the negative values when you have x^2, but now I've warned you, you won't.

Graphical Inequalities

These questions always involve <u>shading a region on a graph</u>. The method sounds very complicated, but once you've seen it in action with an example, you see that it's OK...

Method

1) <u>CONVERT each INEQUALITY to an EQUATION</u>
by simply putting an '=' in place of the '<' or '>'

2) <u>DRAW THE GRAPH FOR EACH EQUATION</u>

3) <u>Work out WHICH SIDE of each line you want</u>
Put x=0 and y=0 into the inequality to see if the <u>ORIGIN</u> is on the correct side.

4) <u>SHADE THE REGION</u> this gives you

Example

> "Shade the region represented by:
> x + y < 5, y > x + 2 and y > 1"

1) <u>CONVERT EACH INEQUALITY TO AN EQUATION</u>:
   The inequalities become x + y = 5, y = x + 2 and y = 1

2) <u>DRAW THE GRAPH FOR EACH EQUATION</u> (see p.91).

3) <u>WORK OUT WHICH SIDE OF EACH LINE YOU WANT</u>.
   This is the fiddly bit. Substitute x = 0 and y = 0 (the origin) into each inequality and see if this makes the inequality <u>true</u> or <u>false</u>.

   <u>In x + y < 5</u>:
   x = 0, y = 0 gives 0 < 5 which is <u>true</u>.
   This means the <u>origin</u> is on the <u>correct</u> side of the line.

   <u>In y > x + 2</u>:
   x = 0, y = 0 gives 0 > 2 which is <u>false</u>.
   So the origin is on the <u>wrong side</u> of this line.

   <u>In y > 1</u>:
   x = 0, y = 0 gives 0 > 1 which is <u>false</u>.
   So the origin is on the <u>wrong side</u> of this line too.

The <u>dotted lines</u> mean the solution <u>doesn't</u> include the points on the line. If your inequality had a ≤ or ≥ instead of a < or >, you'd draw a <u>solid line</u>.

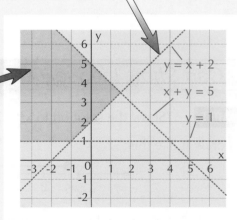

4) <u>SHADE THE REGION</u>.
   You want the region that satisfies all of these:
   – below x + y = 5 *(because the origin <u>is</u> on this side)*
   – left of y = x + 2 *(because the origin <u>isn't</u> on this side)*
   – above y = 1 *(because the origin <u>isn't</u> on this side).*

Just draw the graphs and shade the region

Drawing the graphs is easy as long as you've remembered the methods of graph sketching from p.91. Then you have to make sure you get the right region — pick a point (usually (0,0)) and try it.

Warm-up and Worked Exam Questions

Inequalities — a lovely algebra topic, if you ask me... Anyway, love them or hate them, you have to do them. It's just a case of learning the method and practising lots of questions...

Warm-Up Questions

1) List all integer values for x where $12 < x < 17$.
2) Find all integer values of n if $-3 \leq n \leq 3$.
3) Find all integer values of x such that $8 < 4x < 20$.
4) Solve the inequality $2q + 2 \leq 12$.
5) Solve the inequality $4p + 12 > 30$.
6) a) Using the same axes, draw the graphs of $y = 0$, $y = 2x$, $y = 6 - x$.
   b) R is the region defined by the inequalities $y \leq 2x$, $y \leq 6 - x$, $y \geq 0$. Shade this region and label it R.

Worked Exam Questions

Inequality exam questions are all the same, more or less... than or equal to...

1 Find all integer values of *n* such that $6 < 3n < 20$.

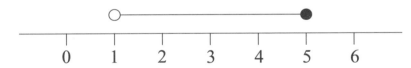

....Dividing by 3 gives $2 < n < 6.666...$;..

....n must be an integer, so the only values it can take are: 3, 4, 5, 6...........................

(2 marks)

2 Draw on a number line all values of *n* such that $1 < n \leq 5$.

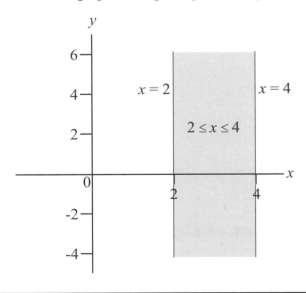

Remember, the circle above the number must be shaded in if that number IS allowed. If it is NOT allowed, it should be left hollow.

(2 marks)

3 Sketch on a graph the region specified by the inequality $2 \leq x \leq 4$.

$x = 2$ $x = 4$

$2 \leq x \leq 4$

*Use solid lines to draw x = 2 and x = 4, then shade between them.
See p.98 for more on sketching regions satisfied by inequalities.*

(2 marks)

Exam Questions

Non-calculator Exam Questions:

4   List all integer values of x such that $-4 < x \le 2$.

....
(2 marks)

5   Draw a number line to represent those values of n where $10 < n \le 15$.

(2 marks)

6   Solve the inequality $5a - 10 > 50$.

....
(2 marks)

7   Solve the inequality $13 < 4t + 3 < 27$.

....
(3 marks)

8   Solve the inequality $-3x > 12$.

....
(2 marks)

9   The graph of $y = x^2 - 4x + 2$ for the values of x from 0 to 4 is shown below.

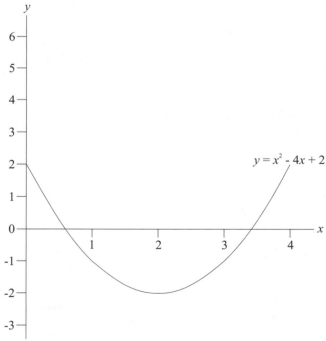

$y = x^2 - 4x + 2$

R is the region defined by the inequalities $x \ge 1.5$, $y \le 1$, $y \le 6 - 2x$ and $y \ge x^2 - 4x + 2$.
Shade this region and label it R.

(4 marks)

Revision Summary for Unit 2 — 2

Unit 2 is the really nasty one — grisly algebra. But grisly or not, you still have to learn it.
So here's another set of questions to test what you know. Don't forget, you've got to keep trying
these <u>over and over again</u>. Making sure that you can do these questions is the <u>best revision</u>
you can possibly do. Just keep practising till you can glide through them all with ease.

Keep learning the basic facts until you know them

1) What does 'factorising a quadratic' mean you have to do?

2) What check should you do to make sure you've done it right?

3) What difference does it make when factorising a quadratic if 'a' is not 1?

4) How exactly do you get solutions to a quadratic equation once you've factorised it?

5) What are the four main steps for turning a quadratic into a 'completed square'?

6)* Jacob stocks the tuck shop with chocolate bars each week.
Last week he spent £3.00 buying 5 chocolate bars and 3 pints of milk for his mum.
This week he spent £4.00 on 10 chocolate bars and 2 pints of milk (for his mum again).
His receipts weren't itemised and he needs to know how much money to take back
from the tuck shop for the chocolate bars (all the chocolate bars are the same price).
a) Write simultaneous equations for Jacob's two receipts.
b) Solve the equations to calculate how much money Jacob is owed.

7) What does stating the rule to extend a number pattern actually boil down to?

8) What's the formula for the nth term of a "common difference" number sequence?

9) What are the four types of straight lines you should know?

10) What does a straight line equation look like?

11)* Joe makes curtains for a living. He knows that the length of material needed for a curtain is the
length of the window plus one tenth of the length again. He works out the equation $y = x + \frac{1}{10}x$,
to show this. He decides to draw a graph so staff can just read the values off that.
a) Will Joe's graph be a straight line or a curve?
b) Use the 'table of 3 values' method to draw Joe's graph.

12) What does '$y = mx + c$' have to do with? What do 'm' and 'c' represent?

13) List the five steps necessary to draw the graph of '$5x = 2 + y$' using '$y = mx + c$'.

14) List the three steps for obtaining the equation from a straight line graph.

15) How are the gradients of parallel lines related?

16) Give three important details relating to distance-time graphs.

17) Give four important details relating to velocity-time graphs.

18) Draw a typical example of both types and label the important features.

19) What do you need to do if you divide an inequality by a negative number?

20) What is the four-stage method for graphical inequalities?

* The answers to these questions can be found on page 224.

Some Harder Graphs to Learn

In the exam you'll be expected to be able to recognise the shape of a graph from its equation. As well as straight line graphs (p.87-88), there are four more types of graph for you to know about — two on this page, and two on the next.

x^2 *Bucket Shapes*: $y = ax^2 + bx + c$ (where b and/or c can be zero)

These graphs all have the same <u>symmetrical bucket shape</u>.
If the x^2 bit has a '–' in front of it then the bucket is <u>upside down</u>.

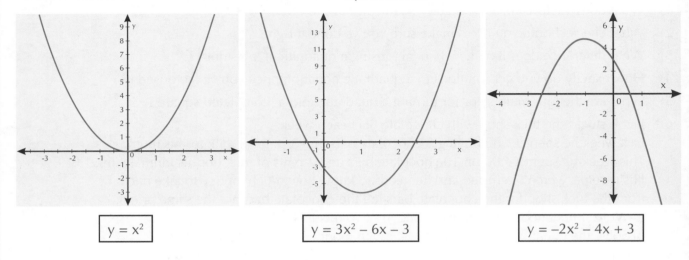

$y = x^2$	$y = 3x^2 - 6x - 3$	$y = -2x^2 - 4x + 3$

x^3 *Graphs*: $y = ax^3 + bx^2 + cx + d$ (b, c and/or d can be zero)

All x^3 graphs have the <u>same wiggle</u> in the middle —
sometimes it's a flat wiggle, sometimes it's more pronounced.

   $-x^3$ graphs always go <u>down from top left</u>,
   $+x^3$ ones go <u>up from bottom left</u>.

(Note that x^3 must be the highest power and there must be no other bits like 1/x etc.)

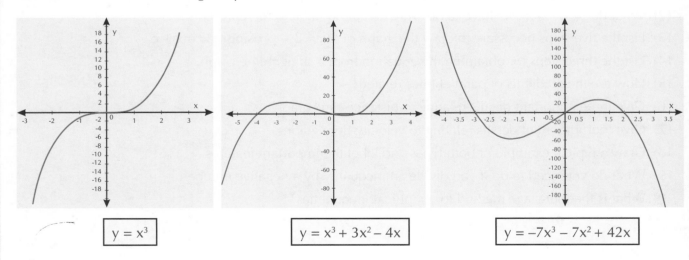

$y = x^3$	$y = x^3 + 3x^2 - 4x$	$y = -7x^3 - 7x^2 + 42x$

These shapes will come up again and again — so learn them

The x^2 bucket is a bit trickier than straight line graphs, and the x^3 wiggle can be downright confusing. All you really need to do, though, is recognise the general shape and the basic properties.

Some Harder Graphs to Learn

1/x Graphs: $y = A/x$, or $xy = A$ (A is any number — positive or negative)

These are <u>all the same basic shape</u>, except the negative ones are in opposite quadrants to the positive ones (as shown). The two halves of the graph don't touch.

They're all <u>symmetrical</u> about the lines <u>y = x</u> and <u>y = -x</u>.

(You get this type of graph with inverse proportion — see p.111)

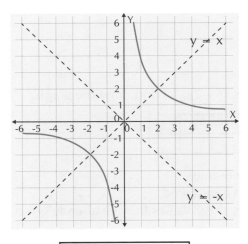

$y = 4/x$ or $xy = 4$

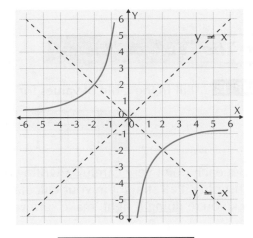

$y = -4/x$ or $xy = -4$

k^x Graphs: $y = k^x$ (k is some positive number)

1) These graphs <u>curve upwards</u> when k > 1.

2) They're always <u>above the x-axis</u>.

3) They all <u>go through the point (0, 1)</u>.

4) For <u>bigger values of k</u>, the graph tails off towards zero <u>more quickly</u> on the left and <u>climbs more steeply</u> on the right.

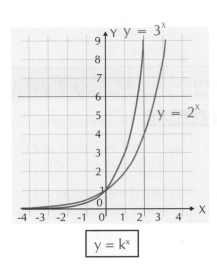

$y = k^x$

Four different graph shapes — do a quick sketch of each to be sure

All these graphs look quite different and so you should be able to recognise the general shapes as easy as pie (though quite how easy pie is I have no idea).

Quadratic Graphs

You need to be able to plot quadratic graphs, and then use them to solve equations.

Plotting and Solving *Quadratic Functions*

Quadratic functions are of the form <u>y = anything with x^2</u> (but not higher powers of x).
Remember that all these x^2 graphs have the same <u>SYMMETRICAL</u> bucket shape (see p.102).

So when you plot a quadratic, remember that you're aiming for a symmetrical bucket shape — anything else and you've gone wrong. Here's how to tackle questions on quadratics.

Fill in *The Table of Values*

EXAMPLE: "Fill in the table of values for the equation $y = x^2 + 2x - 3$ and draw the graph."

x	-5	-4	-3	-2	-1	0	1	2	3
y		5		-3	-4	-3	0		

Work out each point <u>very carefully</u>, writing down all your working.
Don't just plug it all straight in your calculator — you'll make mistakes.
To check you're <u>doing it right</u>, make sure you can <u>reproduce</u> the y-values they've already given you.

Draw *the Curve*

1) <u>PLOT THE POINTS CAREFULLY</u>,
    and don't mix up the x and y values.

2) The points should form a
    <u>COMPLETELY SMOOTH CURVE</u>.
    If they don't, they're <u>wrong</u>.

    *NEVER EVER let one point drag your line off in another
    direction. When a graph is generated from an equation,
    you never get spikes or lumps — only MISTAKES.*

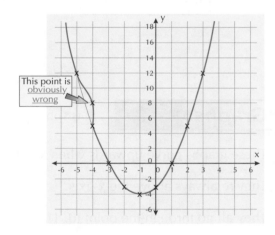

This point is obviously wrong

Read off the *Solutions*

EXAMPLE: "Use your graph to solve the equation $x^2 + 2x - 3 = 0$."

1) Look — the equation you've been asked to solve is what you get
    when you put <u>y = 0</u> into the graph's equation, $y = x^2 + 2x - 3$.

2) To solve the equation, all you do is read the x-values where y = 0,
    i.e. where it crosses the x-axis.

3) So the solutions are <u>x = -3</u> and <u>x = 1</u>. (Quadratic equations usually have 2 solutions.)

Tables of values, plotting — easy marks, as long as you're accurate

Both of these examples are easy questions, but too many people rush them and make silly errors. Take your time and get them right — check and see if the points in the table or on the graph are sensible.

Warm-up and Worked Exam Questions

The warm-up questions run quickly over the basic facts you'll need in the exam. The exam questions come later — but unless you've learnt the facts first you'll find the exams tougher than stale bread.

Warm-Up Questions

1) a) Complete the table of values for $y = x^2 - 2x - 1$.

x	-2	-1	0	1	2	3	4	5
x^2	4							
-2x	4							
-1	-1							
$y = x^2 - 2x - 1$	7							

   b) Plot the x and y values from the table and join the points up to form a smooth curve.
   c) Use your curve to find the value of y when x = 3.5.
   d) Find the two values of x when y = 5.

2) Draw the graph of $y = x^2 - 3x$ for values of x from -2 to 5.
   Use your graph to solve the following equations.
   a) $x^2 - 3x = 0$.
   b) $x^2 - 3x = 3$.

Worked Exam Question

Wow, an exam question — with the answers helpfully written in. It must be your birthday.

1 (a) Complete the table of values for $y = 5x - 4x^3 + 2$.

x	-1.5	-1	-0.5	0	0.5	1	1.5
y	8	1	0	2	4	3	-4

(2 marks)

(b) On the axes below, draw the graph of $y = 5x - 4x^3 + 2$ for values of x from -1.5 to 1.5.

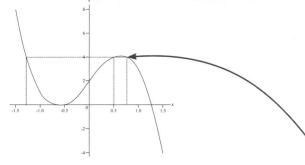

(2 marks)

Hint: Find the x values of the points of intersection for y = 5x – 4x³ + 2 and y = 4.

(c) Use your graph to solve the equation $5x - 4x^3 = 2$.

$5x - 4x^3 = 2; \quad 5x - 4x^3 + 2 = 2 + 2; \quad 5x - 4x^3 + 2 = 4; \quad y = 4.$

Any value between 0.75 and 0.8 is acceptable.

$x = 0.5, 0.78 \text{ and } -1.28.$

Any value between -1.25 and -1.3 is acceptable.

(3 marks)

Exam Questions

2 Match each of the graphs below to the correct equation.

  A: $y = 2^x$ B: $y = 2x^2 + 5x - 3$ C: $y + x^3 = 2$ D: $xy = 1/2$

(a)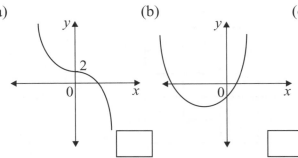

(b)

(c)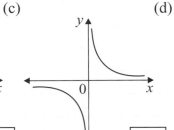

(d)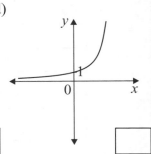

(1 mark)   *(1 mark)*   *(1 mark)*   *(1 mark)*

3 Teenagers Nick and Tom have a competition to see who can kick a football to the greatest height.

The graph shows the path followed by Nick's football which is described by the equation $h = 6t - 1.2t^2$ where h is height in metres and t is time in seconds.

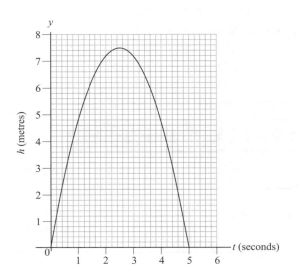

(a) The path followed by Tom's football is described by $h = 4.2t - 0.7t^2$.
     Complete the table of values for Tom's football and plot the curve on the graph above.

t	0	1	2	3	4	5	6
$h = 4.2t - 0.7t^2$	0						

(4 marks)

(b) Who wins the competition?

     ....
     (1 mark)

(c) Calculate the difference in maximum heights reached by Nick and Tom's footballs.

     ....
     (2 marks)

(d) If Nick and Tom both kick their footballs at the same time, at what time do the footballs reach the same height?

     ....
     (1 mark)

Simultaneous Equations and Graphs

When you have two graphs which represent two separate equations, there are two ways the question can present it: two simultaneous equations or a single merged equation. In either case the solutions will simply be where the two graphs cross...

1) Two *Graphs* and Two *Separate Equations*

Example 1:

"Draw the graphs for "$y = 2x + 3$" and "$y = 6 - 4x$" and then use your graphs to solve the equations."

Just draw the graphs and read off the x- and y- values where they cross...

$x = ½$ and $y = 4$

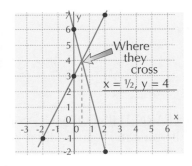

Where they cross
$x = ½$, $y = 4$

Example 2:

"By drawing graphs, solve the simultaneous equations $y = x^2 + 2x - 8$ and $y = 2x + 1$."

1) <u>DRAW BOTH GRAPHS</u>.
   Plot them as you usually would by filling in a table of values for each one (see p.104 for how to plot quadratic graphs).

2) <u>LOOK FOR WHERE THE GRAPHS CROSS</u>.
   The straight line crosses the curve at two points.
   Reading the x and y values of these points gives the solutions:

   $x = 3$, $y = 7$ and $x = -3$, $y = -5$

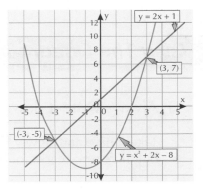

$y = 2x + 1$
$(3, 7)$
$(-3, -5)$
$y = x^2 + 2x - 8$

2) Two *Graphs* but *Just One Equation*, or *so it seems...*

Example:

"Using the graphs shown for $y = 4 + ½x$ and $y = 6 - x^2/3$, <u>solve the equation</u>: $x^2/3 + ½x - 2 = 0$."

<u>ANSWER</u>: <u>Learn</u> these important steps:

1) <u>Equating the equations</u> of the two graphs gives this:
   $6 - x^2/3 = 4 + ½x$ (a sort of '<u>merged</u> equation')

2) Now bring it all onto <u>one side</u> and you end up with:
   $x^2/3 + ½x - 2 = 0$ (the equation in the question!)

3) Hence the <u>solutions</u> to that equation are where the two initial equations ($y = 4 + ½x$ and $y = 6 - x^2/3$) are <u>equal</u> — i.e. where their <u>graphs cross</u>, which as the graph shows is at: <u>$x = 1.8$</u> or <u>$x = -3.3$</u>.

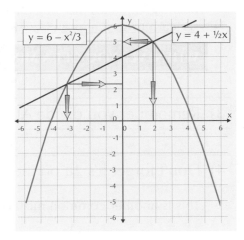

$y = 6 - x^2/3$
$y = 4 + ½x$

A point which satisfies two graphs is the point where they cross

This is pretty obvious but it's the key to these questions. When you are solving two simultaneous equations you are finding a point which satisfies both graphs. So draw them and see where they cross.

The Quadratic Formula

As well as solving quadratic equations by factorising and completing the square (p.76-78), you need to be able to solve them by using the quadratic formula.

You Need to **Learn** the **Quadratic Formula**

The solutions to any quadratic equation $ax^2 + bx + c = 0$ are given by this formula:

$$x = \frac{-b \pm \sqrt{b^2 - 4ac}}{2a}$$

LEARN THIS FORMULA —
If you can't learn it, there's no way you'll be able to use it in the exam, even if they give it to you.

Using it should, in principle, be quite straightforward.
As it turns out though there are quite a few pitfalls, so TAKE HEED of these crucial details:

Using The **Quadratic Formula**

1) Always write it down <u>in stages</u> as you go.

Take it nice and slowly — any fool can rush it and get it wrong, but there's no marks for being a fool.

2) <u>MINUS SIGNS</u>.

Throughout the whole of algebra, minus signs cause untold misery <u>because people keep forgetting them</u>.
In this formula, there are two minus signs that people keep forgetting: <u>the -b and the -4ac</u>.

The -4ac causes particular problems <u>when either 'a' or 'c' is negative</u>, because it makes the -4ac effectively +4ac —
<u>so learn to spot it as a HAZARD before it happens</u>.

WHENEVER YOU GET A MINUS SIGN, <u>THE ALARM BELLS SHOULD ALWAYS RING!</u>

3) Remember you <u>divide ALL of the top line by 2a</u>, not just half of it.

4) Don't forget it's <u>2a</u> on the bottom line, not just a.

This is another common mistake.

Looks nightmarish — but you'll soon be chanting it in your sleep

This formula looks difficult to use and learn but after you've said "minus b plus or minus the square root of b squared minus four a c all over two a" a few times you'll wonder what all the fuss is about.

The Quadratic Formula

Example:

"Find the solutions of $3x^2 + 7x = 1$ to 2 decimal places."

The mention of decimal places in exam questions is a <u>very big clue</u> to use the formula rather than trying to factorise it.

Method:

1) First get it into the form <u>$ax^2 + bx + c = 0$</u>:

$$3x^2 + 7x - 1 = 0$$

2) Then carefully identify a, b and c:

$$\underline{a = 3, \quad b = 7, \quad c = -1}$$

3) Put these values into the quadratic formula and <u>write down each stage</u>:

$$x = \frac{-b \pm \sqrt{b^2 - 4ac}}{2a} = \frac{-7 \pm \sqrt{7^2 - 4 \times 3 \times -1}}{2 \times 3}$$

$$= \frac{-7 \pm \sqrt{49 + 12}}{6}$$

$$= \frac{-7 \pm \sqrt{61}}{6}$$

$$= \frac{-7 \pm 7.81}{6}$$

$$= 0.1350 \text{ or} -2.468$$

So to 2 DP, the solutions are: <u>$x = 0.14$ or -2.47</u>

4) Finally, <u>as a check</u> put these values back into the <u>original equation</u>:

E.g. for $x = 0.1350$:

$$3 \times 0.135^2 + 7 \times 0.135 = 0.999675, \text{ which is 1, as near as...}$$

Not so nightmarish after all — just stick the numbers in the formula

Minus b plus or minus the square root of b squared minus four a c all over two a, minus b plus or minus the square root of b squared minus four a c all over two a, scream if you want to go faster...

Trial and Improvement

In principle, this is an easy way to find approximate answers to quite complicated equations.
<u>BUT</u>... you have to make an effort to <u>LEARN THE FINER DETAILS</u> of this method,
otherwise you'll never get the hang of it.

Method:

1) <u>SUBSTITUTE TWO INITIAL VALUES</u> into the equation that give <u>OPPOSITE CASES</u>.
   These are usually suggested in the question. If not, you'll have to think of your own.
   'Opposite cases' means <u>one answer too big, one too small</u>. If your values don't give opposite cases <u>try again</u>.

2) Now CHOOSE YOUR NEXT VALUE <u>IN BETWEEN</u> THE PREVIOUS TWO,
   and <u>SUBSTITUTE it into the equation</u>.
   <u>Continue this process</u>, always choosing a new value <u>between the two closest opposite cases</u>,
   (and preferably nearer to the one which is closest to the answer you want).

3) <u>AFTER ONLY 3 OR 4 STEPS</u> you should have <u>2 numbers</u> which are to the
   <u>right degree of accuracy but DIFFER BY 1 IN THE LAST DIGIT</u>.
   For example if you had to get your answer to 2 DP then you'd eventually end up with
   say 5.43 and 5.44, with these giving OPPOSITE results of course.

4) <u>At this point</u> you ALWAYS take the <u>Exact Middle Value</u> to decide which
   is the answer you want.
   E.g. for 5.43 and 5.44, you'd try 5.435 to see if the real
   answer was <u>between 5.43 and 5.435</u> or between <u>5.435 and 5.44</u> (see below).

Example

"The equation $x^3 + x = 40$ has a solution between 3 and 3.5. Find this solution to 1 DP."

Try x = 3 $3^3 + 3 = 30$ (Too small)
Try x = 3.5 $3.5^3 + 3.5 = 46.375$ (Too big)   ← (2 opposite cases)

40 is what we want and it's closer to 46.375 than it is to 30.
So we'll choose our next value for x closer to 3.5 than 3.

Try x = 3.3 $3.3^3 + 3.3 = 39.237$ (Too small)

Good, this is very close, but we still need to see if 3.4 is too big or too small:

Try x = 3.4 $3.4^3 + 3.4 = 42.704$ (Too big)

Good, now we know that <u>the answer must be between 3.3 and 3.4</u>.
To find out which one it's nearest to, we have to try the <u>EXACT MIDDLE VALUE</u>:   3.35

Try x = 3.35 $3.35^3 + 3.35 = 40.945$ (Too big)

This tells us with certainty that the solution must be between 3.3 (too small)
and 3.35 (too big), and so to 1 DP <u>it must round down to 3.3</u>. ANSWER: x = 3.3

It's like playing a game of higher and lower

You need to commit this method to memory, otherwise you've wasted your time even reading it.
Luckily it's simple — like a guessing game where you guess a number too high, and then too low and
get gradually closer until you get to the right answer. That's really all you're doing with this method.

Direct and Inverse Proportion

Direct Proportion: y = kx

Both <u>INCREASE</u> together

Inverse Proportion: y = k/x

One <u>INCREASES</u>, one <u>DECREASES</u>

---

1) The graph of y against x is a <u>straight line through the origin</u>: $y = kx$:

2) In a table of values the <u>MULTIPLIER</u> is the <u>same for x and y</u>, i.e. if you <u>double</u> one of them, you <u>double</u> the other, if you <u>times one of them by 3</u>, you <u>times the other by 3</u>, etc.

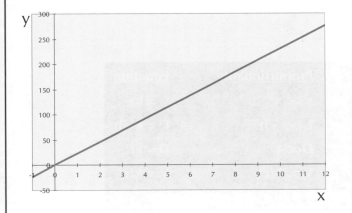

3) The <u>RATIO</u> $\frac{x}{y}$ <u>is the same for all pairs</u> of values, i.e from the table above:

$$\frac{2}{3} = \frac{6}{9} = \frac{8}{12} = \frac{12}{18} = \frac{14}{21} = \frac{56}{84} = 0.6667$$

---

1) The graph of y against x is the well known $y = k/x$ graph:

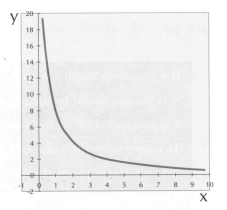

2) In a table of values the <u>MULTIPLIER</u> for one of them becomes a <u>DIVIDER</u> for the other, i.e. if you <u>double one</u>, you <u>half the other</u>, if you <u>treble one</u>, you <u>divide the other by three</u>, etc.

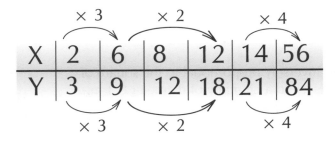

3) The <u>PRODUCT</u> xy (x times y) is the <u>same</u> for <u>all pairs of values</u>, i.e. in the table above:

$$2 \times 30 = 6 \times 10 = 8 \times 7.5 = 12 \times 5$$
$$= 40 \times 1.5 = 10 \times 6 = \underline{60}$$

Direct proportion means x and y increase together

But with inverse proportion, one increases and the other decreases. Remember their main properties — the shape of the graph, the table of values and the ratio x/y, or its equivalent, the product xy.

Direct and Inverse Proportion

This page shows you how to deal with questions which involve statements like these:

'y is proportional to the square of x'   't is proportional to the square root of h'
'D varies with the cube of t'   'V is inversely proportional to r cubed'

To deal successfully with things like this <u>you must remember this method</u>:

Method:

1) <u>Convert the sentence into a proportionality</u>,
   using the symbol '∝' which means '<u>is proportional to</u>'.

2) <u>Replace '∝' with '=k'</u> to make an EQUATION:

The above examples would become:	Proportionality	Equation
'y is proportional to the square of x'	$y \propto x^2$	$y = kx^2$
't is proportional to the square root of h'	$t \propto \sqrt{h}$	$t = k\sqrt{h}$
'D varies with the cube of T'	$D \propto t^3$	$D = kt^3$
'V is inversely proportional to r cubed'	$V \propto 1/r^3$	$V = k/r^3$

(Once you've got it in the form of an equation with k, the <u>rest is easy</u>.)

3) <u>Find a PAIR OF VALUES of x and y</u> somewhere in the question,
   and <u>SUBSTITUTE them into the equation</u> with the <u>sole purpose of finding k</u>.

4) <u>Put the value of k back into the equation</u> and it's now ready to use, e.g. $y = 3x^2$.

5) <u>INEVITABLY, they'll ask you to find y</u>, having given you a value for x (or vice versa).

Example:

The time taken for a duck to fall down a chimney is inversely proportional to the square of the diameter of the flue. If she took 25 seconds to descend a chimney of diameter 0.3 m, how long would it take her to get down one of 0.2 m diameter?

(Notice there's no mention of 'writing an equation' or 'finding k'
— it's up to <u>YOU</u> to remember the method for yourself.)

<u>ANSWER</u>:

1) Write it as a <u>proportionality</u>, then an <u>equation</u>: $t \propto 1/d^2$ i.e. $t = k/d^2$
2) <u>Sub in the given values</u> for the two variables: $25 = k/0.3^2$
3) Rearrange the equation to <u>find k</u>: $k = 25 \times 0.3^2 = 2.25$
4) Put k <u>back in</u> the formula: $t = 2.25/d^2$
5) <u>Sub in new value</u> for d: $t = 2.25/0.2^2 = \underline{56.25 \text{ secs}}$

Remember, "proportional to" can be replaced with "= k"

So any problem about proportion can be made into an equation. These sort of questions can be tricky so take your time. Have another read of this page to make sure you've got it down.

Warm-up Questions

By doing these warm-up questions, you'll soon find out if you've got the basic facts straight.
If not, you'll really struggle, so take the time to go back over the bits you don't know.

Warm-Up Questions

1) The graphs of $2y = 3x - 6$, $y = 0.5x + 3$ and $y + 2x = 8$ are shown.

   Use the graphs to solve the following
   pairs of simultaneous equations.
   a) $2y = 3x - 6$;
   $\quad y = 0.5x + 3$.
   b) $y + 2x = 8$;
   $\quad y = 0.5x + 3$.
   c) $2y = 3x - 6$;
   $\quad y + 2x = 8$.

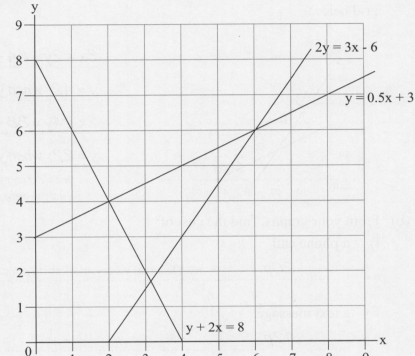

2) Draw the graphs of $y = 4 - 2x^2$ and $y = 1 - x$ for values of x from -2 to +2.
   Use the graphs to solve the equation $2x^2 = x + 3$.

3) Assume the graph of $y = x^2 - 3x + 2$ has been drawn.
   What other graph needs to be drawn to find the solution of the equation $x^2 - 2x - 3 = 0$?

4) Find the solutions of these equations (to 2 decimal places) using the quadratic formula:
   a) $x^2 + 10x - 4 = 0$
   b) $3x^2 - 3x = 2$
   c) $(2x + 3)^2 = 15$

5) The equation $x^3 - 2x = 10$ has a solution between 2 and 3.
   Find it to 1 decimal place, using trial and improvement.

6) Write each of the following as an equation:

   a) A is proportional to the square of r

   b) $D \propto \dfrac{1}{R}$

   c) H is inversely proportional to the cube of D

   d) $V \propto S^3$

Worked Exam Questions

You need to <u>learn</u> the methods from the last few pages — including the quadratic formula. The best way to make sure you remember them and can use them correctly is to practise lots of questions...

1   Natalie and Hannah are both on the same mobile phone tariff. Natalie makes three phone calls and sends two text messages for 84p. Hannah makes two phone calls and sends four text messages for 88p.
Let x represent the cost of a phone call and y represent the cost of a text message.

(a)   From the information given, write down two equations and plot their graphs on the grid below.

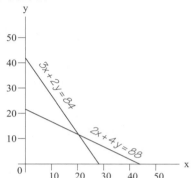

3x + 2y = 84 — when x = 0, 2y = 84,

y = 42; when y = 0, 3x = 84, x = 28.

2x + 4y = 88 — when x = 0, 4y = 88,

y = 22; when y = 0, 2x = 88, x = 44.

See p. 89 for more on plotting graphs using this method.

(4 marks)

(b)   From your graphs, find the cost of:

i)   a phone call

20p   Hint: Read the x and y values at the point of intersection of the 2 graphs.

(1 mark)

ii)   a text message.

12p

(1 mark)

2   Solve $3x^2 + 13x + 3 = 0$ to 2 decimal places, using the quadratic formula.

The best way to start is to write down the quadratic formula and say what a, b and c are.

$$x = \frac{-b \pm \sqrt{b^2 - 4ac}}{2a} \qquad a = 3, b = 13, c = 3$$

Then just plug in all the numbers and be very <u>careful</u>...

$$x = \frac{-13 \pm \sqrt{13^2 - 4 \times 3 \times 3}}{2 \times 3} = \frac{-13 \pm \sqrt{169 - 36}}{6} = \frac{-13 \pm 11.53...}{6}$$

$$x = \frac{-13 + 11.53...}{6} \ or \ x = \frac{-13 - 11.53...}{6}$$

Don't forget to give your answer to 2 decimal places — it's very easy to throw away marks by forgetting this...

So x = -0.24 or x = -4.09 (both to 2 d.p.)

(3 marks)

Worked Exam Questions

3   Find a solution for $x^3 + 5x = 50$ $(3 < x < 4)$ to 2 decimal places by trial and improvement.

You know it's between 3 and 4, so start with 3.5.

x	$x^3 + 5x$
3.5	60.375
3.2	48.768
3.3	52.437
3.25	50.57813
3.22	49.48625
3.23	49.84827
3.24	50.21222
3.235	50.03000

Remember — you're just making guesses for x to get as close to the right hand side (50) as possible.

If it's too low, guess higher.
If it's too high, guess lower.

Keep going until you've got two opposite cases with x values that differ by 1 in the last digit. Then try the middle of these guesses. It sounds confusing, but it'll make sense when you get the hang of it.

.....We can see that x lies between 3.23 and 3.235........

.....So to 2 decimal places, x = 3.23 (because x is definitely less........

.....than 3.235, it must round down to 3.23)........

(4 marks)

4   y is inversely proportional to x^2. When $x = 4$, $y = 3$.

(a) Express y in terms of x.

$$y \propto \frac{1}{x^2} \rightarrow y = \frac{k}{x^2}$$ ← *Start by writing an equation to show how x and y are inversely proportionally related (that's a mouthful).*

Now, putting in the given values of x and y will give you k.

$$x = 4 \text{ when } y = 3 \text{ gives: } 3 = \frac{k}{4^2} \rightarrow k = 3 \times 16 = 48, \text{ so } y = \frac{48}{x^2}$$

(3 marks)

(b) (i) Calculate the value of y when $x = 8$.

$$y = \frac{48}{8^2} = \frac{48}{64} = \frac{3}{4}$$ *Now you've got the equation y = 48 / x², just stick in values for y or x to answer these questions.*

(1 mark)

(ii) Calculate the value of x when $y = 75$.

$$75 = \frac{48}{x^2} \rightarrow x^2 = \frac{48}{75} = 0.64 \rightarrow x = \pm\sqrt{0.64} \rightarrow x = \pm 0.8$$

(2 marks)

Exam Questions

Some of these questions would have lots more space for answers in the real exam. We've just squeezed them in here so you get more practice.

5   (a)   Complete the table of values for $y = 12/x - 1$.

x	1	2	3	4	5	6
y	11					1

(2 marks)

   (b)   Plot the x and y values from the table onto a grid.

(2 marks)

   (c)   By adding a straight line to your graph, solve the equation $12/x = 11 - 2x$.

....

(2 marks)

6   Solve graphically the simultaneous equations $y = 3x + 5$ and $y = x^2 - 3$.

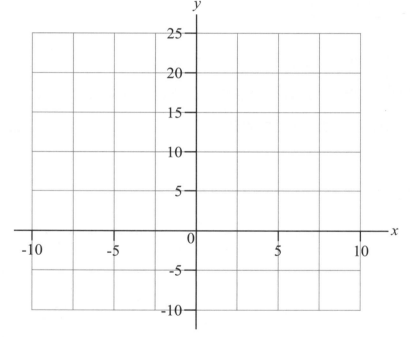

....

(3 marks)

7   Solve $x^2 + 8x - 4 = 0$ to 1 decimal place using the quadratic formula.

....

....

(3 marks)

Exam Questions

8   Find both solutions of $2x^2 + 3x - 4 = 0$ to 2 decimal places.

....
(3 marks)

9   Use the quadratic formula to find the solutions of $3x^2 - 5x = 12$ to 2 decimal places.

....
(3 marks)

10   $x^3 - 3x^2 = 29$ has a solution between 4 and 5.
   Use trial and improvement to find it to 2 decimal places.

....
(4 marks)

11   The company Etto Oil sells oil in various sized containers. The capacity, C litres,
   of an Etto oil container is always directly proportional to the cube of its diameter, d metres.
   One container size has a capacity of 270 litres and a diameter of 1.5 metres.
   (a) Find the equation connecting C and d.

....
(3 marks)

   (b) Another oil container is 1.8 metres in diameter.
        Find out how many litres this container can hold.

....
(2 marks)

   (c) Find the diameter of an oil container which holds 140 litres.

....
(2 marks)

12   F varies inversely as the square of t. $F = 40$ when $t = 5$.
   (a) Express F in terms of t.

....
(3 marks)

   (b) (i) Calculate the value of F when $t = 200$.

....
(1 mark)

        (ii) Calculate the value of t when $F = 50$.

....
(2 marks)

Symmetry

There are <u>TWO types</u> of symmetry and you need to know about them both.

1) *Line* Symmetry

This is where you can draw a <u>MIRROR LINE</u> (or more than one) across a picture and <u>both sides will fold exactly together</u>.

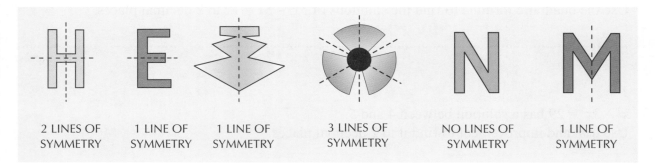

| 2 LINES OF SYMMETRY | 1 LINE OF SYMMETRY | 1 LINE OF SYMMETRY | 3 LINES OF SYMMETRY | NO LINES OF SYMMETRY | 1 LINE OF SYMMETRY |

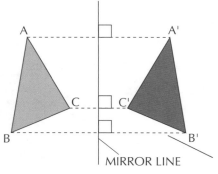

MIRROR LINE

How to Draw a *Reflection*:

1) Reflect each point one by one.
2) Use a line which crosses the mirror line at 90º and goes <u>EXACTLY</u> the same distance on the other side of the mirror line, as shown.

A line which crosses at 90º is called <u>a perpendicular</u>.

2) *Rotational* Symmetry

This is where you can <u>ROTATE</u> the shape or drawing into different positions that <u>all look exactly the same</u>.

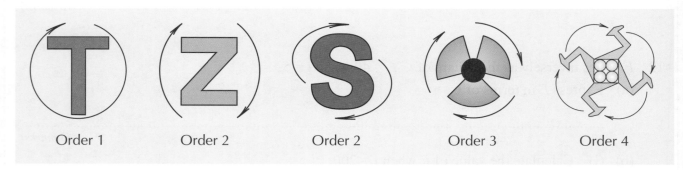

| Order 1 | Order 2 | Order 2 | Order 3 | Order 4 |

The <u>ORDER OF ROTATIONAL SYMMETRY</u> is the posh way of saying: '<u>HOW MANY DIFFERENT POSITIONS LOOK THE SAME</u>'.
E.g. You should say the Z shape above has '<u>Rotational Symmetry order 2</u>'.

BUT... when a shape has <u>ONLY 1 POSITION</u> you can <u>either</u> say that it has '<u>Rotational Symmetry order 1</u>' <u>or</u> that it has '<u>NO Rotational Symmetry</u>'.

Symmetry in Common Shapes

These are easy marks in the exam — make sure you know them all.

Three-sided Shapes — *Triangles*

1) *Equilateral*

<u>3 equal sides</u> and
<u>3 equal angles</u> of <u>60°</u>.
<u>3 lines</u> of symmetry,
rotational symmetry <u>order 3</u> (see p.118).

2) *Right-angled*

1 <u>right angle</u> (<u>90°</u>).

<u>No</u> lines of symmetry unless
the other angles are 45°
(in which case, there's 1).
<u>No</u> rotational symmetry.

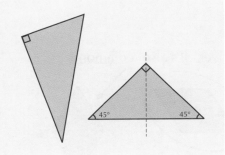

3) *Isosceles*

<u>2 sides</u> the same.
<u>2 angles</u> the same.
<u>1 line</u> of symmetry.
<u>No</u> rotational symmetry.

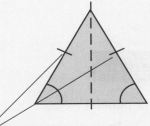

These dashes indicate two sides the same length.

4) *Scalene*

All three sides <u>different</u>.
All three angles <u>different</u>.

No symmetry, pretty obviously.

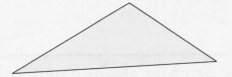

Symmetry in Common Shapes

Four-sided Shapes — Quadrilaterals

1) Square

<u>4 lines</u> of symmetry.
Rotational symmetry <u>order 4</u>.

2) Rectangle

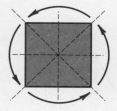

<u>2 lines</u> of symmetry.
Rotational symmetry <u>order 2</u>.

3) Rhombus

A square pushed over. It's also a <u>diamond</u>.

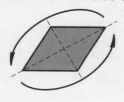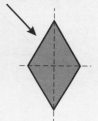

<u>2 lines</u> of symmetry.
Rotational symmetry <u>order 2</u>.

4) Parallelogram

A rectangle pushed over.
<u>Two pairs</u> of parallel sides.

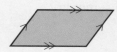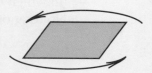

<u>NO lines</u> of symmetry.
Rotational symmetry <u>order 2</u>.

5) Trapezium

<u>One pair</u> of parallel sides.

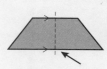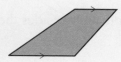

Only the <u>isosceles trapezium</u>
has a <u>line</u> of symmetry.
None have rotational symmetry.

6) Kite

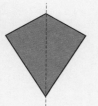

<u>1 line</u> of symmetry.
No rotational symmetry.

Quadrilaterals are just shapes with four sides

Six types of quadrilateral to learn on this page. Make sure you know their features — for example, how many lines of symmetry they have and whether they have rotational symmetry.

Areas

You need to learn <u>all</u> these formulas before you go into the exam.

The area of a <u>trapezium</u> and the <u>trig formula</u> for the area of a <u>triangle</u> will be given on the inside cover of your exam. But I <u>GUARANTEE</u> that if you don't learn them beforehand, you'll be <u>totally incapable</u> of using them in the exam — <u>REMEMBER, I ABSOLUTELY GUARANTEE IT</u>.

You must LEARN these Formulas:

<u>Area of triangle</u> = ½ × base × vertical height

$$A = \tfrac{1}{2} \times b \times h_v$$

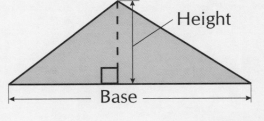

Height

Note that the <u>height</u> must always be the <u>vertical height</u>, not the sloping height.

Base

(Trigonometry is covered on p.154-157)

The alternative formula is this:

<u>Area of triangle</u> = ½ ab sin C

<u>Area of parallelogram</u> = base × vertical height

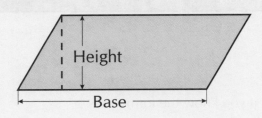

Height

Base

$$A = b \times h_v$$

<u>Area of trapezium</u> = average of parallel sides × distance between them

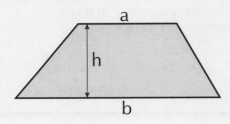

a

h

b

$$A = \tfrac{1}{2} \times (a + b) \times h$$

Areas

Area of circle = π × (radius)²

$$A = \pi \times r^2$$

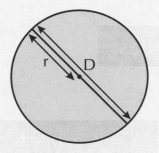

Circumference = π × diameter

$$C = \pi \times D$$

You can use the π button on your calculator for these formulas.
If your calculator doesn't have a π button then use π ≈ 3.14.

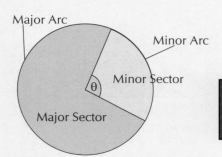

Major Arc

Minor Arc

Minor Sector

Major Sector

$$\text{Area of sector} = \frac{\theta}{360} \times \text{Area of full circle}$$

$$\text{Length of arc} = \frac{\theta}{360} \times \text{Circumference of full circle}$$

<u>FINDING THE AREA OF A SEGMENT</u> is OK if you know the formulas:

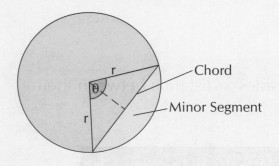

Chord

Minor Segment

1) Find the <u>area of the sector</u> using the formula given above.

2) Find the area of the triangle, then <u>subtract it</u> from the sector's area.

3) You can do this using the '<u>½ ab sin C</u>' formula for the area of the triangle.
This becomes: ½ r²sin θ.

Did I say already — you must learn these formulas

For any exam question on area you should be prepared to make use of Pythagoras (see p.152) and / or trigonometry (p.154). But one step at a time — just get these simple formulas lodged in your brain first.

Surface Area

Surface *Area* and *Nets*

1) <u>SURFACE AREA</u> only applies to solid 3D objects, and it is simply <u>the total area</u> of all the <u>outer surfaces</u> added together. If you were painting it, it's all the bits you'd paint.

2) <u>A NET</u> is just <u>A SOLID SHAPE FOLDED OUT FLAT</u>.

3) So obviously: <u>SURFACE AREA OF SOLID = AREA OF NET</u>.

For example, the surface area of the triangular prism below will be the area of the 3 rectangles plus the 2 triangles.

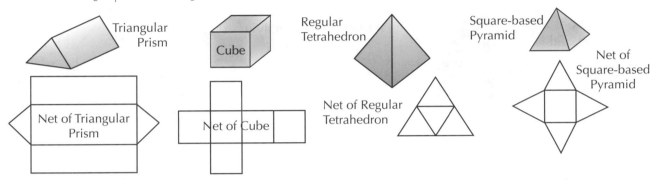

<u>SPHERES, CONES AND CYLINDERS</u> have surface area formulas that you need to learn:

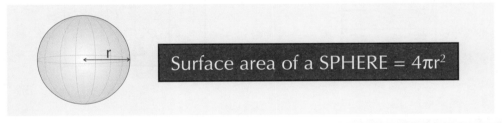

Surface area of a SPHERE = $4\pi r^2$

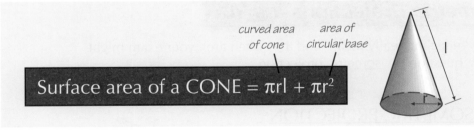

curved area of cone   *area of circular base*

Surface area of a CONE = $\pi r l + \pi r^2$

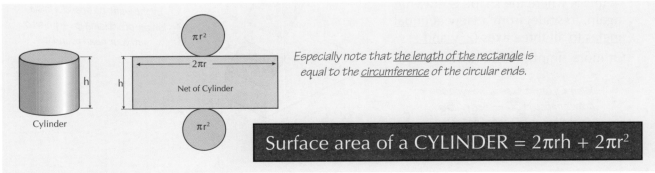

Especially note that <u>the length of the rectangle</u> is equal to the <u>circumference</u> of the circular ends.

Surface area of a CYLINDER = $2\pi rh + 2\pi r^2$

To get the surface area of a solid just add up the area of each face

That's why nets are useful when working out surface area. A net is just all the sides folded out flat, which makes it easier to see which shapes you need to calculate the areas of.

Projections

Projections Show Different Viewpoints

1) A 'projection' shows the shape of an object from the front, the side or the back — they're often called 'elevations'.

2) A 'plan' shows the view of the object from above.

3) Projections and plans are always drawn to scale.

Example:

Draw simplified elevations and a plan of this church.

FRONT ELEVATION
— the view you'd see if you looked from directly in front:

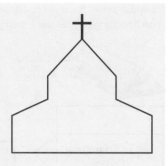

SIDE ELEVATION
— the view you'd see if you looked directly from one side:

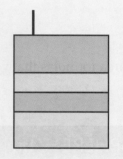

PLAN — the view you'd see if you looked from directly above:

Isometric Projections are 3D

If they're feeling really mean (and they often are), your exam might have a question on isometric projection.

ISOMETRIC PROJECTION
— this is where the shape is drawn (again, to scale) from a view at equal angles to all three axes (x, y and z).
Or more simply, it's a drawing like this:

Using x, y and z axes allows you to draw shapes in 3D — see p.156 for more on 3D coordinates.

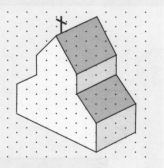

This one's a bit trickier, so you might want to spend a little longer practising it — just to get your head round it.

You'll always be given a grid to draw an isometric projection

You need to be able to draw 2D plans and elevations from 3D shapes, and 3D shapes from plans and elevations. The best way to get to grips with this lot is to get loads and loads of practice.

Volume

You might think you know this already, but I bet you don't know it all. There's only one thing for it...

LEARN these volume formulas...

1) Cuboid (rectangular block)

This is also known as a 'rectangular prism'
— see below to understand why.

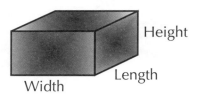

Height

Length

Width

Volume of Cuboid = length × width × height

$$V = L \times W \times H$$

(The other word for volume is <u>CAPACITY</u>.)

2) Prism

A <u>PRISM</u> is a solid (3D) object which is the same shape all the way through — i.e. it has a <u>CONSTANT AREA OF CROSS-SECTION</u>.

Now, for some reason, not a lot of people know what a prism is, but they come up all the time in exams, <u>so make sure YOU know</u>.

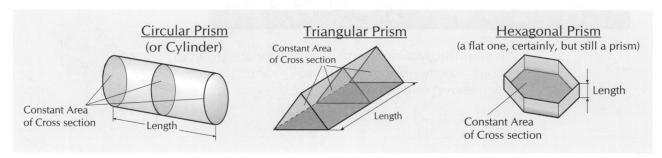

Circular Prism (or Cylinder)
Constant Area of Cross section — Length

Triangular Prism
Constant Area of Cross section — Length

Hexagonal Prism
(a flat one, certainly, but still a prism)
Length — Constant Area of Cross section

$$\text{VOLUME OF PRISM} = \frac{\text{CROSS-SECTIONAL}}{\text{AREA}} \times \text{LENGTH}$$

$$V = A \times L$$

As you can see, the formula for the volume of a prism is <u>very simple</u>. The <u>difficult</u> part, usually, is <u>finding the area of the cross-section</u>.

You have to remember what a prism is

It's the constant area of cross-section which is important — that's what makes a prism a prism. If you remember that, it makes perfect sense that to get the volume you just multiply that area by the length.

Volume

3) *Sphere*

VOLUME OF SPHERE $= \frac{4}{3}\pi r^3$

EXAMPLE: The moon has a radius of 1700 km. Find its volume.

Answer: $V = \frac{4}{3}\pi r^3 = \frac{4}{3} \times 3.14 \times 1700^3 = 2.1 \times 10^{10}$ km³

A hemisphere is just half a sphere. So the volume of a hemisphere is just half the volume of a full sphere, $V = \frac{2}{3}\pi r^3$

4) *Pyramids* and *Cones*

A pyramid is any shape that goes <u>up to a point at the top</u>. Its base can be any shape at all. If the base is a circle then it's called a <u>cone</u> (rather than a circular pyramid).

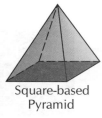
Square-based Pyramid

Tetrahedron

Cone

VOLUME OF PYRAMID $= \frac{1}{3} \times$ BASE AREA $\times$ HEIGHT

VOLUME OF CONE $= \frac{1}{3} \times \pi r^2 \times$ HEIGHT

This surprisingly simple formula is true for <u>any pyramid or cone</u>, whether it goes up 'vertically' (like the three shown above) or off to one side, like this one:

5) *A Frustum* is *Part of a Cone*

A <u>frustum of a cone</u> is what's left when the top part of a cone is cut off parallel to its circular base.

VOLUME OF = VOLUME OF THE _ VOLUME OF THE
FRUSTUM   ORIGINAL CONE   REMOVED CONE

$$= \frac{1}{3}\pi R^2 H - \frac{1}{3}\pi r^2 h$$

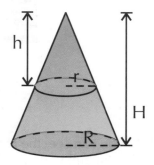

Remember that a cone is just a pyramid with a round base

The pyramid and cone formulas are basically the same because the area of the base = area of a circle $= \pi r^2$. So really just three formulas to learn here, and three important ones at that.

Length, Area and Volume Formulas

You need to be able to work out whether an unknown formula would give you a length, an area or a volume, just by looking at it.

Identifying Formulas Just by Looking at Them

This isn't as bad as it sounds, since we're only talking about the formulas for 3 things:

> LENGTH, AREA and VOLUME

The rules are as simple as this:

> 1) AREA FORMULAS always have LENGTHS MULTIPLIED IN PAIRS
>
> 2) VOLUME FORMULAS always have LENGTHS MULTIPLIED IN GROUPS OF THREE
>
> 3) LENGTH FORMULAS (such as perimeter) always have LENGTHS OCCURRING SINGLY

1) In formulas of course, lengths are represented by letters, so when you look at a formula you're looking for: groups of letters multiplied together in ones, twos or threes.

2) But remember, π is not a length — you can just ignore π and any numbers when you're deciding whether you've got a length, area or volume formula.

Examples:

r^2 means $r \times r$, don't forget (see p.64)

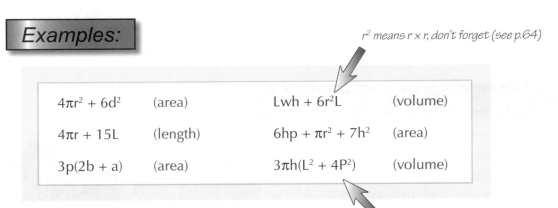

$4\pi r^2 + 6d^2$ (area)		$Lwh + 6r^2L$ (volume)	
$4\pi r + 15L$ (length)		$6hp + \pi r^2 + 7h^2$ (area)	
$3p(2b + a)$ (area)		$3\pi h(L^2 + 4P^2)$ (volume)	

Watch out for tricky ones with brackets — you should multiply out the brackets first (see p.66)

To recognise lengths, areas and volumes, just count the letters

See if the letters appear in ones, twos or threes — one letter on its own means a length, two letters multiplied together means an area and three letters multiplied together means a volume. There are a few examples on the page to make sure you've got the idea.

Regular Polygons

A <u>polygon</u> is a <u>many-sided shape</u>. A <u>regular</u> polygon is one where all the <u>sides</u> and <u>angles</u> are the same. The regular polygons are a never-ending series of shapes with some fancy features. They're very easy to learn.

Here are the first few but they don't stop — you can have one with 12 sides or 25, etc.

EQUILATERAL TRIANGLE
<u>3 sides</u>
<u>3 lines</u> of symmetry
Rot^{nl} symm. <u>order 3</u>

See p.118 for more on symmetry.

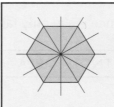

REGULAR HEXAGON
<u>6 sides</u>
<u>6 lines</u> of symmetry
Rot^{nl} symm. <u>order 6</u>

SQUARE
<u>4 sides</u>
<u>4 lines</u> of symmetry
Rot^{nl} symm. <u>order 4</u>

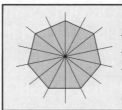

REGULAR HEPTAGON
<u>7 sides</u>
<u>7 lines</u> of symmetry
Rot^{nl} symm. <u>order 7</u>
(A 50p piece is like a heptagon)

REGULAR PENTAGON
<u>5 sides</u>
<u>5 lines</u> of symmetry
Rot^{nl} symm. <u>order 5</u>

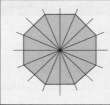

REGULAR OCTAGON
<u>8 sides</u>
<u>8 lines</u> of symmetry
Rot^{nl} symm. <u>order 8</u>

You also need to know the <u>next two</u>, but I'm not drawing them for you. <u>Learn their names</u>:

<u>REGULAR NONAGON</u>
<u>9 sides</u>, etc. etc.

<u>REGULAR DECAGON</u>
<u>10 sides</u>, etc. etc.

REGULAR POLYGONS HAVE LOADS OF SYMMETRY

1) The pentagon shown here has <u>only 3 different angles</u> in the whole diagram.

2) This is <u>typical of regular polygons</u>. They display an amazing amount of symmetry.

3) With a regular polygon, <u>if two angles look the same</u>, <u>they will be</u>. That's not a rule you should normally apply in geometry, and anyway you'll need to <u>prove</u> they're equal.

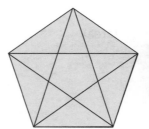

Regular polygons are easier than a round peg in a round hole

You need to learn the names of the polygons (which is pretty straightforward), and then remember what's special about regular polygons. Five minutes of scribbling should knock this page on the head.

Regular Polygons

Another thing that's <u>special</u> and <u>useful</u> about regular polygons
is all the calculations you can do with their angles...

Angles in a Regular Polygon

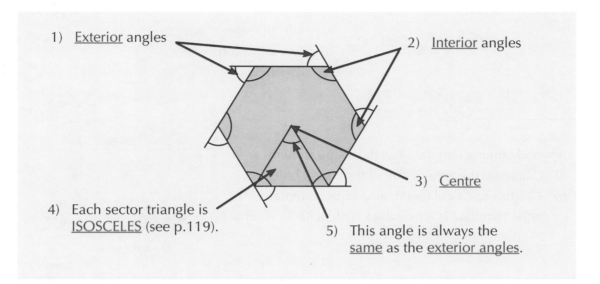

1) <u>Exterior</u> angles

2) <u>Interior</u> angles

3) <u>Centre</u>

4) Each sector triangle is <u>ISOSCELES</u> (see p.119).

5) This angle is always the <u>same</u> as the <u>exterior angles</u>.

There are **Two Formulas** to Learn for **REGULAR Polygons...**

$$\text{EXTERIOR ANGLE} = \frac{360°}{n}$$ (*n* is the number of sides)

$$\text{INTERIOR ANGLE} = 180° - \text{EXTERIOR ANGLE}$$

...and Another **Two Formulas** to Learn for **ALL Polygons**

$$\text{SUM OF EXTERIOR ANGLES} = 360°$$

$$\text{SUM OF INTERIOR ANGLES} = (n - 2) \times 180°$$ (*n* is the number of sides)

Four very simple and very important formulas

There are always all manner of questions they can ask about angles in polygons, but they all come
back to these four basic formulas. So make sure you've learnt them really well.

Warm-up and Worked Exam Questions

There are lots of formulas in this section. The best way to see what you know is to practise these questions. If you find you keep forgetting the formulas, you need more practice.

Warm-Up Questions

1) Calculate the volume of this triangular prism.

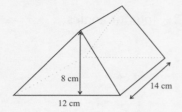

8 cm
14 cm
12 cm

2) From the isometric projection shown draw:
   a) both side elevations
   b) front elevation
   c) plan view

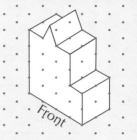

Front

3) A woodworking template has the shape shown.
   a) Calculate the area of one of the round holes.
   b) Use this to calculate the area of the template.
   c) If the template is 4 mm thick, calculate its volume.

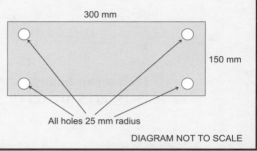

300 mm
150 mm
All holes 25 mm radius

DIAGRAM NOT TO SCALE

Worked Exam Question

This worked exam question is the ideal way to get the hang of the real exam, so work through it carefully.

1 A householder draws a plan of his garden.

The flowerbed and pond are rectangular and his patio is a quarter circle.

He intends to sow lawn seed on the shaded area of his plan.

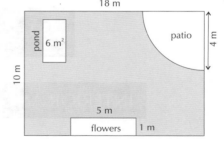

18 m
pond 6 m²
patio 4 m
10 m
5 m
flowers 1 m

DIAGRAM NOT TO SCALE

(a) Calculate the area covered by his new lawn.

Total area of garden = 10 × 18 = 180 m², area of pond = 6 m²,   Work out one bit at a time

area of flowerbed = 5 × 1 = 5 m², area of patio = ¼πr² = ¼ × π × 4² = 12.6 m²

So area of lawn = area of garden − (pond + flowers + patio)

$$= 180 − (6 + 5 + 12.6) = 156.4 \, m²$$

(4 marks)

(b) 0.5 kg of seed covers 10 m². How many kilograms of seed will he need? (Round your answer to the nearest kilogram)

0.5 kg of seed covers 10 m², so 0.5 ÷ 10 = 0.05 kg covers 1 m².

So to cover 156.4 m² need 156.4 × 0.05 = 7.82 kg. Need 8 kg to the nearest kg.

(2 marks)

Exam Questions

2   A tile is made in the shape of
    the regular polygon shown.

(a) Calculate the size of the angle *a*.

....
(2 marks)

(b) Calculate the size of the angle *b*.

....
(1 mark)

3   A metal fastener is produced
    using the dimensions shown.

15 mm

70°

*You'll have lots more
space for working in the
real exam — we've just
removed some lines to
squeeze more questions in.*

Calculate:
(a) the area of metal used to make the fastener.

....
(3 marks)

(b) the perimeter of the fastener.

....
(3 marks)

4   A solid metal sphere has a radius of 3 cm.
    (a) Calculate the volume of the sphere. Give your answer in terms of π.

....
(2 marks)

The sphere is melted down and reformed into a solid cone.
The cone is 4 cm high.
(b) Calculate the radius of the base of the cone. Give your answer in exact form.
     Simplify your answer as much as possible.

....
(3 marks)

Geometry

7 *Simple Rules* — *that's all:*

Spread over the next two pages there are seven simple rules
which will help you solve <u>ANY</u> geometry problem not involving circles.

If you <u>learn them all thoroughly</u>, you'll at least have a fighting chance of tackling geometry problems
— if you're unsure about <u>any</u> of them, then believe me you won't get anywhere with exam questions.

1) Angles in a *triangle*...

...ADD UP TO <u>180°</u>.

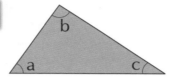

$$a + b + c = 180°$$

2) Angles on a *straight line*...

...ADD UP TO <u>180°</u>.

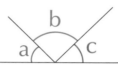

$$a + b + c = 180°$$

3) Angles in a *4-sided shape*... (a <u>quadrilateral</u>)

...ADD UP TO <u>360°</u>.

*You can see <u>why</u> this is if you think of a
quadrilateral as two triangles stuck together.
Each triangle has angles adding up to 180°,
so the two together have angles adding up to
180° + 180° = 360°.*

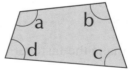

$$a + b + c + d = 360°$$

4) Angles *round a point*...

...ADD UP TO <u>360°</u>.

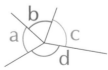

$$a + b + c + d = 360°$$

5) *Exterior Angle* of *Triangle*

<u>EXTERIOR ANGLE</u> of triangle
= <u>SUM OF OPPOSITE INTERIOR ANGLES</u>

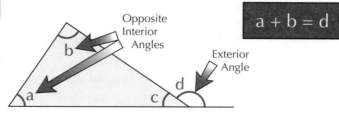

Opposite
Interior
Angles

Exterior
Angle

$$a + b = d$$

Five of seven geometry rules are here — YOU MUST LEARN THEM

That's one page of rules and the first five done — only two more to do. Scribble them down again and
again until they're ingrained in your brain (or desk). Then on to those last two...

Geometry

6) *Isosceles* triangles

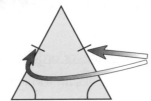

2 sides the same
2 angles the same

These dashes indicate
two sides the same length

In an isosceles triangle, you only need to know <u>one angle</u> to be able to find the other two,
which is very useful if you remember it.

a)

$180° - 40° = 140°$
<u>The two bottom angles are both the same</u> and they must
add up to 140°, so each one must be half of 140°. So <u>x = 70°</u>.

b)

The <u>two bottom angles must be the same</u>, so 50° + 50° = 100°.
All the angles add up to 180° so y = 180° − 100° = <u>80°</u>.

7) *Parallel* Lines

Whenever one line crosses two <u>parallel lines</u>
then the two bunches of angles
<u>are the same</u>, and <u>a + b = 180°</u>.

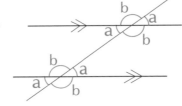

These are called
'<u>vertically
opposite angles</u>'.

You need to be able to spot these <u>characteristic shapes</u>:

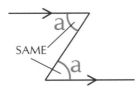

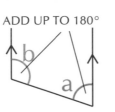

ADD UP TO 180°

In a Z-shape they're called
"<u>ALTERNATE ANGLES</u>"

If they add up to 180° they're called
"<u>SUPPLEMENTARY ANGLES</u>"

In an F-shape they're called
"<u>CORRESPONDING ANGLES</u>"

Alas you're expected to learn these three silly names.

If two lines cross at 90° then you've
got yourself some <u>perpendicular lines</u>.

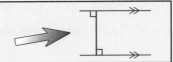

Parallel lines are key things to look out for in geometry

Keep your eyes open for parallel lines and those all important alternate, supplementary and
corresponding angles. Extending the lines can make seeing these things a lot easier.

UNIT 3 — GEOMETRY AND ALGEBRA

Geometry

The **Basic Approach** to Geometry Problems

1) <u>Don't</u> concentrate too much on the angle you have been asked to find.

2) The best method is to find <u>ALL</u> the angles in <u>whatever order</u> they become obvious.

3) <u>Don't</u> sit there waiting for inspiration to hit you. It's all too easy to find yourself staring at a geometry problem and <u>getting nowhere</u>.

4) The method is this:

> <u>GO THROUGH ALL THE RULES OF GEOMETRY, ONE BY ONE</u>,
> and apply each of them in turn <u>in as many ways as possible</u> —
> one of them is bound to work.

Geometry Problem — **Example**

"<u>Find all the other angles in this diagram</u>."

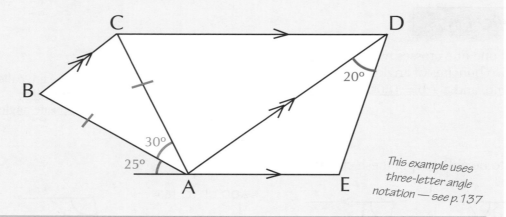

This example uses three-letter angle notation — see p.137

<u>ANSWER:</u>

1) Triangle ABC is isosceles, so angle ABC = <u>angle ACB</u> = ½ × (180 − 30) = <u>75°</u>

2) BC and AD are parallel — so, using <u>alternate angles</u>, if angle ACB = 75° then <u>angle CAD = 75°</u> too.

3) Angles on a straight line means <u>angle EAD</u> = 180 − (25 + 30 + 75) = <u>50°</u>

4) AE and CD are parallel so <u>angle ADC = 50°</u> also.

5) Triangle ACD adds up to 180° so <u>angle ACD</u> = 180 − (75 + 50) = <u>55°</u>

6) Triangle ADE adds up to 180° so <u>angle AED</u> = 180 − (20 + 50) = <u>110°</u>

The most important rule of all — don't panic

Learn each of the last three pages one at a time, and make sure you've got all seven rules clear in your head. If not, go back over them and scribble all seven down again and again.

Circle Geometry

9 Simple Rules — *That's all:*

Unfortunately, as well as the seven geometry rules on pages 132-133, there are nine special rules for circle geometry — four on this page and five on the next.

There's only one thing for it — you have to <u>LEARN THESE TOO</u>...

1) *Angle in a Semicircle = 90°*

A triangle drawn from the <u>two ends of a diameter</u> will <u>ALWAYS</u> make an <u>angle of 90° where it hits</u> the edge of the circle, no matter where it hits.

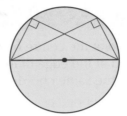

2) *Tangent-Radius Meet at 90°*

A <u>TANGENT</u> is a line that just touches a single point on the edge of the circle.

A tangent always makes an angle of <u>exactly 90°</u> with the <u>radius</u> it meets at this point.

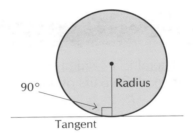

3) *Sneaky Isosceles Triangles Formed by Two Radii*

<u>Unlike other isosceles triangles</u> they <u>don't have the little tick marks on the sides</u> to remind you that they are the same.

The fact that <u>they are both radii</u> is enough to make it an isosceles triangle.

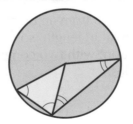

4) *Chord Bisector is a Diameter*

A <u>CHORD</u> is any line <u>drawn across a circle</u>.

And no matter where you draw a chord, the line that <u>cuts it exactly in half</u> (at 90°), will <u>go through the centre of the circle</u> and so will be a <u>DIAMETER</u>.

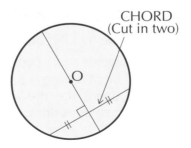

CHORD
(Cut in two)

Four down, five to go

There's just a pile of words (like tangent, chord, bisector...) which make this stuff sound more complicated than it really is. Once you've got them in your head it's just four simple rules to learn.

Circle Geometry

5) *Angles* in the Same Segment *Are Equal*

All triangles drawn from a chord will have <u>the same angle where they touch the circle</u>.

Also, the two angles on opposite sides of the chord <u>add up to 180°</u>.

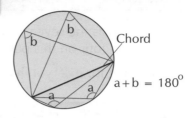

Chord

$a + b = 180^o$

6) *Angle* at the Centre is *Twice* the Angle at the Edge

The angle subtended at the centre of a circle is <u>EXACTLY DOUBLE</u> the angle subtended at the edge of the circle from the same two points (two ends of the same chord).

The phrase '<u>angle subtended at</u>' is nothing complicated, it's just a bit posher than saying '<u>angle made at</u>'.

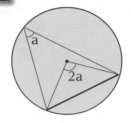

7) *Opposite Angles* of a Cyclic Quadrilateral Add Up to *180°*

A <u>cyclic quadrilateral</u> is a <u>4-sided shape with every corner touching the circle</u>. Both pairs of opposite angles add up to 180°.

$$\underline{a + c = 180°}$$
$$\underline{b + d = 180°}$$

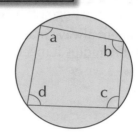

8) *Equality* of Tangents from a Point

The two tangents drawn from an outside point are <u>always equal in length</u>, so creating an 'isosceles' situation, with <u>two congruent right-angled triangles</u>.

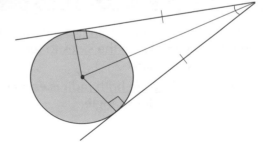

9) Angle in *Opposite Segment* is Equal

This is perhaps the trickiest one to remember.

If you draw a <u>tangent</u> and a <u>chord</u> that meet, then the <u>angle between them</u> is always <u>equal</u> to '<u>the angle in the opposite segment</u>' (i.e. the angle made at the edge of the circle by two lines drawn from the chord).

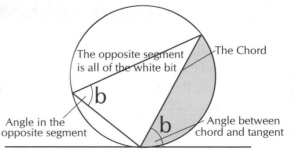

The opposite segment is all of the white bit

The Chord

Angle in the opposite segment

Angle between chord and tangent

And that's your lot

This page is just more of the same: five more rules to cram into your overcrowded brain. But there's no way round learning this stuff, and once you've learnt all nine, circle geometry becomes child's play.

Circle Geometry

3-Letter Notation for Angles

1) Angles are specified using 3 letters, e.g. angle ODC = 48°

2) THE MIDDLE LETTER IS WHERE THE ANGLE IS.

3) THE OTHER TWO LETTERS tell you which lines enclose the angle.
   For example: Angle ODC is at D and enclosed by the lines going
   from O to D and from D to C.

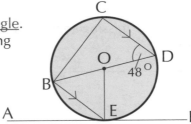

Circle Geometry Problem — Example

This example should tie together all the circle rules from pages 135-136,
the geometry rules from pages 132-133 and 3-letter notation.
If you understand it all, that should mean you've got all this stuff sorted.
If not, you need to go back over those rules again.

"Find all the angles in this diagram."

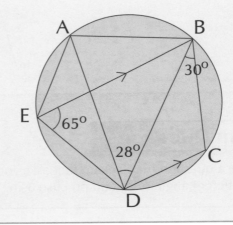

1) PARALLEL LINES — there are actually 4 different lines crossing the 2 parallel
   ones, but the most useful one is ED which tells us that EDC is 115°

2) ANGLES IN SAME SEGMENT — there are potentially eight different chords
   where this rule could apply, but some are more useful than others:
   EAD = EBD,   ADB = AEB (so AEB = 28°)
   ABE = ADE,   DAB = DEB (so DAB = 65°)

3) OPPOSITE ANGLES OF A CYCLIC QUADRILATERAL
   — looking at BEDC gives:
   BCD = 180 – DEB = 180 – 65 = 115°
   — looking at ABDE gives:
   ABD = 180 – AED = 180 – (28 + 65) = 87°

4) ANGLES IN A TRIANGLE ADD UP TO 180° — this, the simplest of all the rules,
   will now find all the other angles for you.

Have you remembered those nine rules?

If this stuff is all still more confusing than a Japanese game show, or you can't remember all the rules,
you need to go back for another look. The rules are essential for all circle geometry questions.

Warm-up and Worked Exam Questions

Oh look at all those lovely big diagrams. But don't just look at them — you need to work through them one by one and make sure that you've remembered all those rules...

Warm-Up Questions

1) Find the missing angles a-d. State any angle laws used.

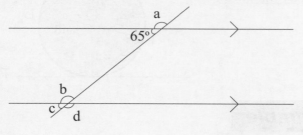

2) PQR and RST are tangents to the circle.
Find the missing angles L, M and N. ➡

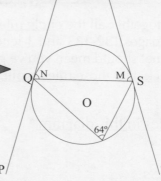

Worked Exam Questions

There'll probably be a question in the exam that asks you to find angles. That means you have to remember all the different angle rules and practise using them in the right places...

1   Calculate angles *a* and *b*.

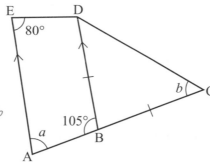

If you're asked to find two angles, finding the first one will usually help you find the second one.

Diagram NOT drawn accurately

Write down all your reasoning — that way, you could get method marks even if you get the answer wrong.

__Angle a and angle ABD are supplementary angles,__

.... __so angle a = 180 − 105 = 75°__ ....

__Angle a and angle CBD are corresponding angles, so angle CBD = 75°__

You could also have used the fact that angles on a straight line sum to 180°

__Triangle BCD is isosceles,__

.... __so angle b = ½ (180 − 75) = 52.5°__ ....

(3 marks)

Worked Exam Questions

2   The line joining P to T is a tangent to the circle at the point C.
O is the centre of the circle and the angle APT is 30°.

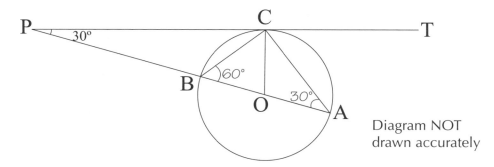

Diagram NOT
drawn accurately

Giving reasons and stating any theorems used, determine the size of angles:

(a) OBC

   PCT is a tangent and OC is a radius, so angle PCO = 90°

   Angles in a triangle total 180°, so angles PCO + COP + OPC = 180°

   90° + COP + 30° = 180° ⇒ COP = 60°

   Two radii form an isosceles triangle, therefore triangle OBC is isosceles, so:

   angle OBC = ½(180° – COP) = ½(180° – 60°)

   angle OBC = 60°   Notice that triangle OBC actually turns out to be equilateral.

(3 marks)

(b) OAC

   From part (a), angle COP = 60°

   So, using angles on a straight line, angle AOC = 180° – 60° = 120°

   Triangle OAC is isosceles because two of its sides are radii of the circle, so

   angle OAC = ½(180° – AOC) = ½(180° – 120°)

   angle OAC = 30°

(2 marks)

(c) ACT

   Triangle OAC is isosceles, so angle OCA = angle OAC = 30°

   Angle ACT = angle OCT – angle OCA, so

   angle ACT = 90° – 30° = 60°

(2 marks)

Exam Questions

3   The lines AT and BT are tangents to the circle with centre O.
    Angle BAT is 60°.

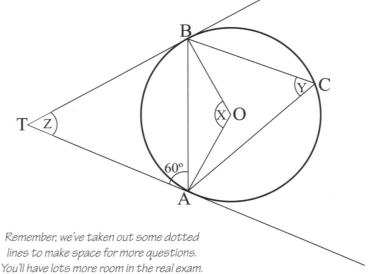

*Remember, we've taken out some dotted
lines to make space for more questions.
You'll have lots more room in the real exam.*

Calculate the missing angles, giving reasons for your calculations at each step.

(a)   X

    ....
                                                                                                              (3 marks)

(b)   Y

    ....
                                                                                                              (2 marks)

(c)   Z

    ....
                                                                                                              (2 marks)

4   ABC is a scalene triangle.

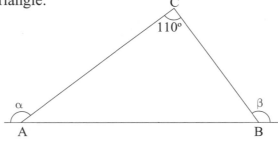

Prove that $\alpha + \beta = 290°$.

    ....
                                                                                                              (3 marks)

The Four Transformations

Transformations are about the most fun you can have without laughing.

1) Use the name <u>TERRY</u> to remember the 4 types.
2) You must always specify <u>all the details</u> for each type.
3) It'll help if you remember which properties remain <u>unchanged</u> in each transformation, too.

T	ranslation	—	**ONE Detail**
E	nlargement	—	**TWO Details**
R	otation	—	**THREE Details**
R	eflection	—	**ONE Detail**
Y			

1) Translation

<u>You must specify this ONE detail</u>:

1) The <u>VECTOR OF TRANSLATION</u> $\left(\begin{smallmatrix} X \to \\ \uparrow Y \end{smallmatrix}\right)$
(See p.177 on vector notation)

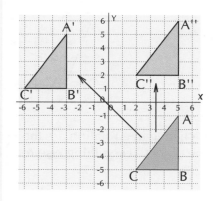

ABC to A'B'C' is a <u>translation of</u> $\left(\begin{smallmatrix} -8 \\ 6 \end{smallmatrix}\right)$

ABC to A''B''C'' is a <u>translation of</u> $\left(\begin{smallmatrix} 0 \\ 7 \end{smallmatrix}\right)$

All that changes in a translation is the POSITION of the object — <u>everything else</u> remains <u>unchanged</u>.

2) Enlargement

<u>You must specify these 2 details</u>:

1) The <u>SCALE FACTOR</u>

2) The <u>CENTRE</u> of Enlargement

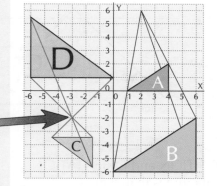

From <u>A to B</u> is an enlargement of <u>scale factor 2</u>, and <u>centre (2,6)</u>

From <u>B to A</u> is an enlargement of <u>scale factor 1/2</u> and <u>centre (2,6)</u>

The ANGLES of the object and RATIOS of the lengths remain <u>unchanged</u>.
The ORIENTATION is unchanged unless the scale factor is negative.

You must remember to give specific details

It's no good just saying it's a translation, you need to give the vector of translation. And be careful with enlargements — it's easy to forget to give the centre of enlargement, and that's marks gone.

The Four Transformations

Two down, two to go...

3) Rotation

You must specify these 3 details:

1) <u>ANGLE</u> turned

2) <u>DIRECTION</u> (Clockwise or anticlockwise)

3) <u>CENTRE</u> of Rotation

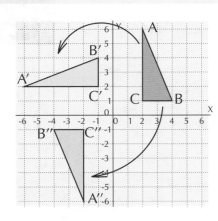

ABC to A'B'C' is a rotation of <u>90°</u>, <u>anticlockwise</u>, <u>ABOUT the origin</u>.

ABC to A"B"C" is a rotation of <u>half a turn (180°)</u>, <u>clockwise</u>, <u>ABOUT the origin</u>.

The only things that change in a rotation are the POSITION and the ORIENTATION of the object. <u>Everything else</u> remains <u>unchanged</u>.

4) Reflection

You must specify this <u>ONE detail</u>:

1) The <u>MIRROR LINE</u>

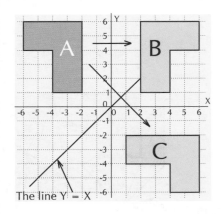

A to B is a <u>reflection in the y-axis</u>.

A to C is a <u>reflection in the line y = x</u>

With reflection, the POSITION and ORIENTATION of the object are the <u>only things that change</u>.

Remember four types — *Translation, Enlargement, Rotation, Reflection, Y*

The key thing is to get your head around the details you need for each type of transformation. Without the details the transformations mean nothing — the devil's in the detail.

Combinations of Transformations

In exam questions they'll often do something <u>horrid</u> like <u>stick two transformations together</u> and then ask you what combination gets you from shape A to shape B. Be <u>ready</u> — those examiners are brutal.

*The **Better** You **Know Them All** — The **Easier** it is*

These kinds of question aren't so bad — but <u>ONLY</u> if you've <u>LEARNT</u> the <u>four transformations</u> on the last two pages <u>really well</u> — if you don't know them, then you certainly won't do too well at spotting a <u>combination</u> of one followed by another. That's because the method is basically <u>try it and see...</u>

Example:

"What combination of two transformations takes you from triangle A to triangle B?"

(There are usually a few different ways of getting from one shape to the other — but remember you only need to find <u>ONE</u> of them.)

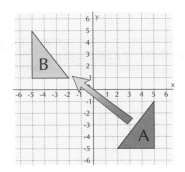

Method:

*Try an **Obvious Transformation** first, and **See**...*

If you <u>think</u> about it, the answer can <u>only</u> be a combination of two of the <u>four types</u> shown on the last two pages, so you can immediately start to <u>narrow it down</u>:

1) Since the shapes are the <u>same size</u> we can <u>rule out enlargements</u>.

2) Next, <u>try a reflection</u> (in either the x-axis or the y-axis). Here we've tried a reflection in the <u>y-axis</u>, to give shape A':

3) You should now easily be able to see the <u>final step</u> from A' to B — it's a <u>translation</u> of $\begin{pmatrix} 0 \\ 6 \end{pmatrix}$.

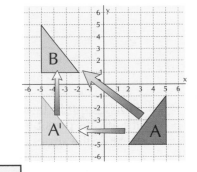

And that's it <u>DONE</u> — from A to B is simply a combination of:

A <u>REFLECTION IN THE Y-AXIS</u> followed by a <u>TRANSLATION OF</u> $\begin{pmatrix} 0 \\ 6 \end{pmatrix}$

At least that's <u>one answer</u> anyway. If instead we decided to reflect shape A in the <u>x-axis</u> first (as shown here) then we'd get another answer — a reflection in the x-axis followed by a rotation of 180° about the point (0, 3). But both are right.

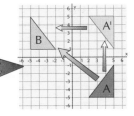

*"But **Which Transformation** do I try first?" I hear you cry*

Well it just depends on <u>how it looks</u>.
But the <u>more transformation questions</u> you do, the more obvious that first guess becomes.
In other words: the more you <u>practise</u>, the <u>easier</u> you'll be able to do it.

This is just a case of trial and error

Try out a few different transformations and you'll eventually reach the right answer. As you saw above there's often more than one right answer — this doesn't happen often in maths so make the most of it.

Congruence and Similarity

Congruence is another ridiculous maths word which sounds really complicated when it's not.
If two shapes are congruent, they are simply <u>the same</u> — the <u>same size</u> and the <u>same shape</u>.
That's all it is. They can however be <u>mirror images</u>.

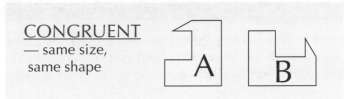

CONGRUENT
— same size,
same shape

Congruent Triangles — are they or aren't they?

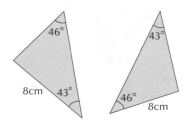

Probably the <u>trickiest area</u> of congruence is deciding whether
<u>two triangles</u>, like the ones shown here, are <u>CONGRUENT</u>.

In other words, from the skimpy information given, are the two going
to be the same or different. There are <u>THREE IMPORTANT STEPS</u>:

1) The Golden Rule is definitely to <u>draw them both</u> in the <u>same orientation</u> —
only then can you compare them properly:

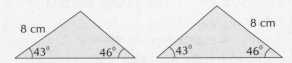

2) <u>Don't jump to hasty conclusions</u> — although the 8 cm sides are clearly in different positions,
it's always possible that <u>both top sides are 8 cm</u>. In this case we can work out that they're <u>not</u>
because the angles are different (so they can't be isosceles).

3) Now see if any of these <u>conditions are true</u>. If <u>ONE</u> of the conditions holds,
the triangles are <u>congruent</u>.

SSS	three sides match up
AAS	two angles and a side match up
SAS	two sides and the angle between them match up
RHS	a right angle, the hypotenuse (longest side) and one other side all match up

For two triangles to be congruent, <u>ONE OR MORE</u> of these four conditions must hold.

(<u>If none are true</u>, then you have proof that the triangles <u>aren't congruent</u>.)

Congruent just means same size, same shape

The trick is just being sure if things are congruent. Take your time and think about it carefully.
The shapes are only congruent if all the angles and lengths are the same.

Congruence and Similarity

Similar Shapes — *Same Shape, Different Size*

1) If two shapes are <u>similar</u>, they are exactly the <u>same shape</u> but different sizes.
2) <u>Any</u> two shapes are <u>similar</u> if all the pairs of <u>angles</u> match up and all the pairs of <u>sides</u> are proportional (i.e. the <u>ratio</u> of the side lengths is constant).

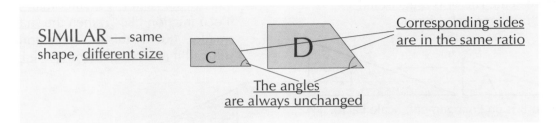

<u>SIMILAR</u> — same shape, <u>different size</u>

Corresponding sides are in the same ratio

The angles are always unchanged

Congruence and *Transformations*

Remember <u>transformations</u>? (See pages 141-142 if you don't.) Well...

When a shape is <u>translated</u>, <u>rotated</u> or <u>reflected</u>, the image is congruent to the original shape. <u>Enlargements</u> don't follow this rule.

EXAMPLE

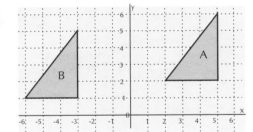

A to B is a <u>translation</u> of $\begin{pmatrix} -8 \\ -1 \end{pmatrix}$.
The lengths and angles are unchanged, so <u>A is congruent to B</u>.

EXAMPLE

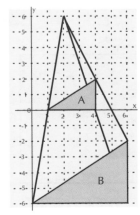

A to B is an <u>enlargement</u> of scale factor 2, and centre (2, 6).

The angles are unchanged but not the lengths, so <u>A is not congruent to B</u>, A is <u>similar</u> to B.

Similar means the same shape but a different size

Make sure you really know the difference between congruent and similar shapes. And make sure you understand why the shapes you get from rotations, enlargements, etc. are similar or congruent.

Enlargements

You first met enlargements back on page 141 (have a look back for a reminder if you need one). Well, now it's time for some more — you'll soon be an expert in scale factors.

Scale Factors — 4 Key Features

1) If the <u>Scale Factor is bigger than 1</u> the <u>shape gets bigger</u>.

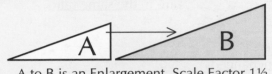

A to B is an Enlargement, Scale Factor 1½

2) If the <u>Scale Factor is smaller than 1</u> (i.e. a fraction like ½) then the <u>shape gets smaller</u>. (Really this is a reduction, but you still call it <u>an Enlargement, Scale Factor ½</u>.)

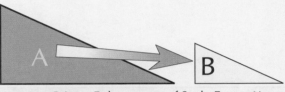

A to B is an Enlargement of Scale Factor ½

3) If the <u>Scale Factor is NEGATIVE</u> then the shape pops out the other side of the enlargement centre. If the scale factor is -1, it's exactly the same as a rotation of 180°.

A to B is an enlargement of scale factor -2. B to A is an enlargement of scale factor -½.

4) The <u>Scale Factor</u> also tells you the <u>relative distance</u> of old points and new points <u>from the Centre of Enlargement</u> — this is <u>very useful for drawing an enlargement</u>, because you can use it to trace out the positions of the new points:

9cm

3cm

A   B
D   C

2cm

4.2cm

12.6cm

THE CENTRE OF ENLARGEMENT

A'   B'

6cm

D'   C'

ABCD to A'B'C'D' is an enlargement of scale factor 3.

Enlargement questions are always appearing on exam papers

You need to make sure you've got these four key features straight, or you'll be very muddled. Remember, enlargements can actually result in the shape getting smaller or moving about.

Enlargements

Areas and Volumes of Enlargements

This catches everybody out.

The increase in area and volume is <u>BIGGER</u> than the scale factor.
<u>For example</u>, if the <u>Scale Factor is 2</u>, the lengths are <u>twice as big</u>,
each area is <u>4 times</u> as big, and the volume is <u>8 times</u> as big.

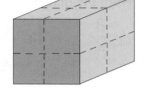

The rule is this:

For a SCALE FACTOR N:		Or... expressed AS RATIOS:		
The **SIDES** are	N times bigger	Lengths	$a : b$	e.g. **3 : 4**
The **AREAS** are	N^2 times bigger	Areas	$a^2 : b^2$	e.g. **9 : 16**
The **VOLUMES** are	N^3 times bigger	Volumes	$a^3 : b^3$	e.g. **27 : 64**

Simple... but <u>VERY FORGETTABLE</u>

EXAMPLE

2 spheres have surface areas of 16 m² and 25 m².
Find the ratio of their volumes.

ANSWER 16 : 25 is the areas ratio which must be $a^2 : b^2$,
i.e. $a^2 : b^2 = 16 : 25$
and so $a : b = 4 : 5$
and so $a^3 : b^3 = \underline{64 : 125}$ — the volumes ratio.

Converting Area and Volume Measurements

$$1 \text{ m}^2 = 100 \text{ cm} \times 100 \text{ cm} = 10\,000 \text{ cm}^2$$

1) To change area measurements from m² to cm² multiply the area in m² by 10 000 (e.g. 3 m² = 30 000 cm²).

2) To change area measurements from cm² to m² divide the area in cm² by 10 000 (e.g. 45 000 cm² = 4.5 m²).

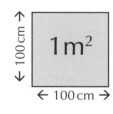

$$1 \text{ m}^3 = 100 \text{ cm} \times 100 \text{ cm} \times 100 \text{ cm} = 1\,000\,000 \text{ cm}^3$$

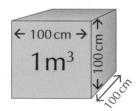

1) To change volume measurements from m³ to cm³ multiply the volume in m³ by 1 000 000 (e.g. 3 m³ = 3 000 000 cm³).

2) To change volume measurements from cm³ to m³ divide the volume in cm³ by 1 000 000 (e.g. 4 500 000 cm³ = 4.5 m³).

When you make lengths bigger, **areas get bigger** *and* **volumes even bigger**

It's easy to make the mistake of thinking that length, area and volume all get bigger at the same rate — make sure you've got the rule on this page very clear in your mind to avoid a lot of confusion.

Warm-up and Worked Exam Questions

The warm-up questions run quickly over the basic facts you'll need in the exam. The exam questions come later — but unless you've learnt the facts first you'll find the exams tougher than old boots.

Warm-Up Questions

1) From the diagram below, pick out:

   a) a pair of congruent shapes
   b) a pair of similar shapes

2) What pair of transformations will convert shape C into shape D?
   What pair will convert shape D to shape C?

3) What translation would map the point (1, 3) onto (-2, 6)?

4) Triangle DEF is an enlargement of triangle ABC.
   a) What is the scale factor of the enlargement?
   b) What is the length of DF?

5) Two similar cones have volumes of 27 m³ and 64 m³.
   If the surface area of the smaller one is 36 m², find the surface area of the other one.

6) Convert these area measurements: a) 23 m² → cm²   b) 34 500 cm² → m²

7) Convert these volume measurements: a) 5.2 m³ → cm³   b) 100 000 cm³ → m³

Worked Exam Questions

I'm afraid this helpful blue writing won't be there in the exam, so if I were you I'd make the most of it and make sure you fully understand it now.

1

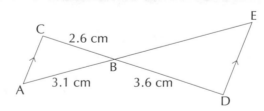

(a) Explain why the triangles ABC and BDE are similar.

   ABC = DBE (vertically opposite angles are equal). CAB = BED and ACB = BDE

   (alternate angles on parallel lines equal). So the triangles have the same angles,

   i.e. same shape, so are similar.

   (2 marks)

(b) Find the length of BE, correct to 1 decimal place.

(use two given
corresponding
sides)   *Scale factor = 3.6 ÷ 2.6 = 1.384615385*   *do not round the answer at this stage*

   So BE = 1.384615385 × 3.1 = 4.2923 = 4.3 cm (to 1 d.p.)

   (3 marks)

Worked Exam and Exam Questions

2
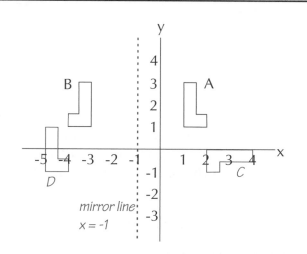

mirror line
x = -1

(a) What is the equation of the line of reflection to map A onto B?

.... x = -1 ....

(1 mark)

(b) Rotate A 90° clockwise about centre (1, 0). Label the new shape C.

(2 marks)

(c) Translate A by vector $\binom{-6}{-2}$.
Label this shape D.

(1 mark)

Exam Questions

3   These cones are similar.
Find the height of the smaller cone.

....

(2 marks)

4   This rectangle is enlarged by a scale factor of 2½.

8.5 cm

12 cm

What are the dimensions of the enlarged rectangle?

....

(2 marks)

UNIT 3 — GEOMETRY AND ALGEBRA

Exam Questions

5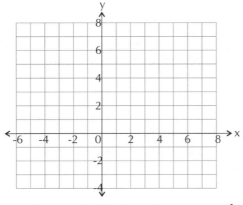

(a) On the grid, plot the following points to draw quadrilateral ABCD:
A (6, 7), B (3, 1), C (-3, 4), D (0, 6).
(1 mark)

(b) Enlarge ABCD with a scale factor $\frac{1}{3}$, using (0, 1) as the centre of enlargement.
Label the vertices of the transformed quadrilateral A′B′C′D′.
(2 marks)

(c) What are the coordinates of point B′?

....
(1 mark)

6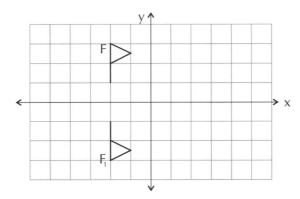

(a) Describe fully the transformation which maps F onto F_1.

....
(2 marks)

(b) Draw the reflection of F in the *y* axis. Label it F_2.
(1 mark)

(c) What single transformation would map F_1 onto F_2?

....
(2 marks)

7 A swimming pool is 20 metres long and 6 metres wide. It is filled with water up to a
height of 1.2 metres. Calculate the volume of water in the swimming pool,
giving your answer in cubic centimetres.

....
(2 marks)

Revision Summary for Unit 3 — 1

More difficult questions, but just keep reminding yourself that they're the very best revision you can do. These questions don't ask anything too tricky, they just check whether or not you've actually learnt all the basic facts in this part of the Unit. It's really important to keep practising these as often as you can.

Keep learning the basic facts until you know them

1) List the four 'harder' types of graph that you should recognise.

2) Describe in words and with a sketch the forms of these graphs:
$y = ax^2 + bx + c$; $y = ax^3 + bx^2 + cx + d$; $xy = a$

3) Describe how you could solve a quadratic equation using a graph.

4) Describe the simple method for solving simultaneous equations graphically.

5) Write down the formula for solving quadratics.

6) Write down the 4 steps of the trial and improvement method.

7) List the three key features of both direct proportion and inverse proportion.

8) Name and describe the two types of symmetry.

9) There are five formulas for area you should know straight off. Write them all down.

10)* Clive is re-carpeting his lounge, which is rectangular. The room is 12 m long and 7 m wide. The carpet he wants costs £12 per m². How much will it cost Clive to carpet his lounge?

11) What is meant by a net? How is it related to surface area?

12)* A confectionery company is designing the packaging for a new brand of biscuits. The packaging will be cylindrical, with a diameter of 4 cm and a height of 15 cm. Calculate the surface area of the packaging.

13) Sketch the nets for these shapes:
a) triangular prism b) cylinder   c) cube   d) square-based pyramid.

14)* An architect has drawn up plans for an extension to a house, shown on the right. Using the scale 4 mm : 1 m, draw:
a) the front elevation b) the side elevation c) the plan view.

15) There are six formulas for volume you should know. Write them all down.

16)* A juice company makes apple squash in batches of 9000 cm³. The squash is sold in cylindrical cans that have a cross-sectional area of 12 cm² and a height of 6 cm. How many of these cans can the company fill from one batch of apple squash?

17) What is a prism? Sketch three different ones.

18) What are the three rules for identifying formulas as length, area or volume?

19) What are regular polygons? Name the first eight.

20) List the special features that regular polygons have.

21) What do you know about their symmetry?

22) Write down the first six easy rules of geometry.

23) Give five extra details on parallel lines.

24) Write down the nine simple rules for circle geometry.

25) What is three-letter notation? Give an example.

26) List the four types of transformation. What details must be specified for each type?

27) What do "congruent" and "similar" mean?

28) What are the rules for deciding if two triangles are congruent or not?

29) Draw a typical enlargement, showing the two important details.

30) What three types of scale factor are there and what is the result of enlarging by each?

31)* Geoff has built a scale model of a garden shed that he hopes to supply to garden centres. His model is 30 cm wide, 60 cm long and 50 cm high. He has used a scale factor of 0.2. Give the width, length and height of the actual sheds.

* The answers to these questions can be found on page 227.

Pythagoras' Theorem

Pythagoras' theorem sounds hard but it's actually <u>really simple</u>.
It's also really important, so make sure you really get your teeth into it.

Pythagoras' Theorem — $a^2 + b^2 = h^2$

1) <u>PYTHAGORAS' THEOREM</u> always goes hand in hand with <u>sin</u>, <u>cos</u> and <u>tan</u> because they're both involved with <u>RIGHT-ANGLED TRIANGLES</u>.

There's more about sin, cos and tan on pages 154-155.

2) The big difference is that Pythagoras does not involve any <u>angles</u> — it just uses <u>two sides</u> to find the <u>third side</u>. (Sin, cos and tan always involve <u>ANGLES</u>.)

3) The <u>BASIC FORMULA</u> for Pythagoras is:

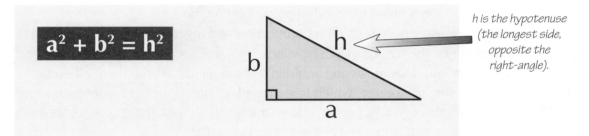

$$a^2 + b^2 = h^2$$

h is the hypotenuse (the longest side, opposite the right-angle).

4) <u>PLUG THE NUMBERS IN</u> and work it out.

5) But get the numbers in the <u>RIGHT PLACE</u>. The 2 shorter sides (squared) add to equal the longest side squared.

6) Always <u>CHECK</u> that your answer is <u>SENSIBLE</u>.

EXAMPLE:

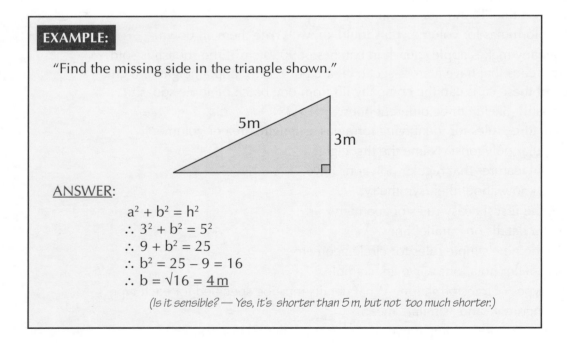

"Find the missing side in the triangle shown."

<u>ANSWER</u>:

$a^2 + b^2 = h^2$
$\therefore 3^2 + b^2 = 5^2$
$\therefore 9 + b^2 = 25$
$\therefore b^2 = 25 - 9 = 16$
$\therefore b = \sqrt{16} = \underline{4\,m}$

(Is it sensible? — Yes, it's shorter than 5 m, but not too much shorter.)

Finding lengths in a right-angled triangle? Pythagoras is your man

This is probably one of the most famous of all maths formulas. It will be in your exam at some point. If you haven't learnt it and practised some questions you might as well kiss good grades goodbye.

Bearings

Bearings describe the direction of one place from another. The direction is given as the number of degrees clockwise from due north.

Bearings

To find or plot a bearing you must remember the three key words:

1) 'FROM'

Find the word 'FROM' in the question, and put your pencil on the diagram at the point you are going 'from'.

2) NORTHLINE

At the point you are going FROM, draw in a NORTHLINE.

The bearing of A from B

3) CLOCKWISE

Now draw in the angle CLOCKWISE from the northline to the line joining the two points. This angle is the required bearing.

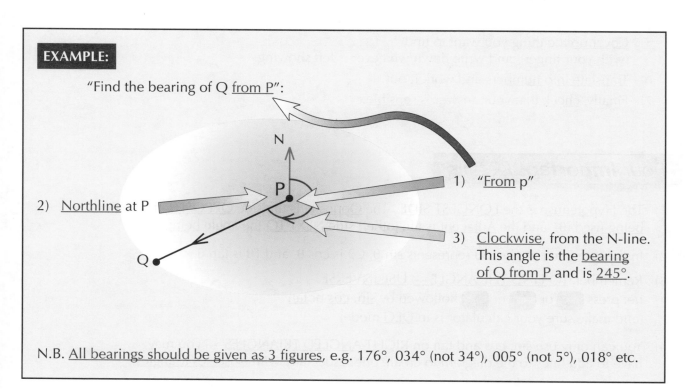

EXAMPLE:

"Find the bearing of Q from P":

1) "From p"

2) Northline at P

3) Clockwise, from the N-line. This angle is the bearing of Q from P and is 245°.

N.B. All bearings should be given as 3 figures, e.g. 176°, 034° (not 34°), 005° (not 5°), 018° etc.

From... Northline... Clockwise — that's all you need to remember...

This is a very straightforward exam topic. Make sure you get the bearing from the right place, draw a northline and measure clockwise... From, Northline, Clockwise — am I going on...

Trigonometry — Sin, Cos and Tan

Trigonometry — it's a big scary word. But although it's <u>important</u> and <u>always cropping up</u> in exams, just follow the method below and it won't be a big scary topic.

Method

There are several methods for doing Trig and they're all pretty much the same.
However, the method shown below has a number of advantages, mainly because the <u>formula triangles</u> mean the <u>same method</u> is used <u>every time</u>, (no matter which side or angle is being asked for).
This makes the whole topic a lot simpler, and you'll find that once you've learned this method, the answers automatically come out right every time.

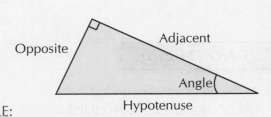

1) <u>Label</u> the three sides <u>O, A and H</u>
    (Opposite, Adjacent and Hypotenuse).

2) Write down <u>from memory</u> 'SOH CAH TOA'.

3) Decide which <u>two sides</u> are <u>involved</u>: O,H A,H or
    O,A and select <u>SOH</u>, <u>CAH</u> or <u>TOA</u> accordingly.

4) Turn the one you choose into a <u>FORMULA TRIANGLE</u>:

Formula triangles are explained in detail on page 172.

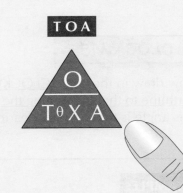

5) <u>Cover up</u> the thing you want to find
    (with your finger), and write down whatever is left showing.

6) <u>Translate into numbers</u> and work it out.

7) Finally, <u>check</u> that your answer is <u>sensible</u>.

Four **Important** Details

1) The <u>Hypotenuse</u> is the <u>LONGEST SIDE</u>. The <u>Opposite</u> is the side <u>OPPOSITE</u> the angle
    being used (θ), and the <u>Adjacent</u> is the (other) side <u>NEXT TO</u> the angle <u>being used</u>.

2) In the formula triangles, Sθ represents sin θ, Cθ is cos θ, and Tθ is tan θ.

3) Remember, <u>TO FIND THE ANGLE — USE INVERSE</u>.
    i.e. press [INV] or [SHIFT] or [2nd], followed by <u>sin</u>, <u>cos</u> or <u>tan</u>
    (and make sure your calculator is in <u>DEG</u> mode).

4) You can only use sin, cos and tan on <u>RIGHT-ANGLED TRIANGLES</u> — you may
    have to add lines to the diagram to create one, especially with <u>isosceles triangles</u>.

H = longest, O = opposite, A = next to, and remember SOH CAH TOA

It's vital to practise exam questions, but don't make the mistake of thinking it's pointless learning these seven steps first. If you don't know them all thoroughly, you'll just keep on getting questions wrong.

Trigonometry — Sin, Cos and Tan

And now for some lovely examples to help you through the trials of trigonometry.

Examples:

EXAMPLE 1: "<u>Find x in the triangle shown</u>."

1) Label O, A, H
2) Write down 'SOH CAH TOA'
3) Two sides <u>involved</u>: O, H
4) So use

5) We want to find H so cover up H to leave: $H = \dfrac{O}{s\theta}$

6) Translate: $x = \dfrac{15}{\sin 35}$

Press 15 ÷ SIN 35 = `26.151702`   So ans = <u>26.2 m</u>

Check it's sensible: yes it's about twice as big as 15, as the diagram suggests.

Hyp, Opp, 15 m, x, 35°, Adj

EXAMPLE 2: "<u>Find the angle θ in this triangle</u>."

1) Label O, A, H
2) Write down 'SOH CAH TOA'
3) Two sides <u>involved</u>: A, H
4) So use

5) We want to find θ so cover up Cθ to leave: $C\theta = \dfrac{A}{H}$

6) Translate: $\cos \theta = \dfrac{15}{25} = 0.6$

<u>NOW USE INVERSE</u>:   θ = INV cos (0.6)

Press INV COS 0.6 = `53.130102`   So ans. = <u>53.1°</u>

25 m, 25 m, θ, 30 m

NOTE THE USUAL WAY OF DEALING WITH AN ISOSCELES TRIANGLE: SPLIT IT <u>DOWN THE MIDDLE</u> TO GET A RIGHT ANGLE:

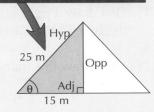

Hyp, 25 m, Opp, θ, Adj, 15 m

Finally, is it sensible? — Yes, the angle looks like about 50°.

Angles of *Elevation* And *Depression*

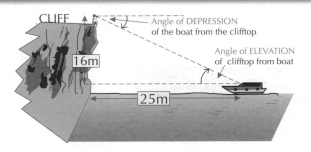

CLIFF
Angle of DEPRESSION of the boat from the clifftop
Angle of ELEVATION of clifftop from boat
16m
25m

1) The <u>Angle of Depression</u> is the angle <u>downwards</u> from the horizontal.

2) The <u>Angle of Elevation</u> is the angle <u>upwards</u> from the horizontal.

3) The Angles of Elevation and Depression are <u>EQUAL</u>.

You need to have learnt all seven steps on page 154

Here you can see the seven steps from the last page being put into action. You can see how easy it is to apply those steps, but only if you can remember them and practise using them — so practise.

3D Pythagoras and Trigonometry

3D questions on Pythagoras and trig are a bit tricky. But they're definitely not fiendishly difficult
— all you need is to follow the same old rules. But first, a bit about 3D coordinates...

Z Coordinates are for *3D* space

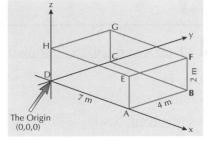

1) All z-coordinates do is extend the normal x-y
coordinates into a third direction, z, so that
all positions then have 3 coordinates: (x,y,z)

2) This means you can give the coordinates of
the corners of a box or any other 3D SHAPE.

For example, in this drawing the coordinates of **B** and **F** are **B**(7, 4, 0)   **F**(7, 4, 2).

Angle Between *Line* and *Plane* — Use a *Diagram*

1) Make a RIGHT-ANGLED triangle using the line, a line in the plane
and a line between the two.
2) Draw this right-angled triangle again so that you can see it
clearly. Label the sides. You might have to use Pythagoras to
work out the length of one of the sides.
3) Use trigonometry to calculate the angle.

EXAMPLE: "ABCDE is a square-based pyramid.
It is 12 cm high and the square base
has sides of length 7 cm. Find the angle
the edge AE makes with the base."

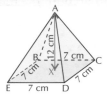

*X is the centre of
the square base.*

1) First draw a right-angled triangle using the edge AE, the base and a line between
the two (in this case the central height). Call the angle you're trying to find **θ**.

2) Now draw this triangle clearly and label it.

To find θ, you need to know the length of side EX.

So, using Pythagoras — $EX^2 = 3.5^2 + 3.5^2 = 24.5 \Rightarrow EX = \sqrt{24.5}$ cm

3) Now use trigonometry to find the angle θ:

*You know the lengths of
the opposite and adjacent
sides, so use tan.*

$$\tan \theta = \frac{12}{\sqrt{24.5}} = 2.4... \quad \theta = \underline{67.6°} \text{ (1 d.p.)}$$

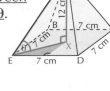

Use *Right-Angled Triangles* To Find *Lengths* too

EXAMPLE: "Find the lengths FH and BH shown in the diagram."

First use Pythagoras to find the length FH.

$FH^2 = 3^2 + 3^2 = 18 \Rightarrow FH = \sqrt{18}$ cm

Now use Pythagoras again to find the length BH.

$BH^2 = 3^2 + (\sqrt{18})^2 = 27 \Rightarrow BH = \sqrt{27}$ cm = $\underline{5.2 \text{ cm}}$ (1 decimal place)

The Sine and Cosine Rules

Normal trigonometry using SOH CAH TOA etc. <u>can only be applied to right-angled</u> triangles. <u>The Sine and Cosine Rules</u>, on the other hand, allow you to tackle <u>any triangle at all</u>.

Labelling The Triangle

This is very important. You must label the sides and angles properly so that the letters for the sides and angles correspond with each other:

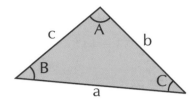

Remember, <u>side 'a' is opposite angle A</u> etc.

It doesn't matter which sides you decide to call a, b, and c, just as long as the angles are then labelled properly.

Three Formulas to Learn:

These first two formulas let you work out <u>sides</u> and <u>angles</u>:

The Sine Rule

You don't use the whole thing with both '=' signs of course, so it's not half as bad as it looks — you just choose the two bits that you want:

$$\frac{a}{\sin A} = \frac{b}{\sin B} = \frac{c}{\sin C}$$

e.g. $\frac{b}{\sin B} = \frac{c}{\sin C}$ or $\frac{a}{\sin A} = \frac{b}{\sin B}$

The Cosine Rule

$$a^2 = b^2 + c^2 - 2bc \cos A$$

or $\cos A = \dfrac{b^2 + c^2 - a^2}{2bc}$

Area of the Triangle

Of course, you already know the simple formula when you have the <u>base</u> and <u>vertical height</u>:

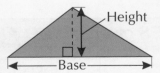

Area = ½ base × height

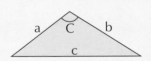

Well, here's a fancier formula that you can use when you know <u>two sides</u> and the angle <u>between them</u>:

Area of triangle = ½ ab sin C

You need to <u>LEARN</u> all of these formulas off by heart and practise using them. If you don't, you won't be able to use them in the exam, even if they give them to you.

That cosine rule looks complicated, but you just have to learn it

Once you have learnt it, it's just like any other formula — plug the numbers in and Bob's your uncle. So you just have to scribble it over and over until it's burnt into the inside of your eyeballs.

The Sine and Cosine Rules

Amazingly, there are only <u>FOUR</u> question types where the <u>Sine</u> and <u>Cosine</u> rules would be applied. So learn the exact details of these four examples and you'll be laughing.

The Four **Examples**

You might get any of these question types in 3D but <u>DON'T PANIC.</u> You answer them in <u>exactly</u> the same way as you would if they were in 2D.

TWO ANGLES given plus ANY SIDE

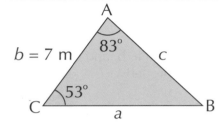

— SINE RULE NEEDED | For example, to find c:

1) Don't forget the obvious: $B = 180 - 83 - 53 = \underline{44°}$

2) Then use $\dfrac{b}{\sin B} = \dfrac{c}{\sin C} \Rightarrow \dfrac{7}{\sin 44} = \dfrac{c}{\sin 53}$

3) Which gives, $c = \dfrac{7 \times \sin 53}{\sin 44} = \underline{8.05\,m}$

TWO SIDES given plus an ANGLE NOT ENCLOSED by them

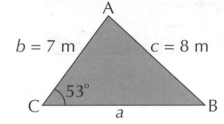

— SINE RULE NEEDED | For example, to find B:

1) Use: $\dfrac{b}{\sin B} = \dfrac{c}{\sin C} \Rightarrow \dfrac{7}{\sin B} = \dfrac{8}{\sin 53}$

2) $\Rightarrow \sin B = \dfrac{7 \times \sin 53}{8} = 0.6988 \Rightarrow B = \sin^{-1}(0.6988) = \underline{44.3°}$

TWO SIDES given plus THE ANGLE ENCLOSED by them

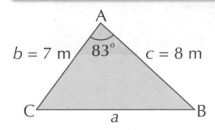

— COSINE RULE NEEDED | For example, to find a:

Use: $a^2 = b^2 + c^2 - 2bc \cos A$
$= 7^2 + 8^2 - 2 \times 7 \times 8 \times \cos 83$
$= 99.3506 \Rightarrow a = \sqrt{99.3506} = \underline{9.97\,m}$

ALL THREE SIDES given but NO ANGLES

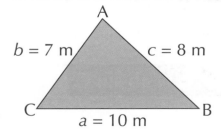

— COSINE RULE NEEDED | For example, to find A:

1) Use: $\cos A = \dfrac{b^2 + c^2 - a^2}{2bc}$
$= \dfrac{49 + 64 - 100}{2 \times 7 \times 8} = \dfrac{13}{112} = 0.11607$

2) Hence $A = \cos^{-1}(0.11607) = \underline{83.3°}$

Learn which rule you need for which question type

Rather than fret about which equation to use and how to do it, you just need to learn these four basic question types and practise them. It'll save you loads of time and stress on the big day.

Warm-up and Worked Exam Questions

Learning facts and practising exam questions is the only recipe for success.
That's what the questions on these pages are all about. All you have to do — is do them.

Warm-Up Questions

1) In a right-angled triangle, the two shorter sides are 10 cm and 8.4 cm. Find:

   a) the length of the longest side, correct to 3 significant figures.

   b) the smallest angle, correct to the nearest degree.

2) In this triangle, find the
length of AC, correct to 1 decimal place.

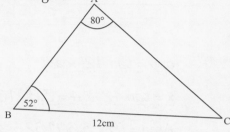

3) A triangle has sides of 4 cm, 6 cm and 8 cm.
Calculate the largest angle, correct to 1 d.p.

Worked Exam Questions

There's a knack to using the facts you've stored away in your brain box in the right way to get marks in
the exam. These worked examples will really help you see how...

1   The radar location of a ship in distress is given as 143 km north and 89.5 km east of a
port, P. The rescue ship leaves P travelling on a bearing of 032°, to the ship in trouble.

(a)   How far does the rescue team travel, to the nearest km?

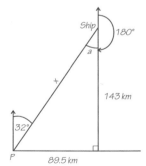

Call the distance x.

By Pythagoras $143^2 + 89.5^2 = x^2$

$x^2 = 28459.25$, so $x = 169$ km

(3 marks)

(b)   What bearing does the rescue team need to return to port P?

The two parts of the bearing are $180° + a$

$a = 32°$ (the NORTH lines are parallel and the

angles are equal alternate angles)

Bearing required $= 180 + 32 = 212°$

Remember — draw in the North line
from the required point
(in this case, the ship in trouble)
and then mark in the angle turned
clockwise to face port P.

(1 mark)

Worked Exam and Exam Questions

2 (a) Find the area of the cross section of this prism.

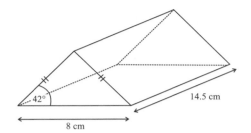

Always check if you can make a right-angled triangle.

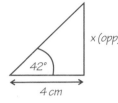

$opp = tan\ 42° \times adj.$

$x = tan\ 42° \times 4 = 3.60162\ cm$

$Area = (8 \times 3.60162) \div 2 = 14.40646 = 14.4\ cm^2$

(3 marks)

(b) Find the volume of the prism.

$14.40646 \times 14.5 = 208.8937 = 209\ cm^3$

Volume is just cross section area × length.

(2 marks)

Exam Questions

3 To 3 significant figures, find:

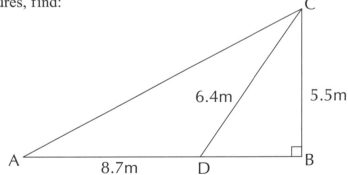

(a) BD ....

(3 marks)

(b) AB ....

(1 mark)

(c) AC ....

(3 marks)

Exam Questions

4   A surveyor needs to find the height of a tower (shown in grey on the diagram).
    Points A and B are 24 m and 31 m respectively from the base of the tower.
    She measures the angle of elevation of the top of the tower from point A as 52.1°.

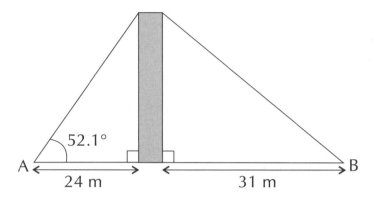

Calculate:

(a)   the height of the tower.

    ....
                                                                                                                    (3 marks)

(b)   the angle of elevation of the top of the tower from point B.

    ....
                                                                                                                    (3 marks)

5   A triangular sail has a bottom edge 3.1 m long, which slopes at an angle of 85° to the mast.
    The top of the sail makes an angle of 41° with the mast.

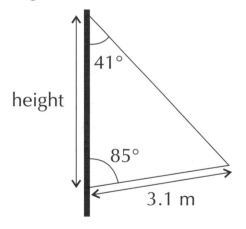

(a)   Calculate the height of the sail.

    ....
                                                                                                                    (4 marks)

(b)   Hence calculate the area of the sail.

    ....
                                                                                                                    (3 marks)

The Graphs of Sin and Cos

<u>You are expected to know these graphs</u> and be able to <u>SKETCH</u> them <u>from memory</u>.

Y = SIN X   **Y = COS X**

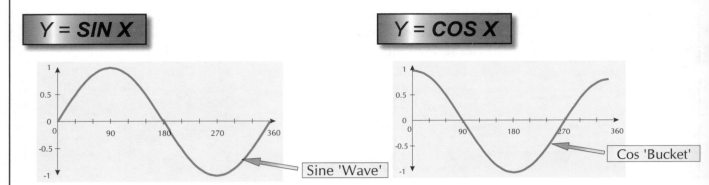

Sine 'Wave'   Cos 'Bucket'

<u>For 0° – 360°</u>, the shapes you get are a <u>Sine 'Wave'</u> (one peak, one trough) and a <u>Cos 'Bucket'</u> (starts at the top, dips, and finishes at the top).

Extending the Sin and Cos Graphs

The underlying shape of both the sin and cos graphs are <u>identical</u> (as shown below) when you extend them (indefinitely) in both directions:

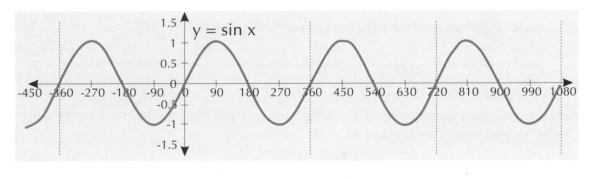

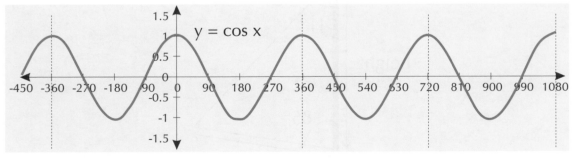

1) The only difference is that the <u>sin graph</u> is shifted right by 90° compared to the cos graph.

2) Note that both graphs wiggle between <u>y-limits of exactly +1 and -1</u>.

3) The key to drawing the extended graphs is to first draw the 0 – 360° cycle of either the <u>Sine 'WAVE'</u> or the <u>Cos 'BUCKET'</u> and then <u>repeat it</u> in <u>both directions</u> as shown.

You should recognise these graphs like the back of your hand

Sin and cos graphs are very similar — the only difference is that they're 90° apart.
You need to remember what the graphs look like and all the properties in the numbered list.

Graphs: Shifts and Stretches

Don't be put off by <u>function notation</u> involving f(x) — it's just a fancy way of saying "an equation in x". In other words "y = f(x)" just means "y = some totally mundane equation in x, which we won't tell you, we'll just call it f(x) instead to see how many of you get in a flap about it".

Graph **Transformations**

In a question on transforming graphs they will either use <u>function notation</u> or they'll use a <u>known function</u> instead. There are only four different types of graph transformations:

The 'known function' might be one of the ones from p.102-103, or even the sin and cos graphs on p.162 — make sure you know what they all look like.

1) **y-Stretch**: $y = k \times f(x)$

This is where the original graph is <u>stretched along the y-axis</u> by multiplying the whole function by a number, i.e. <u>y = f(x)</u> becomes <u>y = kf(x)</u> (where k = 2 or 5 etc.). If k is less than 1, then the graph is <u>squashed down</u> in the y-direction instead:

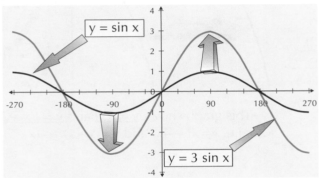

This graph shows <u>y = f(x)</u> and <u>y = 3f(x)</u>
(y = sin x and y = 3 sin x)

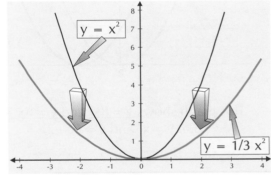

This graph shows <u>y = f(x)</u> and <u>y = 1/3 f(x)</u>
(y = x² and y = $\frac{1}{3}$ x²)

2) **y-Shift**: $y = f(x) + a$

This is where the whole graph is <u>slid up or down</u> the y-axis <u>with no distortion</u>, and is achieved by simply <u>adding a number</u> onto the <u>end</u> of the equation: <u>y = f(x) + a</u>.

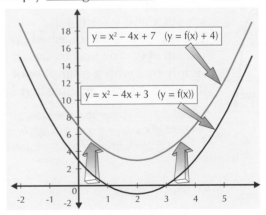

This shows <u>y = f(x)</u> and <u>y = f(x) + 4</u>
i.e. y = x² – 4x + 3, and
y = (x² – 4x + 3) + 4
or y = x² – 4x + 7

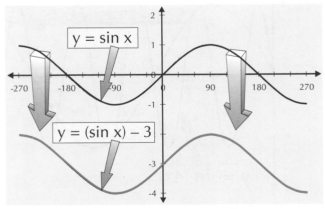

This shows <u>y = f(x)</u> and <u>y = f(x) – 3</u>
i.e. y = sin x and y = (sin x) – 3

Remember f(x) just means an equation in x

Graphs can be stretched or squashed along the y-axis by multiplying the whole function by a number. Or they can slide up or down by adding a number to the function. That's all I'm trying to say.

Graphs: Shifts and Stretches

Keep going, there are two more transformations to learn before you're done with shifts and stretches.

3) *x-Shift*: y = f(x − a)

This is where the whole graph <u>slides to the left or right</u> and it only happens when you replace '<u>x</u>' everywhere in the equation <u>with 'x – a'</u>. These are a bit tricky because they go '<u>the wrong way</u>'. In other words if you want to go from <u>y = f(x)</u> to <u>y = f(x – a)</u> you must move the whole graph a distance 'a' in the <u>positive</u> x-direction → (and vice versa).

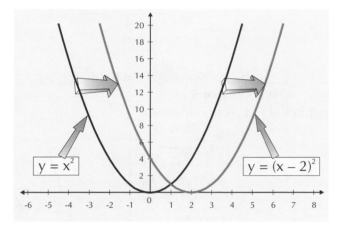

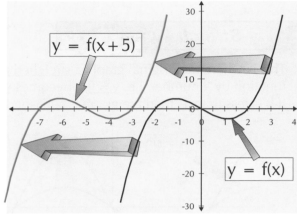

This graph shows <u>y = f(x)</u> and <u>y = f(x − 2)</u>
i.e. y = x² and y = (x − 2)²

This graph shows <u>y = f(x)</u> and <u>y = f(x + 5)</u>
i.e. y = x³ − 4x, and y = (x + 5)³ − 4(x + 5)

4) *x-Stretch*: y = f(kx)

These go '<u>the wrong way</u>' too — when k is a '<u>multiplier</u>' it <u>scrunches the graph up</u>, whereas when it's a '<u>divider</u>', it <u>stretches</u> the graph out. (The opposite of the y-stretch.)

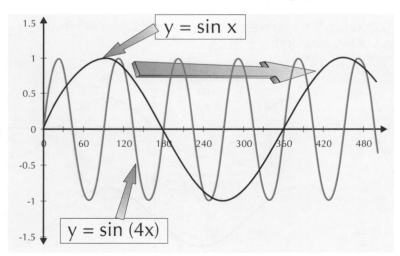

This graph shows
<u>y = sin x</u> and <u>y = sin(4x)</u>.
The one that is all squashed up is
y = sin (4x). The way to sketch it is
simply that with a multiplier of 4,
it will be 4 times as squashed up.

(Each full cycle of up-and-down takes ¼ the amount of x-axis as the original graph, so you fit 4 of them into 1 of the other graph)

Remember, if k is a <u>divider</u>, then the graph <u>spreads out</u>. So if the squashed up graph above was the original, <u>y = f(x)</u>, then the more spread out one would be <u>y = f(x/4)</u>.

Two more slightly trickier shifts and stretches

Graphs can also slide left or right when x is replaced with x – a. Or be stretched or squashed along the x-axis when x is replaced with kx. These are trickier than the last page but the principle is the same.

Warm-up and Exam Questions

You should know the script by now — go through these warm-up questions to make sure you know the basics. If you struggle with anything, go back over the last few pages and learn it again.

Warm-Up Questions

1) Name one important similarity and one difference between the following pair of graphs:
   $y = \sin x$ and $y = \cos x$

2) Sketch the graph of $y = \sin x$ for x between 0° and 360°.

3) Graphs are drawn showing the functions $y = f(x)$ and $y = f(x) + 2$.
   Describe how the shape and position of the two graphs are related.

Exam Question

Exam questions don't vary that wildly, the basic format is the same.
So you'd be mad not to spend a bit of time learning how to answer a common question.
There are no answers written in for you this time, though — so you're on your own...

1   Below is a sketch of the curve with equation $y = f(x)$.

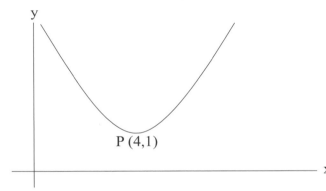

P (4,1)

There is just one minimum point and that is P (4,1).
Write down the coordinates of the minimum point for curves with the following equations.

(a) $y = f(x - 2)$

   ....
   (1 mark)

(b) $y = f(4x)$

   ....
   (1 mark)

(c) $y = f(x) + 3$

   ....
   (1 mark)

Loci and Construction

A <u>LOCUS</u> (another ridiculous maths word) is simply:

A LINE that shows <u>all the points which fit in with a given rule</u>.

Make sure you learn how to do these <u>PROPERLY</u> using a <u>ruler</u> and <u>compasses</u> as shown on these two pages.

1) ## The locus of points which are '<u>*A fixed distance from a given point*</u>'

This locus is simply a <u>CIRCLE</u>.

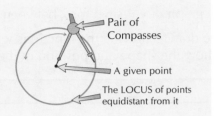

Pair of Compasses

A given point

The LOCUS of points equidistant from it

2) ## The locus of points which are '<u>*A fixed distance from a given line*</u>'

This locus is an <u>OVAL SHAPE</u>.

It has <u>straight sides</u> (drawn with a <u>ruler</u>) and <u>ends</u> which are <u>perfect semicircles</u> (drawn with compasses).

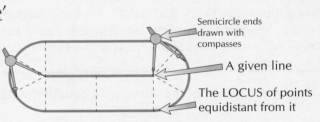

Semicircle ends drawn with compasses

A given line

The LOCUS of points equidistant from it

3) ## The locus of points which are '<u>*Equidistant from two given lines*</u>'

1) Keep the compass setting <u>THE SAME</u> while you make <u>all four marks</u>.

2) Make sure you <u>leave</u> your compass marks <u>showing</u>.

3) You get <u>two equal angles</u> — i.e. this <u>LOCUS</u> is actually an <u>ANGLE BISECTOR</u>.

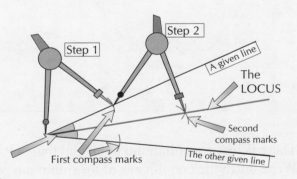

Step 1

Step 2

A given line

The LOCUS

Second compass marks

First compass marks

The other given line

4) ## The locus of points which are '<u>*Equidistant from two given POINTS*</u>'

<u>This LOCUS</u> is all points which are the <u>same distance</u> from A as they are from B.

This time the locus is actually the <u>PERPENDICULAR BISECTOR</u> of the line joining the two points.

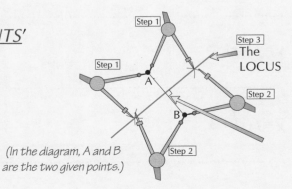

Step 1

Step 1

Step 3

The LOCUS

Step 2

Step 2

A

B

(In the diagram, A and B are the two given points.)

Loci and Construction

Don't just read the page through once and hope you'll remember it — get your ruler, compasses and pencil out and have a go. It's the only way of testing whether you really know this stuff.

Constructing accurate **60°** angles

1) They may well ask you to draw an <u>accurate 60° angle</u>.

2) One thing they're needed for is drawing <u>equilateral triangles</u>.

3) Make sure you <u>follow the method</u> shown in this diagram, and that you can do it <u>entirely from memory</u>.

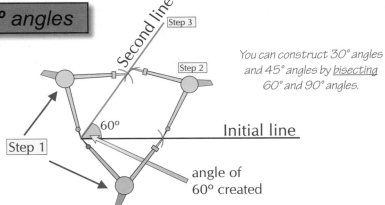

You can construct 30° angles and 45° angles by <u>bisecting</u> 60° and 90° angles.

Constructing accurate **90°** angles

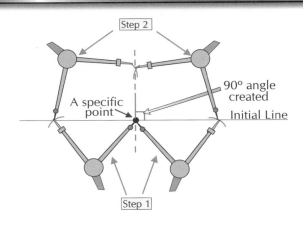

1) They might want you to draw an <u>accurate 90° angle</u>.

2) They won't accept it just done '<u>by eye</u>' or with a ruler — if you want the marks you've got to do it <u>the proper way</u> with <u>compasses</u> like I've shown you here.

3) Make sure you can <u>follow the method</u> shown in this diagram.

Drawing the **Perpendicular** from a **Point** to a **Line**

1) This is similar to the one above but <u>not quite the same</u> — make sure you can do <u>both</u>.

2) Again, they won't accept it just done '<u>by eye</u>' or with a ruler — you've got to do it <u>the proper way</u> with <u>compasses</u>.

3) <u>Learn</u> the diagram.

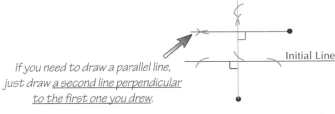

If you need to draw a parallel line, just draw <u>a second line perpendicular to the first one you drew</u>.

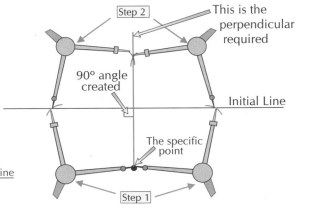

Constructions are basically tricks for maths drawings

There's nothing too 'mathsy' about this page. It's just a few simple tricks to use to draw different angles accurately — it's almost art. So get it learnt quick-smart so you can get back to the maths.

Warm-up and Worked Exam Questions

You need to work through these one by one and make sure you really know what you're doing with your ruler and compasses. Look back over the last few pages if you get stuck.

Warm-Up Questions

1) Using a compass and ruler, construct an equilateral triangle with sides of length 4 cm.

2) Draw the locus of the point P that moves around this kite at a constant distance of 1 cm.

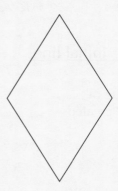

3) Construct four 90° angles to form a square with side length 5.5 cm.

4) Draw a line and a point and construct the perpendicular from the point to the line.

Worked Exam Question

One worked example, and then it's over to you.

1   The triangle ABC is drawn below.
    Using a ruler and compasses, plot the locus of the point P, which moves around the outside
    of the triangle at a constant distance of 1 cm.

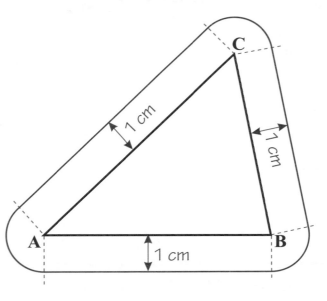

Hint: Always think carefully about the shape of the locus when passing around corners. In general the locus will be an arc.

(5 marks)

Exam Questions

2   A ball of radius *r* rests at the top of a series of ramps.

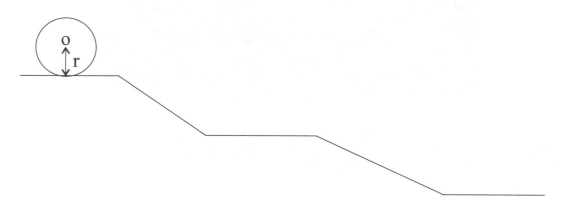

It is pushed towards the top of the first ramp and rolls downwards. If the ball remains in contact with the ramps at all times, plot the locus of the point O, the centre of the ball.

(3 marks)

3   A and B are two towns.
Plot the locus of points which are equidistant from A and B.

A
●

B
●

(3 marks)

4   Draw the line which bisects angle DEF.

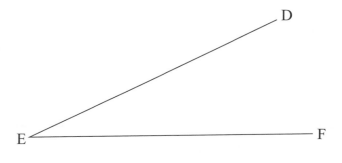

(3 marks)

Conversion Factors

Conversion factors are a mighty powerful tool for dealing with a wide variety of questions. And what's more the method is <u>real easy</u>. Learn it now. It's ace.

> 1) Find the <u>Conversion Factor</u> (always easy)
>
> 2) <u>Multiply</u> by it AND <u>divide</u> by it
>
> 3) Choose the <u>common sense</u> answer

Using **Scales** on **Maps** and **Scale Drawings**

A <u>scale</u> on a map or drawing is a common type of conversion factor.
Here's an example of how to use one:

> "<u>A map has a scale of 1:20 000.</u>
> <u>How big in real life is a distance of 3 cm on the map?</u>"
>
> 1) Conversion Factor = 20 000
>
> 2) 3 cm × 20 000 = 60 000 cm (looks OK)
>   3 cm ÷ 20 000 = 0.00015 cm (not good)
>
> 3) So <u>60 000 cm</u> is the answer.
>   How do we convert to metres?
>
> <u>To convert 60 000 cm to m</u>:
> 1) C.F. = 100 (cm ↔ m)
> 2) 60 000 × 100 = 6 000 000 m
>   (hmm)
>   60 000 ÷ 100 = <u>600 m</u> (more like it)
> 3) So answer = <u>600 m</u>

Two Other Important **Examples**

  "<u>Convert 2.55 hours into minutes.</u>" — (N.B. This is NOT 2 hrs 55 mins)

1) Conversion factor = <u>60</u> — (simply because 1 hour = <u>60</u> mins)

2) 2.55 hrs × 60 = 153 mins (makes sense)
    2.55 hrs ÷ 60 = 0.0425 mins (ridiculous answer!)

3) So plainly the answer is that 2.55 hrs = <u>153 mins</u>

  "<u>If £1 = 1.7 US Dollars, how much is 63 US dollars in £s?</u>"

1) Obviously, conversion factor = <u>1.7</u>   (The "exchange rate")

2) 63 × 1.7 = £107.10
    63 ÷ 1.7 = £37.06

3) Not quite so obvious this time, but since 1.7 US dollars = £1, you're
    clearly going to have <u>less</u> pounds than you had dollars (roughly half).
    So the answer has to be <u>less than</u> 63, which means it must be <u>£37.06</u>

Just three steps to simple conversions

Read through these examples and make sure you fully understand how to use conversion factors.
Don't forget, scale 1:25 000 means 1 cm on the map = 25 000 cm in real life. And take care with time
questions — don't mix up minutes with hundredths of hours, or seconds with hundredths of minutes.

Metric and Imperial Units

A nice easy page for a change — just some <u>facts</u> to learn.

Metric Units

1) <u>Length</u>   mm, cm, m, km
2) <u>Area</u>   mm², cm², m², km²,
3) <u>Volume</u>   mm³, cm³, m³, ml, litres
4) <u>Weight</u>   g, kg, tonnes
5) <u>Speed</u>   km/h, m/s

MEMORISE THESE KEY FACTS:	
1 cm = 10 mm	1 tonne = 1000 kg
1 m = 100 cm	1 litre = 1000 ml
1 km = 1000 m	1 litre = 1000 cm³
1 kg = 1000 g	1 cm³ = 1 ml

Imperial Units

1) <u>Length</u>   Inches, feet, yards, miles
2) <u>Area</u>   Square inches, square feet, square yards, square miles
3) <u>Volume</u>   Cubic inches, cubic feet, gallons, pints
4) <u>Weight</u>   Ounces, pounds, stones, tons
5) <u>Speed</u>   mph

IMPERIAL UNIT CONVERSIONS

1 Foot = 12 Inches
1 Yard = 3 Feet
1 Gallon = 8 Pints
1 Stone = 14 Pounds (lbs)
1 Pound = 16 Ounces (Oz)

You don't need to know these for the exam, but you should be able to <u>use</u> the conversions.

Metric-Imperial Conversions

<u>YOU NEED TO LEARN THESE</u> — they don't promise to give you these in the exam and if they're feeling mean (as they often are), they won't.

APPROXIMATE CONVERSIONS

1 kg ≈ 2.2 pounds

1 inch ≈ 2.5 cm

1 gallon ≈ 4.5 litres

1 mile ≈ 1.6 km (or 5 miles ≈ 8 km)

Using Metric-Imperial Conversion Factors

1) Convert 10 pounds into kg.
   CF = 2.2, so × and ÷ by 2.2, to get 22 kg or <u>4.5 kg</u>. ◄— *A kilogram is heavier than a pound, so there must be fewer kilograms than pounds in the same mass.*

   If you're not sure, multiply <u>and</u> divide by the conversion factor. Then:

2) Convert 5.45 litres into gallons.
   CF = 4.5, so × and ÷ by 4.5, to get 25.5 or <u>1.21 gallons</u>. ◄— *A gallon is more than a litre, so there must be fewer gallons than litres in the same volume.*

There's no way round it — you just have to learn all these factors

There's loads of conversion factors to learn here so keep scribbling them down until you remember every one. Then use your common sense to make sure you don't divide when you should be multiplying.

Formula Triangles

You may have already come across these in physics, because they are <u>extremely potent tools</u> for dealing <u>swiftly and reliably</u> with a lot of common formulas.
They are <u>very easy</u>, so make sure you know how to use them.

Where do you put the letters?

If 3 things are related by a simple formula...

E.g. $A = B \times C$ or $B = \dfrac{A}{C}$

...then you can put them into a <u>FORMULA TRIANGLE</u>.

1) <u>A = B×C</u>   If there are <u>TWO LETTERS MULTIPLIED TOGETHER</u> they must go <u>ON THE BOTTOM</u> of the formula triangle, and so the other must go on the top. For example, the formula <u>A = B×C</u> becomes:

2) <u>B = A/C</u>   If there is <u>ONE THING DIVIDED BY ANOTHER</u> then the one <u>ON TOP OF THE DIVISION</u> goes <u>ON TOP IN THE FORMULA TRIANGLE</u>, and so the other two letters must go on the bottom (it doesn't matter which way round). For example, the formula B = A/C will produce the formula triangle shown above.

How do you use it?

> 1) <u>COVER UP</u> the thing you want to find and just <u>WRITE DOWN</u> what is left showing.
>
> 2) Now <u>PUT IN THE VALUES</u> for the other two things and <u>WORK IT OUT</u>.

Density = Mass ÷ Volume

You can put the above formula for density into a formula triangle like this:
You might think this is physics, but density is specifically mentioned in the maths syllabus.

One way or another you <u>MUST</u> remember this formula for density, because they promise nothing and without it you'll be stuck. The best method by far is to <u>remember the order of the letters</u> in the formula triangle as D^MV or <u>DiMoV</u> (The Russian Agent!).

Example:

"Find the volume of an object with a mass of 40 g and a density of 6.4 g/cm³."

To find volume, <u>cover up V</u>. This leaves M/D, <u>so V = M ÷ D</u> = 40 ÷ 6.4 = <u>6.25 cm³</u>.

Putting the equation into a formula triangle makes life easier

Once you've got the formula triangle sorted, then you only need to cover up whichever letter you are trying to work out and the formula you need is right there. What could be simpler?

Formula Triangles

Speed-distance-time questions are <u>very common</u>, and they never give you the formula.
Either you learn it beforehand or you wave goodbye to several easy marks.

Speed = *Distance ÷ Time*

Formula triangles are dead handy for speed questions. Of course you have
to <u>remember the order of the letters</u> in the triangle (SDT), but you can use the
word <u>SoDiT</u> to help you. So if it's a question on speed, distance and time
just say: <u>SOD IT</u>.

Example: "A car travels 90 miles at 36 miles per hour. How long does it take?"

> We want to find the <u>time</u>, so <u>cover up T</u> in the triangle which leaves D/S,
> so T = D/S = Distance ÷ speed = 90 ÷ 36 = <u>2.5 hours</u>.

> **IF YOU <u>LEARN THE FORMULA TRIANGLE</u>, YOU WILL FIND
> QUESTIONS ON SPEED, DISTANCE AND TIME <u>VERY EASY</u>.**

Units — Getting them Right

By <u>units</u> we mean things like <u>cm, m, m/s, km²</u>, etc. and quite honestly they should always be
in your mind when you <u>write an answer down</u>. When you're using a FORMULA, there is one
special thing you need to know. It's simple enough but you must know it:

> The <u>UNITS you get out</u> of a formula
> <u>DEPEND ENTIRELY</u> upon <u>the UNITS you put into it</u>.

For example, if you put a <u>distance in cm</u> and a <u>time in seconds</u> into the formula triangle to work
out SPEED, the answer must come out in <u>cm per second</u> (cm/s).

If the <u>time is in hours</u> and the speed in <u>miles per hour</u> (mph) then the distance you calculate will
come out in <u>miles</u>. It's pretty simple when you think about it.

But Don't Mix Units

E.g.   Don't mix <u>Miles Per HOUR</u> in a formula with a <u>time in MINUTES</u> (convert it to <u>hours</u>).
        Don't mix <u>DENSITY IN g/cm³</u> in a formula with a <u>MASS IN kg</u> (convert it to g).

Example: "A boy walks 800 m in 10 minutes. Find his speed in km/h."

> If you use 800 m and 10 minutes your answer will be a speed in
> <u>metres per minute</u> (m/min).
> Instead you must <u>convert</u>: 800 m = <u>0.8 km</u>,
>   10 mins = <u>0.1667 hours</u> (mins ÷ 60).
> Then you can divide 0.8 km by 0.1667 hours to get <u>4.8 km/h</u>.

Be careful with units when using formula triangles

Remember to read these questions carefully to see if you need to convert any units before putting
the numbers into the formula triangle. Then it's just a case of plugging the numbers in.

Estimating

Estimating gives you a rough idea of the <u>size</u> of the proper answer. So if you estimate an answer to be about 20 and the exact answer comes out as 2.13, then it's probably wrong and you can redo it.

Estimating **Calculations**   This is <u>VERY EASY</u>, so long as you don't <u>over-complicate it</u>.

> 1) <u>ROUND EVERYTHING OFF</u> to nice easy <u>CONVENIENT NUMBERS</u>.
> 2) Then <u>WORK OUT THE ANSWER</u> using these nice easy numbers — that's it!

<u>EXAMPLE</u>: Estimate the value of $\dfrac{127.8 + 41.9}{56.5 \times 3.2}$ showing all your working.

<u>ANSWER</u>: $\dfrac{127.8 + 41.9}{56.5 \times 3.2} \approx \dfrac{130 + 40}{60 \times 3} = \dfrac{170}{180} \approx 1$

In the exam you'll need to <u>show all the steps</u>, to prove you didn't just use a calculator.

(" $\approx$ " means "roughly equal to")

Estimating **Areas** *and* **Volumes**

> 1) Draw or imagine a <u>RECTANGLE OR CUBOID</u> of similar size to the object.
> 2) <u>ROUND OFF</u> all lengths to the <u>NEAREST WHOLE</u>, and work it out — easy.

<u>EXAMPLES</u>: "Estimate the area of this shape and the volume of the bottle:"

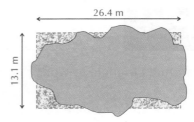

26.4 m

13.1 m

Area ≈ rectangle
26 m × 13 m = <u>338 m²</u>
(or without a calculator:
30 × 10 = 300 m²)

12.7 cm

5.2 cm

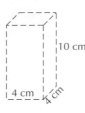

10 cm

4 cm   4 cm

Volume ≈ cuboid
= 4 × 4 × 10
= <u>160 cm³</u>

Estimating **Sizes**

This needs a bit of <u>common sense</u> on top of some basic rules to remember.
Have a look at this example:

EXAMPLE: Assuming the man is of average height, <u>estimate</u> the height of the tree, in m.

1) Firstly, decide on a reasonable height for the man. About <u>1.8 m</u> is fine, but you could get away with anywhere from 1.5 to 2 m.

2) Looking at the picture, the tree is about <u>3 times</u> the man's height.

3) Using 1.8 m as the man's height:

   Height of tree = 3 × 1.8 m = <u>5.4 m</u>

Warm-up and Worked Exam Questions

I know you'll be champing at the bit to get into the exam questions, but these basic warm-up questions are invaluable to get the basic facts straight first.

Warm-Up Questions

1) Convert 12.7 kg into grams.
2) Convert 1430 cm into metres.
3) 10 lbs of apples weigh about how many kilograms?
4) A lump of lead, weighing 374 g has a volume of 33 cm^3.
   What is the approximate density of the lead (to 3 s.f.)?
5) A solid plastic building block measures 5 cm × 4 cm × 6 cm.
   The density of the plastic is 0.8 g/cm^3. What is the mass of the block?
6) A cheetah runs 100 m in 4 seconds, what is its average speed in km per hour?
7) A cyclist travels for ¾ hour at a speed of 12 km per hour. What distance does he travel?
8) By rounding to 1 significant figure, estimate the answer to $\dfrac{94 \times 1.9}{0.328 + 0.201}$.

Worked Exam Questions

Take your time to go through this example and make sure you understand it all.
If any of the facts are baffling you, it's not too late to take another peek over the section.

1   A map has a scale of 1 : 40 000.
    How long is a road that appears as 3 cm long on the map?

   40 000 × 3 cm = 120 000 cm = 1200 m = 1.2 km.

   (2 marks)

2   A solid silver bar is in the shape of a cuboid. The bar is 10 cm long,
    7.4 cm wide and 7.4 cm thick. The bar has a mass of 5749.8 g.
    What is the density of the silver? State the units clearly.

   Density = mass ÷ volume.

   Volume = length × width × thickness = 10 × 7.4 × 7.4 = 547.6 cm³

   Density = 5749.8 ÷ 547.6 = 10.5 g/cm³

   These questions are all about using the formula triangles. But be extra careful with the units — they're the main thing that could catch you out.

   (4 marks)

3   The distance from the Earth to the Sun is 149 000 000 km.
    The speed of light is 300 000 km per second.
    How long does it take light to travel from the Sun to the Earth, to the nearest minute?

   Time = distance ÷ speed = 149 000 000 ÷ 300 000

   = 496.667 seconds.

   To make into minutes ÷ 60 = 8.277 minutes = 8 to nearest minute.

   (3 marks)

Exam Questions

4   Daniel went to a bank to buy some holiday money. He exchanged £250 for €295.25.
    What was the exchange rate?

    ....
                                                                                                                        (1 mark)

5   A signpost says "Paris 24 km". Approximately how many miles is this?

    ....
                                                                                                                        (1 mark)

6   A bunch of bananas are weighed on some old scales. The dial reads 5 lbs.
    Approximately how many kilograms is this?

    ....
                                                                                                                        (1 mark)

7   A car has a fuel economy of 36.5 miles per gallon. Petrol costs £1.12 per litre.
    How much will it cost to buy enough petrol for a journey of 120 miles?

    ....
                                                                                                                        (3 marks)

8   A cube container is filled to the brim with mercury.
    The sides of the container are 4 cm long. The density of the mercury is 13.55 g/cm^3.
    Find the mass of mercury in the container.

    ....
                                                                                                                        (3 marks)

9   A train travels 495 km in 4 hours.
    What is its average speed in km/h, to 2 significant figures?

    ....
                                                                                                                        (2 marks)

10 A car is travelling along the M6. It passes Hilton Park service station at 13.20 hrs and
    then gets stuck in a traffic jam. It finally passes Stafford service station at 16.00 hrs.
    The service stations are 30 km apart.
    What was the average speed of the car on this part of the journey in km/h?

    ....
                                                                                                                        (2 marks)

11 By rounding to 1 significant figure, estimate the answer to $\dfrac{29 \times 2.9}{9.1 - 6.9}$.

    ....
                                                                                                                        (2 marks)

Vectors

The next three pages contain several monstrously important things you need to know about <u>vectors</u>.

The Four **Notations**

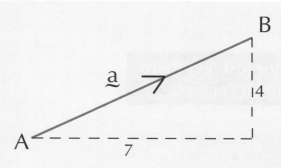

The vector shown here can be referred to as:

It's pretty obvious what these mean.

Just make sure you know which number is which in the column vector — $\left(\begin{smallmatrix} x & \rightarrow \\ y & \uparrow \end{smallmatrix}\right)$,
and what a negative value means — $\left(\begin{smallmatrix} -x & \leftarrow \\ -y & \downarrow \end{smallmatrix}\right)$.

Adding *And* Subtracting *Vectors*

Vectors must always be added <u>end to end</u>,
so that the <u>arrows all point with</u> each other, <u>not against</u> each other.

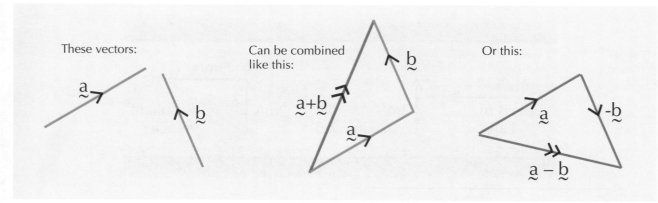

These vectors: Can be combined like this: Or this:

Adding and subtracting <u>COLUMN VECTORS</u> is really easy:

E.g. if $\underline{a} = \left(\begin{smallmatrix}5\\3\end{smallmatrix}\right)$ and $\underline{b} = \left(\begin{smallmatrix}-2\\4\end{smallmatrix}\right)$ then $2\underline{a} - \underline{b} = 2\left(\begin{smallmatrix}5\\3\end{smallmatrix}\right) - \left(\begin{smallmatrix}-2\\4\end{smallmatrix}\right) = \left(\begin{smallmatrix}12\\2\end{smallmatrix}\right)$

To multiply a vector by a number (called a <u>scalar</u>), just multiply both bits of the vector by the number, e.g. $2\underline{a} = \left(\begin{smallmatrix}10\\6\end{smallmatrix}\right)$.

This is called the <u>resultant vector</u> (it's the result of combining vectors).

That's two vital vector facts done

But the facts are only really 'done' if you've learnt them. So be sure you know how vectors are written (there are four ways remember) and how to add and subtract vectors — then you're done.

Typical Vector Questions

These are the types of vector question you're most likely to stumble across in the exam, so make sure you learn all the little tricks on the next two pages.
They'll stop you coming a cropper. Or at least reduce the chances of it.

A *Typical* Exam Question

This is a common type of question and it illustrates a very important vector technique:

> ### To obtain the <u>unknown vector</u> just '<u>get there</u>' by any route <u>made up of known vectors</u>.

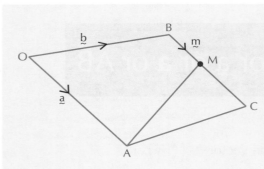

Applying this rule we can easily obtain the following vectors in terms of $\underset{\sim}{a}$, $\underset{\sim}{b}$ and $\underset{\sim}{m}$ (given that M is the mid point of the line BC):

$\overrightarrow{AM} = -\underset{\sim}{a} + \underset{\sim}{b} + \underset{\sim}{m}$ (i.e. get there via O and B)

$\overrightarrow{OC} = \underset{\sim}{b} + 2\underset{\sim}{m}$ (i.e. get there via B and M)

$\overrightarrow{AC} = -\underset{\sim}{a} + \underset{\sim}{b} + 2\underset{\sim}{m}$ (A to C via O, B and M)

The Old '*Swimming Across the River*' Question

EXAMPLE: "A swimmer crosses a river by swimming directly towards the opposite bank. He swims at a speed of 2 m/s. As he swims he is carried downstream by the river, which is flowing at a speed of 3 m/s. Find his resultant speed and direction of travel."

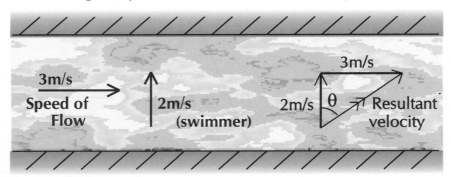

Overall Speed $= \sqrt{3^2 + 2^2}$
$= \sqrt{13} = 3.6\,\text{m/s}$
Direction: $\tan\theta = 3 \div 2$
$\theta = \tan^{-1}(1.5) = 56.3°$

This is a really easy question: You just <u>ADD</u> the two velocity vectors <u>END TO END</u> and draw the <u>RESULTANT VECTOR</u> which shows both the <u>speed</u> and <u>direction</u> of the final course.

As usual with vectors, you'll need to use <u>Pythagoras and Trig</u> to find the length and angle, but that's relatively straightforward. Just make sure you LEARN the two methods in this question. The example shown above is pretty standard stuff and you should definitely see it that way, rather than as one random question of which there may be hundreds — there aren't.

If you know $\overrightarrow{AB}$ *and* $\overrightarrow{BC}$ — *then add them to get* $\overrightarrow{AC}$

It's worth learning these questions, because very similar ones are likely to come up on the exam. So make sure you can do them all. Turn over for two more typical exam questions on vectors.

Typical Vector Questions

The Old 'Swimming Slightly Upstream' Question

EXAMPLE: "A river is flowing at a speed of 1 m/s. A girl swims slightly upstream across the river, at a speed of 2 m/s, to reach a point directly opposite her starting point. Find the angle she swims at and her resultant speed."

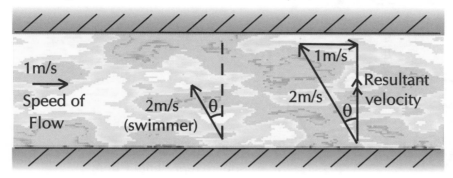

1) $\sin\theta = \text{OPP}/\text{HYP}$
   $= 1/2$
   $so\ \theta = \sin^{-1}(0.5) = 30°$

2) Speed $= \sqrt{2^2 - 1^2}$
   $= \sqrt{3} = 1.73\,\text{m/s}$

The general idea here is to end up going <u>directly across the river</u>, and once again the old faithful method of drawing a <u>vector triangle</u> makes light work of the whole thing — 2 vectors joined end to end to give the resultant velocity.

However, in this case the resultant is drawn in <u>first</u> (straight across), so that the angle θ has to be worked out <u>to fit</u> as shown above.

The Old 'Queen Mary's Tugboats' Question

The problem here is to find the overall force from the two tugs.

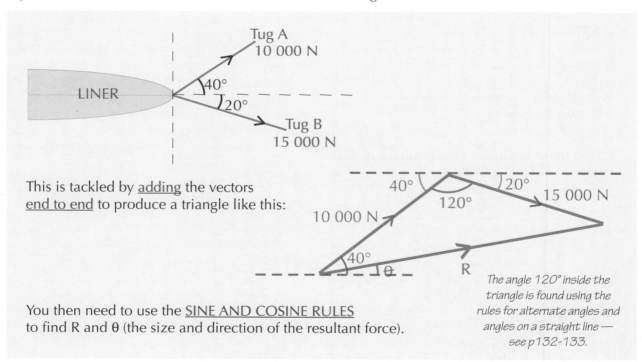

This is tackled by <u>adding</u> the vectors <u>end to end</u> to produce a triangle like this:

You then need to use the <u>SINE AND COSINE RULES</u> to find R and θ (the size and direction of the resultant force).

The angle 120° inside the triangle is found using the rules for alternate angles and angles on a straight line — see p132-133.

If you learn how to answer these questions you will get marks

Two more questions which are very likely to come up on your exam, almost like a hint as to what to learn — it's as close to cheating as you can get without cheating — so learn them.

Warm-up Questions

Vector questions can be pretty tricky until you get your head around the basics. That's what these warm-up questions are all about — work through them carefully and check any bits you don't know.

Warm-Up Questions

1)

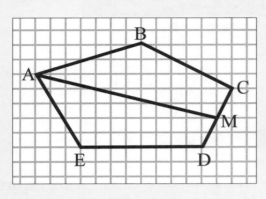

In the diagram, each square represents 1 unit.

Write the following as a column vector.

a) $\vec{AB}$　　b) $\vec{BC}$　　c) $\vec{ED}$　　d) $\vec{CD}$　　e) $\vec{AM}$

2) If $\mathbf{a} = \begin{pmatrix} 5 \\ 3 \end{pmatrix}$, $\mathbf{b} = \begin{pmatrix} -1 \\ 6 \end{pmatrix}$, $\mathbf{c} = \begin{pmatrix} 0 \\ 4 \end{pmatrix}$, $\mathbf{d} = \begin{pmatrix} -2 \\ 0 \end{pmatrix}$ find:

a) $\mathbf{a} + \mathbf{b}$　　b) $\mathbf{b} - \mathbf{c}$　　c) $\mathbf{c} + \mathbf{a}$　　d) $\mathbf{d} - \mathbf{b}$　　e) $\mathbf{b} + \mathbf{c} - \mathbf{d}$

3)

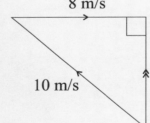

Find the magnitude of the resultant vector.

4)

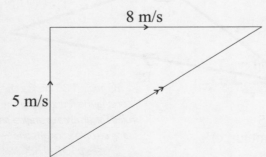

A model aeroplane that flies at a speed of 5 m/s in still air, heads due north.
There is an 8 m/s crosswind blowing from west to east, which makes the aeroplane drift off its intended heading. Find the speed and direction of the resultant course of travel.

Worked Exam Questions

Worked Exam Question

Get through these exam questions, then it'll be time to put your feet up... have a nice glass of ginger beer... a chocolate biscuit... mmm. (But don't relax too much — there's still the revision summary and the practice exam...)

1

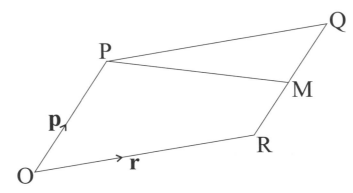

OPQR is a parallelogram. M is the midpoint of QR. $\overrightarrow{OP} = \mathbf{p}$, $\overrightarrow{OR} = \mathbf{r}$.

(a) Find in terms of **p** and **r** expressions for the following vectors.

(i) $\overrightarrow{OQ}$

$$\overrightarrow{OQ} = \overrightarrow{OP} + \overrightarrow{PQ} = \mathbf{p} + \mathbf{r} \qquad (because\ \overrightarrow{PQ} = \overrightarrow{OR})$$

(1 mark)

(ii) $\overrightarrow{MR}$

$$\overrightarrow{MR} = \tfrac{1}{2}\,\overrightarrow{QR} = \tfrac{1}{2}\,\overrightarrow{PO} = -\tfrac{1}{2}\mathbf{p}$$

(1 mark)

(b) S is a point positioned three quarters along $\overrightarrow{PM}$. Find, in terms of **p** and **r**:

(i) $\overrightarrow{PS}$

$$\overrightarrow{PS} = \tfrac{3}{4}\,\overrightarrow{PM} = \tfrac{3}{4}\,(\mathbf{r} - \tfrac{1}{2}\mathbf{p})$$

(1 mark)

(ii) $\overrightarrow{OS}$

$$\overrightarrow{OS} = \overrightarrow{OP} + \overrightarrow{PS} = \mathbf{p} + \tfrac{3}{4}\,(\mathbf{r} - \tfrac{1}{2}\,\mathbf{p})\ or\ \tfrac{3}{4}\,\mathbf{r} + \tfrac{5}{8}\mathbf{p}$$

(1 mark)

Exam Questions

2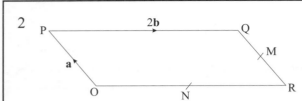

OPQR is a parallelogram. $\overrightarrow{OP} = \mathbf{a}$, $\overrightarrow{PQ} = 2\mathbf{b}$.
M is the midpoint of QR. N is the midpoint of OR.

(a) Find in terms of **a** and **b** the vectors:

(i) $\overrightarrow{OQ}$ ....
(1 mark)

(ii) $\overrightarrow{OM}$ ....
(1 mark)

(b) The lines PQ and NM are extended to meet at S. Find in terms of **a** and **b** the vectors:

(i) $\overrightarrow{RS}$ ....
(1 mark)

(ii) $\overrightarrow{NQ}$ ....
(1 mark)

(c) What can you say about the lines RS and NQ?

....
(2 marks)

3

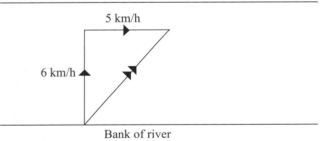

A boat, whose speed in still water is 6 km/h, is making its way across a river flowing
at 5 km/h. The boat sets off at right angles to the bank.

(a) Find its resultant velocity and its direction relative to the bank.

....
(2 marks)

(b) The boat owner wants to cross the river at right angles to the bank.
At what angle relative to the bank must he point the boat upstream?

....
(2 marks)

(c) The boat is pointed upstream, 60° to the bank. The speed of the current has changed.
If the boat is moving at right angles to the bank, what is the current's speed?

....
(2 marks)

Revision Summary for Unit 3 — 2

Here we are again — one more lovely set of questions for you to test yourself with.

Remember you have to practise these questions <u>over and over again</u> until you can answer them <u>all</u>. Seriously, you do. That's the best kind of revision there is because the whole idea is to find out what you <u>don't know</u> and then learn it <u>until you do</u>. Enjoy.

Keep learning the basic facts until you know them

1) What is the formula for Pythagoras' theorem? In what sort of triangle can you use Pythagoras?

2) How do you decide which numbers go where? What final check do you make?

3)* A museum has a flight of stairs up to its front door (see diagram). A ramp is to be put over the top of the steps for wheelchair users. Calculate the length that the ramp would need to be.

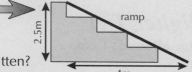

4) What are the three key words for bearings? How must bearings be written?

5) Write down the important steps of a good solid method for doing TRIG.

6) What are the advantages of using formula triangles to do sin, cos and tan?

7)* Most avalanches happen on slopes that are at angles of between 15° and 60°. Jane decided to estimate the angle of the slope she was on to see whether she was at high risk from an avalanche. She created a right-angled triangle using two ice axes and estimated the measurements shown. Calculate angle x — the angle of the slope.

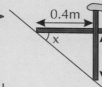

8) Draw a diagram to illustrate angles of elevation and depression.

9) What three steps allow you to find the angle between a line and a plane?

10) Write down the SINE and COSINE RULES and draw a properly labelled triangle.

11) What is the formula (involving sin) for the area of any triangle? Demonstrate its use.

12) List the 4 different types of sine/cosine rule questions and which rule you need for each.

13) Draw the graphs of sin and cos, over 0-360º and then –1080º to 1080º.

14) How many types of shift and stretch are there for graphs? Illustrate each of the different types.

15) Explain how the equation is modified for each of these.

16) Give an example of each type, both the modified equation and a sketch.

17) What is a locus?

18) Demonstrate how to accurately draw the bisector of an angle and the perpendicular bisector of a line.

19)* Kylie is on holiday in South Africa, where £1 = 12.12 rand. She pays 250 rand to go to a safari park. How much has she spent in pounds?

20) Give 8 metric conversions, 5 imperial ones, and 4 metric-to-imperial.

21)* Kevin is filling in a form to join the gym and needs to give his weight in kg. He knows he weighs 10 st 4 lbs. How much is this in kg?

22) How do you put the formulas A=B×C and A=B/C into formula triangles?

23) What are the 2 steps for using a formula triangle?

24) What is the formula triangle for density?

25) What is the formula triangle for speed, distance and time?

26) What two main rules apply to the units involved with formula triangles?

27) What are the two steps for estimating the answer to a calculation?

28) What are the two steps for estimating the area or volume of a shape?

29) What are the four vector notations?

30) What's the main rule for adding vectors?

31) In a typical exam question, what is the basic rule for finding an unknown vector?

32) Produce your own 'swimming across the river' and 'swimming slightly upstream' questions and work them out.

33) Produce your own 'Queen Mary's tugboats' question and do it using the SINE and COSINE rules.

* The answers to these questions can be found on page 228.

Once you've been through all the questions in each unit, you should feel pretty confident about the unit exam.
As final preparation, here are three practice exams — one for each unit, to really get you set for the real things.
These papers are designed to give you the best possible preparation for your AQA modular exams.

GCSE Mathematics
AQA Modular

Unit 1: Calculator

Higher Tier
Time allowed: 1 hour

Centre name				
Centre number				
Candidate number				

In addition to this paper you should have:
- A ruler.
- A protractor.
- A pair of compasses.
- A calculator.

Tracing paper may be used.

Surname	
Other names	
Candidate signature	

Instructions to candidates
- Write your name and other details in the spaces provided above.
- Answer **all** questions in the spaces provided.
- In calculations show clearly how you worked out your answers.
- Do all rough work on the paper.
- You are allowed to use a calculator.

Information for candidates
- The marks available are given in brackets at the end of each question.
- You may get marks for method, even if your answer is incorrect.
- There are 12 questions in this paper.
- There are 54 marks available for this paper.
- In questions labelled with an asterisk *, you will be assessed on the quality of your written communication — take particular care here with spelling, punctuation and the quality of explanations.

For examiner's use

Q	Attempt Nº 1	2	3	Q	Attempt Nº 1	2	3
1				7			
2				8			
3				9			
4				10			
5				11			
6				12			
Total							

Advice to candidates
- Work steadily through the paper.
- Don't spend too long on one question.
- If you have time at the end, go back and check your answers.

Amanda is setting up a game for her school summer fair.

A player will flip an ordinary coin, and roll an ordinary unbiased 6-sided dice.

If they get heads on the coin and roll a 1 or a 6 on the dice, they win some money.

If they get heads on the coin and roll a 2, 3, 4 or 5 on the dice, they win a lucky dip prize.

She draws the table below to help her work out the probabilities of people winning.

	1	2	3	4	5	6
Heads	H1					
Tails						

(a) Complete the table above to show the possible combinations.

(1 mark)

(b) Find the probability that a player wins some money.
Give your answer as a fraction in its lowest form.

....

....

Answer (b) _____

(2 marks)

(c) How many lucky dip prizes should Amanda expect to give out if 60 people play her game?
You must show your working.

....

....

....

Answer (c) _____

(3 marks)

2   Dee is investigating whether there is a correlation between the weight and head circumference of newborn babies. Her hypothesis is that there is no correlation between weight and head circumference.

She collects data on 12 babies, which is shown on the scatter graph below.

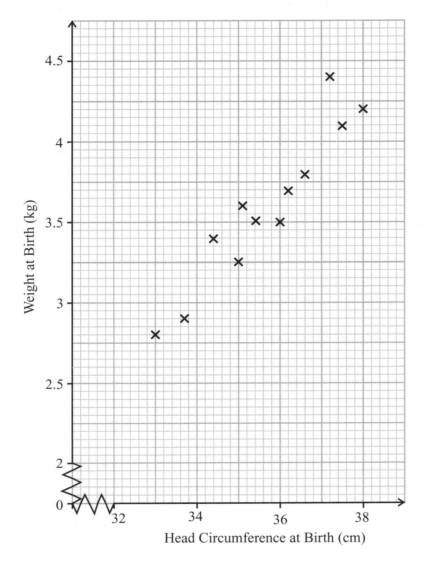

(a) Explain whether the data supports Dee's hypothesis.

....

....

(1 mark)

(b) Dee says that a baby with a head circumference of 39 cm would weigh about 4.6 kg. Comment on this assumption.

....

....

(1 mark)

The table below gives information about the heights of the children in Class A.

Height in cm (h)	Frequency
$130 \leq h < 140$	5
$140 \leq h < 150$	10
$150 \leq h < 160$	14
$160 \leq h < 170$	8
$170 \leq h < 180$	3

(a) Calculate an estimate for the mean height of the children in Class A.

....

....

Answer (a) _____ *cm*

(3 marks)

(b)* Below are two frequency polygons showing the heights of the children in Classes A and B.
By using any two measures of average, compare the heights in the two Classes.

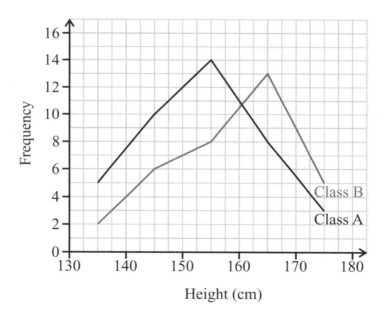

Height (cm)

....

....

....

....

....

(3 marks)

4   Mrs Jones is trying to sell her house. She decides to advertise her house with an estate agent, with an asking price of £190 000. She asks two estate agents what fees they will charge.

Shirleys	Tibbersons
Fees for selling your house with us: Fixed Price £3700	Our selling fees are 1.95% of the actual selling price

(a) Mrs Jones expects the actual selling price of her house to be 10% below her asking price. Explain which estate agent will be cheapest to use if this happens.

....

....

....

(3 marks)

(b) Mrs Jones finds a house she wants to buy. It has an asking price of £212 500. She is told that the asking price was dropped by 15% six months ago. What was the price six months ago?

....

....

....

*Answer (b) £*_____

(3 marks)

A large supermarket chain is planning to open a new store in a town called Digton.
Residents of Digton are asked to complete a questionnaire to give their views on this idea.

(a)   Here is one of the questions from the questionnaire:

> 'There is nowhere in Digton that sells a good range of products,
> so Digton needs a new supermarket. Do you agree?'

   (i)   Write down one criticism of this question.

   ....

   ....
   (1 mark)

   (ii)   Suggest a more suitable question that could be used instead.

   ....

   ....
   (1 mark)

(b)   The questionnaire is distributed to shoppers in the town centre every morning from
Monday to Friday, during one week.
Will this method of distributing the questionnaire produce reliable data? Explain your answer.

....

....

....
(2 marks)

6   An area of rainforest is 840 520 000 acres in size. The area contains an estimated 1.7×10^{11} trees.

   (a)   Use this information to estimate the number of trees per acre of rainforest.
       Give your answer correct to the nearest ten trees per acre.

       ....

       ....

Answer (a) _____

(2 marks)

   (b)   The area of rainforest has been shrinking by an average of 0.7% per year.
       Assuming this trend continues, estimate the size of the rainforest in a year's time.
       Give your answer in standard form, correct to the nearest million acres.

       ....

Answer (b) _____*acres*

(3 marks)

7   Reena inherits £4500. She decides to place the money in a savings account, and is considering two different accounts.

   Account 1 pays a simple interest rate of 5% per year.
   Account 2 pays a compound interest rate of 3.5%, compounded yearly.

   Reena wants to invest her money for 10 years. In which account will her savings grow the most in this time? Show your working clearly.

   ....

   ....

   ....

   ....

(3 marks)

Megan is the manager of a health club. She wants to know if the BMIs (Body Mass Indexes) of the female members have improved since she last surveyed them. She intends to publish her findings in an information leaflet. The cumulative frequency curve below shows the new data she's collected from the 40 female members.

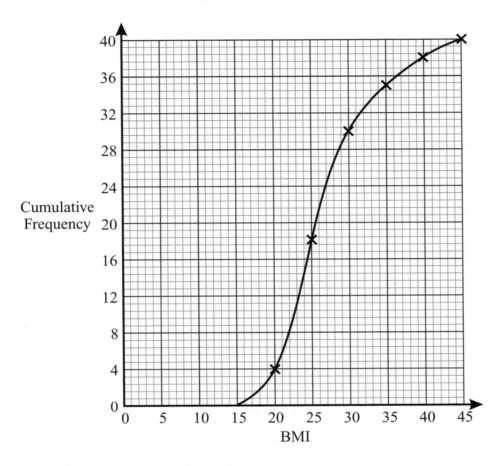

(a) Estimate the median BMI.

....

Answer (a) _____

(1 mark)

(b) Estimate the interquartile range (IQR).

....

....

Answer (b) _____

(2 marks)

(c)* Megan also wants to include a comparison of the BMIs of the men and women in the health club in her information leaflet. A box-plot giving information on the BMIs of the men is shown below.

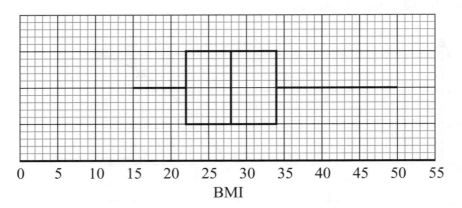

BMI

Compare the BMIs of the women to the BMIs of the men.

....

....

....

....

(2 marks)

9   Aaron is deciding which brand of tea he should serve during tea breaks. He wants to take a sample of workers in his company and ask them which brand they prefer. He wants the sample to proportionally represent the age distribution of workers within the company.

(a)   What sampling method should he use?

....

(1 mark)

(b)   The table below shows the age distribution of workers in the company.

Age range	Proportion of the workers in that range
16 to 24	21%
25 to 44	63%
45 to 65	16%

Aaron decides to sample 38 people.
Calculate how many people he should sample from each age range.

....

....

....

(3 marks)

0   The table and unfinished histogram below give information about the length of time 100 cars
spent parked in a supermarket car park.

Amount of time spent in the car park (minutes, m)	Number of cars
$0 < m \leq 20$	24
$20 < m \leq 30$	24
$30 < m \leq 40$	16
$40 < m \leq 60$	20
$60 < m \leq 80$	12
$80 < m \leq 120$	4

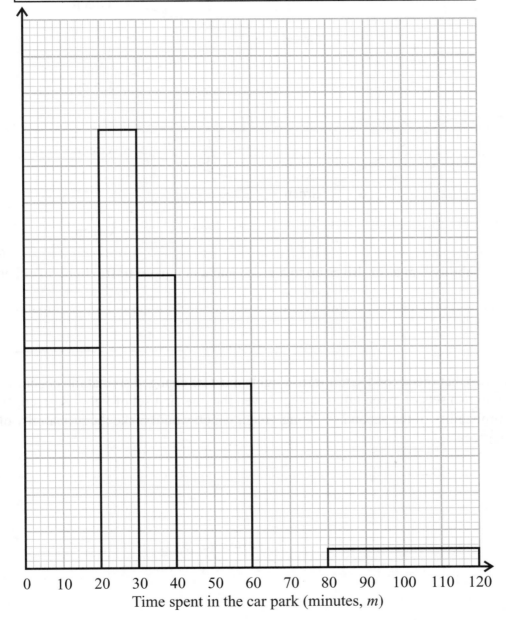

(a) Use the information given in the table and histogram to put values on the
frequency density axis.

....

(2 marks)

(b) Use the table to complete the histogram.

....

(1 mark)

10

11 Janice works for the city council, and is investigating how well a sequence of two sets of traffic
    lights works to reduce jams. The lights are set up so that the likelihood of the second set being
    green as a car approaches depends on the colour of the first set.
    Janice drives between the lights many times and records how often each set is on green.
    From her results, she estimates the probabilities shown in the tree diagram below.

(a) Complete the tree diagram by filling in the missing probabilities.

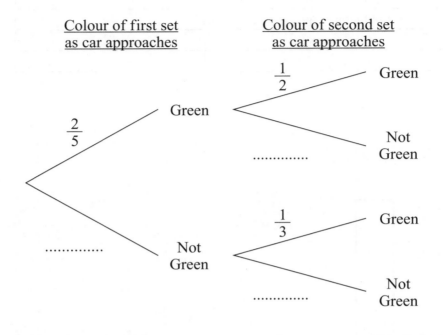

(2 marks)

(b) Find the probability that a car drives up to a green and a not green traffic light, in either order.

....

Answer (b) _____

(2 marks)

(c) Janice decides that the second set of traffic lights must be changed so that the chance of
    driving up to two sets of green lights is $\frac{3}{10}$. Given that the first set of lights is green, find the
    required probability of the second set being green, which would make the probability of both
    sets being green $\frac{3}{10}$.

....

....

Answer (c) _____

(2 marks)

2* Jim has to deliver a load of metal rods on his truck.
Each rod is cut so that it weighs 80 kg (correct to the nearest 5 kg).
All the rods must be strapped onto wooden pallets to make them easier to transport.
Pallets weigh exactly 20 kg, and a maximum of 10 rods can be strapped onto each pallet.

The maximum load that the truck can take is 1900 kg, to the nearest 10 kg. What is the greatest number of rods that Jim can put onto his truck while being sure that all rods are strapped onto pallets and the truck is loaded within safe limits? Explain your reasoning clearly.

....

....

....

....

....

(4 marks)

GCSE Mathematics
AQA Modular
Unit 2: Non-calculator

Higher Tier
Time allowed: 1 hour 15 minutes

Centre name				
Centre number				
Candidate number				

In addition to this paper you should have:
- A ruler.
- A protractor.
- A pair of compasses.

Tracing paper may be used.

Surname	
Other names	
Candidate signature	

Instructions to candidates
- Write your name and other details in the spaces provided above.
- Answer **all** questions in the spaces provided.
- In calculations show clearly how you worked out your answers.
- Do all rough work on the paper.
- You are **not allowed** to use a calculator.

Information for candidates
- The marks available are given in brackets at the end of each question.
- You may get marks for method, even if your answer is incorrect.
- There are 15 questions in this paper. There are no blank pages.
- There are 66 marks available for this paper.
- In questions labelled with an asterisk *, you will be assessed on the quality of your written communication — take particular care here with spelling, punctuation and the quality of explanations.

For examiner's use

Q	Attempt Nº			Q	Attempt Nº		
	1	2	3		1	2	3
1				9			
2				10			
3				11			
4				12			
5				13			
6				14			
7				15			
8							
Total							

Advice to candidates
- Work steadily through the paper.
- Don't spend too long on one question.
- If you have time at the end, go back and check your answers.

In a working week, Hassan drives 75 miles each day for 5 days.
He is able to claim back 24p for every mile he travels.

Calculate the amount, in pounds, that he can claim back for one working week.

....

....

....

*Answer £*_____

(3 marks)

Dave and Maria decide to split a shopping bill of £45.25 in the ratio 3:2, with Dave paying most.
(a) How much should Dave pay?

....

*Answer (a) £*_____

(2 marks)

(b) £30 of the shopping bill was spent on food and drinks. £17.40 of this was spent on food.
What percentage of the food and drinks bill was spent on drinks?

....

Answer (b) _____*%*

(3 marks)

3   (a) Find the next number in the sequence below.
Explain how you worked the next number out.
57, 46, 35, 24, 13, ...

....

....

(2 marks)

(b)* The *n*th term of a sequence is $2n + 2$.
Rita says that the number 65 will be in the sequence.
Is she correct? Explain your answer.

....

....

(2 marks)

4* A Youth Centre decides to organise a trip to a theme park.
They plan to hire a coach that costs £100 for the day.
The cost to get into the theme park is £15 per person.

The Youth Centre will charge £23 per person for the trip,
which includes the coach journey and entry to the theme park.

The trip can only go ahead if the Youth Centre makes enough money to cover its costs.
Show how many people need to go on the trip for it to go ahead.

....

....

....

....

....

(4 marks)

5 Solve the inequality $\dfrac{5z}{4} \leq 2z - 3$.

....

....

Answer _____

(2 marks)

6 Amelia and Bert get taxis home with the same company. The company charges a fixed
amount (m) per mile and a different fixed amount (t) per minute of the journey.
The total journey cost is the amount for the distance plus the amount for the time taken.

Amelia's 10 mile journey takes 29 minutes and costs her £20.80.
Bert's 2 mile journey takes 7 minutes and costs him £4.40.

Set up and solve a pair of simultaneous equations to find the fixed amount per mile
and the fixed amount per minute of the journey that the taxi company charges.

....

....

....

....

....

(5 marks)

Geoff is setting up a stall selling rain capes at a tourist attraction.
He uses the following formula to estimate how many capes he should buy for the summer:

$$c = \left(r \times \frac{v}{5}\right) + 10\,000,$$ where c is the number of capes he should buy, r is the expected

number of rainy days over the summer and v is the expected number of visitors per day.

He expects there to be 21 rainy days and 19 400 visitors per day to the attraction.
By rounding to 1 significant figure, estimate the number of capes he should buy.

....

....

....

Answer _____

(3 marks)

Find the value of y in the equation below:
$$\frac{2y + 8}{5} = \frac{4y - 40}{3}$$

....

....

Answer y = _____

(3 marks)

(a) Simplify $\dfrac{\sqrt{r}\,s^2 t}{r^{\frac{3}{2}} st^3}$.

....

....

Answer (a) _____

(3 marks)

(b) Factorise $24x^2y - 16xy + 32xy^2$.

....

....

Answer (b) _____

(1 mark)

(c) Fully factorise $8x^2 - 18y^2$.

....

....

Answer (c) _____

(2 marks)

200

10 Becky wants to join a pottery class.

(a) Her local school offers a class which costs £5 per hour, plus a one-off registration fee of £15 to cover equipment costs. Draw a line on the graph below to represent the cost in £ (y) of a given number of class hours (x).

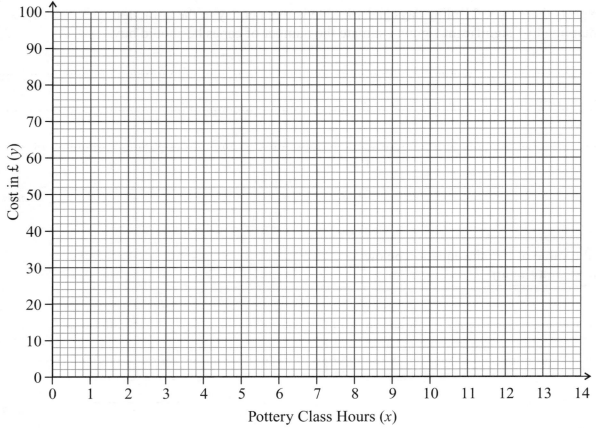

(2 marks)

(b) A nearby college offers a similar class. The first hour for new students is free, and after that it costs £7.50 per hour. Write an equation to represent the cost in £ (y) of a given number of class hours (x).

....

(1 mark)

(c) By plotting your equation from part (b), write down how many hours Becky must spend at a pottery class for it to become cheaper to do it at the local school than the nearby college.

....

(2 marks)

1 Solve $x^2 - 2x = 15$ by factorising.

....

....

....

Answer _____

(3 marks)

2 (a) The diagram below shows a rectangle ABCD.

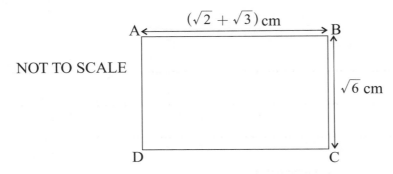

NOT TO SCALE

Calculate the area of the rectangle. Leave your answer in the form $(a\sqrt{3} + b\sqrt{2})$ cm^2, where a and b are integers.

....

....

Answer (a) _____ cm^2

(3 marks)

(b) Multiply out the brackets and simplify the following expression, writing your answer in the form $a\sqrt{b} + c$.

$$(\sqrt{2} + 3)(\sqrt{2} + 2)$$

....

....

....

Answer (b) _____

(2 marks)

13   Rearrange the equations below to make '*b*' the subject in each case:

(a) $a = \dfrac{1}{2}bc^2$

....

Answer (a) b = _____

(2 marks)

(b) $12 = \dfrac{bx + 8}{by - 4}$

....

....

....

Answer (b) b = _____

(3 marks)

(c) $\dfrac{1}{a} + \dfrac{1}{b} = \dfrac{1}{c}$

....

....

....

Answer (c) b = _____

(3 marks)

4 Simplify these algebraic fractions as much as possible:

(a) $\dfrac{4x + 10}{6x + 14}$

....

....

Answer (a) _____

(2 marks)

(b) $\dfrac{x^2 - x - 12}{x^2 + 10x + 21}$

....

....

....

Answer (b) _____

(3 marks)

5* Prove that the squares of any two consecutive multiples of 3 always add up to a multiple of 9.

....

....

....

....

....

....

(5 marks)

GCSE Mathematics
AQA Modular

Unit 3: Calculator

Higher Tier

Time allowed: 1 hour 30 minutes

Centre name				
Centre number				
Candidate number				

Surname	
Other names	
Candidate signature	

In addition to this paper you should have:
- A ruler.
- A protractor.
- A pair of compasses.
- A calculator.

Tracing paper may be used.

Instructions to candidates
- Write your name and other details in the spaces provided above.
- Answer **all** questions in the spaces provided.
- In calculations show clearly how you worked out your answers.
- Do all rough work on the paper.
- You are allowed to use a calculator.
- Take the value of π to be 3.14, or use the π button on your calculator.

Information for candidates
- The marks available are given in brackets at the end of each question.
- You may get marks for method, even if your answer is incorrect.
- There are 15 questions in this paper. There are no blank pages.
- There are 80 marks available for this paper.
- In questions labelled with an asterisk *, you will be assessed on the quality of your written communication — take particular care here with spelling, punctuation and the quality of explanations.

For examiner's use

Q	Attempt Nº 1	2	3	Q	Attempt Nº 1	2	3
1				9			
2				10			
3				11			
4				12			
5				13			
6				14			
7				15			
8				Total			

Advice to candidates
- Work steadily through the paper.
- Don't spend too long on one question.
- If you have time at the end, go back and check your answers.

Formula Sheet: Higher Tier

Area of trapezium $= \dfrac{1}{2}(a + b)h$

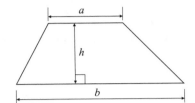

Volume of prism = area of cross-section × length

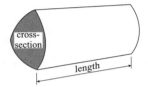

Volume of sphere $= \dfrac{4}{3}\pi r^3$

Surface area of sphere $= 4\pi r^2$

Volume of cone $= \dfrac{1}{3}\pi r^2 h$

Curved surface area of cone $= \pi rl$

For any triangle *ABC*:

Sine rule: $\quad \dfrac{a}{\sin A} = \dfrac{b}{\sin B} = \dfrac{c}{\sin C}$

Cosine rule: $\quad a^2 = b^2 + c^2 - 2bc\cos A$

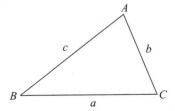

Area of triangle $= \dfrac{1}{2}ab\sin C$

The quadratic equation:

The solutions of $ax^2 + bx + c = 0$, where $a \neq 0$, are given by $x = \dfrac{-b \pm \sqrt{(b^2 - 4ac)}}{2a}$

1   For the equation $x^3 - x - 4 = 0$:

(a) Show that it has a solution between $x = 1$ and $x = 2$.

....

....

(2 marks)

(b) Use trial and improvement to find the solution correct to one decimal place.
     You must show your working.

....

....

....

....

Answer (b) x = _____

(4 marks)

2   Use the diagram below to calculate the given angles.

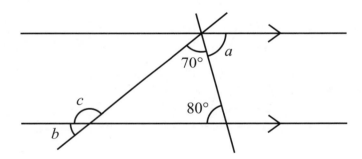

*not drawn
to scale*

(a) Angle a

Answer (a) a = _____ °

(1 mark)

(b) Angle b

Answer (b) b = _____ °

(2 marks)

(c) Angle c

Answer (c) c = _____ °

(1 mark)

* A painter wants to calculate the cost of painting the four outside walls of a warehouse. The diagram below gives the dimensions of the warehouse.

There are 5 windows in the warehouse that each measure 2 m by 1 m and a door that measures 3 m by 2.5 m.

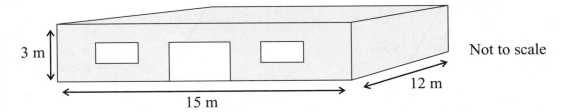

3 m

15 m

12 m

Not to scale

- The paint covers 13 m² per litre.
- The paint can be bought in tins that contain 5 litres or 2.5 litres.
- 5 litre tins cost £20.99
- 2.5 litre tins cost £12.99

Calculate the cheapest price for painting the warehouse. You must show all your working.

....

....

....

....

....

....

....

....

(6 marks)

4

4   A chocolate manufacturer trials a new shape of box for one of its products.

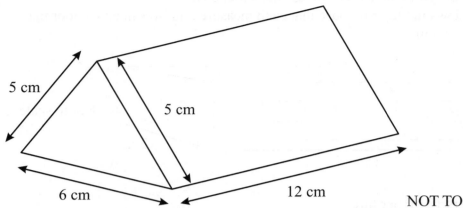

5 cm

5 cm

6 cm

12 cm

NOT TO SCALE

(a)   Find the surface area of the box. Give the correct units in your answer.

....

....

....

Answer (a) _____

(3 marks)

(b)   Find the volume of the box.

....

....

Answer (b) _____ cm^3

(2 marks)

Alice walks to the garage to pick up her car. This journey is shown on the distance-time graph below. She spends 20 minutes at the garage, and then drives home at a speed of 21 mph.

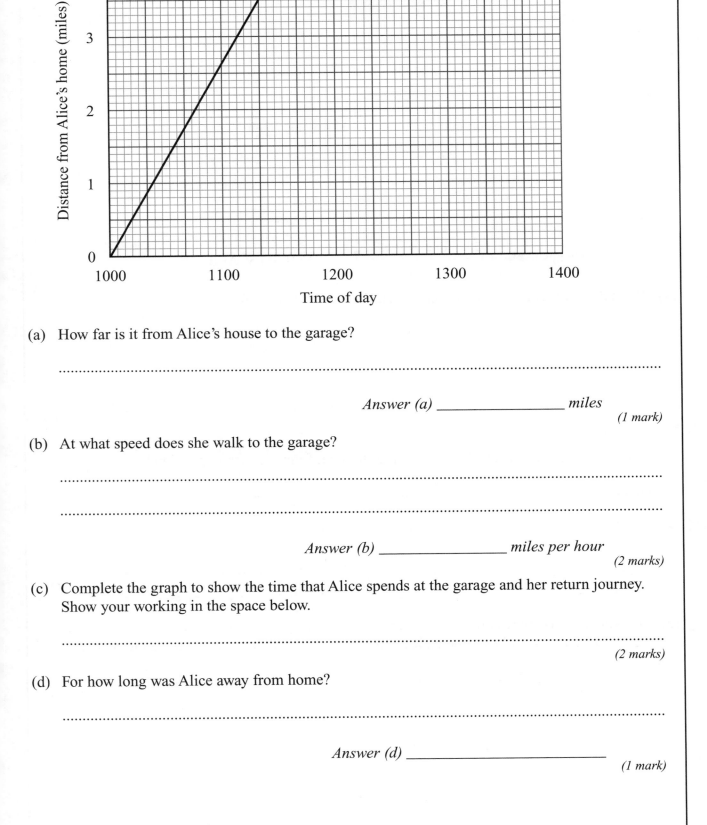

(a) How far is it from Alice's house to the garage?

....

Answer (a) _____ miles

(1 mark)

(b) At what speed does she walk to the garage?

....

....

Answer (b) _____ miles per hour

(2 marks)

(c) Complete the graph to show the time that Alice spends at the garage and her return journey. Show your working in the space below.

....

(2 marks)

(d) For how long was Alice away from home?

....

Answer (d) _____

(1 mark)

6   Todd is out walking on moorland, and needs to reach his campsite as quickly as possible.
    His instructions say that to get to the campsite he needs to walk due south along a path for 12 km,
    and then due west along a path for 5 km. He is thinking about taking a short cut and walking
    directly towards the campsite.

Todd

Short cut

12 km due south

5 km due west

Campsite

NOT TO SCALE

(a) What distance will he have to walk if he takes the short cut to the campsite?

....

....

                                    Answer (a) _____ *km*

                                                                    (2 marks)

(b) What bearing must he travel on to take the short cut from his current position?

....

....

                                    Answer (b) _____°

                                                                    (2 marks)

(c) He estimates that he would walk at 5 km/h along the original route, but only 4 km/h along the
     short cut as it will not be on footpaths. How much time will he save by taking the short cut?

....

....

                                    Answer (c) _____ *minutes*

                                                                    (4 marks)

In the diagram below, shape 'B' is a transformation of shape 'A'.

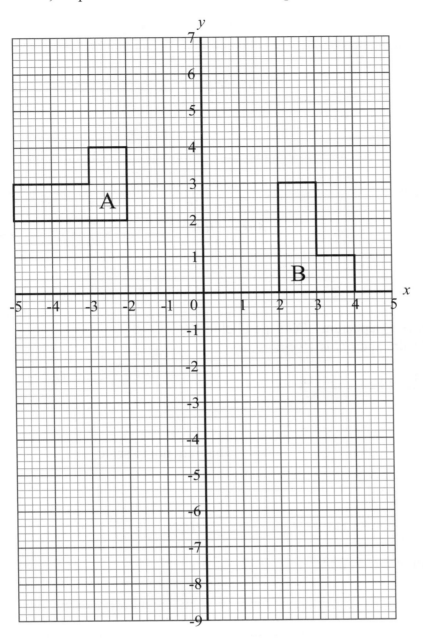

(a) Describe fully the transformation that maps shape 'A' onto shape 'B'.

....

....

....

(3 marks)

(b) Enlarge shape 'B' by a scale factor of -2 from the centre (2, -1).

Label the enlargement 'C'

(2 marks)

8   Fully factorise the following expressions:
(a) $4e - 6ef$

....

Answer (a) _____
(1 mark)

(b) $g^2 - 16$

....

....

Answer (b) _____
(2 marks)

9   The diagram below shows a trapezium. *FG* is parallel to *EH*.
EH is 15.5 cm, *EF* is 4.8 cm and *FG* is 10 cm

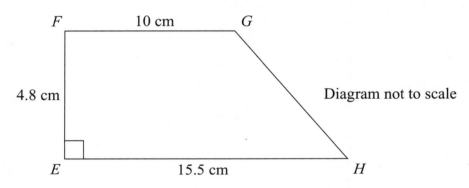

Diagram not to scale

(a) Calculate the length of *GH*.

....

....

....

Answer (a) _____ *cm*
(3 marks)

(b) Calculate the size of angle *EHG*. Give your answer correct to 1 decimal place.

....

....

....

Answer (b) _____ °
(3 marks)

0 The diagram below shows a triangle RST in which RS is 8.5 cm long and ST is 10 cm long. The triangle has an area of 35 cm^2.

Leave blank

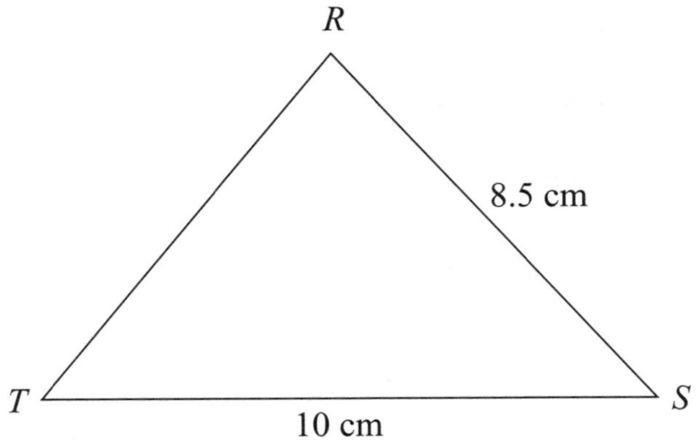

(a) Calculate the size of angle RST. Give your answer correct to 1 decimal place.

....

....

....

Answer (a) ______________________ °

(3 marks)

(b) Calculate the length RT. Give your answer correct to 3 significant figures.

....

....

....

Answer (b) ______________________ *cm*

(3 marks)

11   Solve the equation $x^2 - 8x + 3 = 0$ using the quadratic formula.
     Leave your answer in surd form.

     ....

     ....

     ....

                                          Answer _____
                                                                              (3 marks)

12   A company is testing an air pressure gauge that is based on a gas-filled ball.
     Air pressure is inversely proportional to the cube of the diameter of the ball.
     When the air pressure, p, is 60 bars, the diameter of the ball, d, is 2 cm.

     Write down a formula connecting p and d.

     ....

     ....

     ....

                                          Answer _____
                                                                              (3 marks)

3   The height, *h* metres, of a stone thrown by a catapult is related to its horizontal distance from the catapult, *d* metres, as described by the equation $h = 2d - 0.02d^2$.

(a)   Complete this table for the graph of $h = 2d - 0.02d^2$.

d	0	20	40	50	60	80	100
h	0	32	48		48	32	0

(1 mark)

(b)   Draw the graph of $h = 2d - 0.02d^2$.

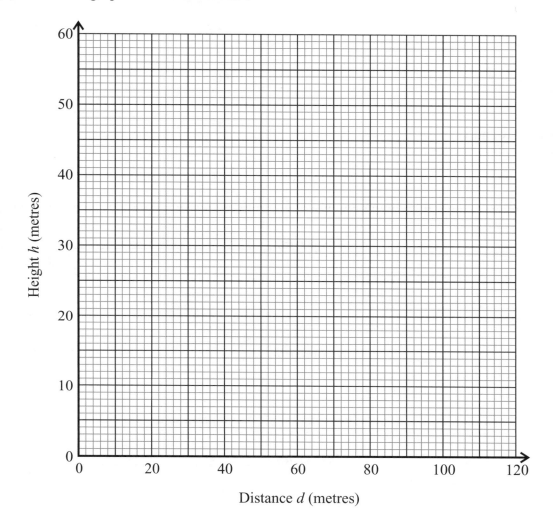

Distance *d* (metres)

(2 marks)

(c)   The catapult throws a stone up a hill with a gradient of 1 in 10. By drawing an appropriate line on the graph, find the horizontal distance travelled by the stone.

Answer (c) _____ *m*

(3 marks)

12

216

14 ABCD is a parallelogram. PQRS are the mid-points of the sides. $\overrightarrow{SP} = \mathbf{y}$ and $\overrightarrow{SD} = \mathbf{x}$.
Triangles PSD and ACD are similar.

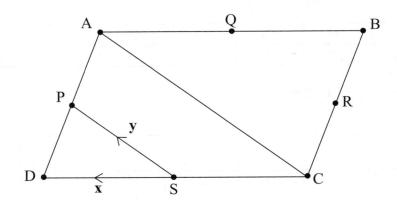

Find in terms of **x** and **y**:

(a) $\overrightarrow{DC}$

....

Answer (a) _____

(1 mark)

(b) $\overrightarrow{CA}$

....

Answer (b) _____

(1 mark)

(c) $\overrightarrow{QB}$

....

Answer (c) _____

(2 marks)

(d) $\overrightarrow{DB}$

....

Answer (d) _____

(2 marks)

5   In the diagram below, O is the centre of the circle. The angle *a* is 36°.

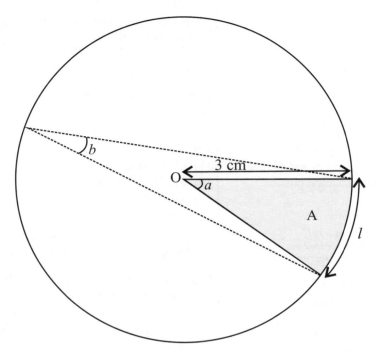

(a)   What is the size of angle *b*?

....

Answer (a) b = _____ °

(1 mark)

(b)   Calculate the area of the minor sector A. Leave your answer in terms of π.

....

....

....

Answer (b) _____ *cm²*

(3 marks)

(c)   Calculate the length of the minor arc, *l*, in terms of π. Give your answer in its lowest terms.

....

....

Answer (c) _____ *cm*

(3 marks)

Page 9 (Warm-up Questions)

1) (a) 40.22   (b) 39.9   (c) 28
2) 2.5×10^5 miles
3) 2.7×10^{-6} seconds
4) 0.0000000000000000000000027 g
5) 1.2×10^8

Page 10 (Exam Questions)

3) Maximum dimensions of the room are 4.15 m × 3.65 m.
   So maximum area of the room is 15.1475 m².
   Ethan must buy at least 16 m² of carpet. *[2 marks]*
4) The upper bounds of a and b are 8.5 and 5.5, and the lower
   bounds are 7.5 and 4.5. We want the smallest possible
   answer in each case, so:
   (a) $a + b = 7.5 + 4.5 = 12$. *[2 marks]*
   (b) $a \div b = 7.5 \div 5.5 = 1.363636...$ *[2 marks]*
   Note that in (b) the smallest value is NOT given by the lower bounds.
   It depends on the operation you're carrying out. So the lowest value of a ÷ b is given
   by a small value for a and a big one for b.
5) Upper bound = $60.5 \times 60.5 \times 60.5 = 221445.125$ mm³.
   Lower bound = $59.5 \times 59.5 \times 59.5 = 210644.875$ mm³.
   [3 marks]
6) (a) 1 cubic mm of blood = 5×10^6 red blood cells
       1 cubic cm of blood = $5 \times 10^6 \times 1000$
       1 litre of blood = $5 \times 10^6 \times 1000 \times 1000$
       6 litres of blood = $5 \times 10^6 \times 1000 \times 1000 \times 6$
       = 3×10^{13} red blood cells *[2 marks]*
   (b) $3 \times 10^{13} \div 120$
       = 2.5×10^{11} *[2 marks]*
7) $1.7 \times 10^{10} + 3.71 \times 10^{11}$ m²
   = 3.88×10^{11} m² *[2 marks]*

Page 16 (Warm-up Questions)

1) £13.50 *(0.15 × 90 = 13.5)*
2) 74% *(double both numbers to make it out of 100, which is a
   percentage, or do 37 ÷ 50 × 100 on your calculator.)*
3) £3376.53
4) (a) 1:2   (b) 2:9   (c) 5:4
5) 450 g of flour *(300 g ÷ 2 = 150 g; 150 g × 3 = 450 g)*

Page 17 (Exam Questions)

4) 35% of £2200 = 0.35 × £2200 = £770.
   So Alexander takes home £2200 − £770 = £1430. *[2 marks]*
5) The amount of money she lost was £95 − £57 = £38.
   As a percentage of what she paid: 38 ÷ 95 × 100 = 40%.
   [2 marks]
6) £329 is 100% + 17.5% = 117.5% of the price before VAT.
   So 1% of the price before VAT = $\frac{329}{117.5}$ = £2.80
   Price before VAT = £2.80 × 100 = £280 *[3 marks]*
7) Final amount = £5000 × (1 + 4 ÷ 100)⁴ = £5000 × 1.04⁴
   = £5849.29. So the amount of interest earned is:
   £5849.29 − £5000 = £849.29. *[3 marks]*
8) 12 500 × 0.92⁵ = £8238.52. *[3 marks]*
   These questions are very standard —
   if you're at all confused, look back to page 13.
9) Investment value is 6000 × 1.038ⁿ, where n is number of
   years. Just try different values of n until you find the lowest
   value for which investment is greater than £7000.
   Answer: $n = 5$. *[3 marks]*

10) Need 1.5 times as much, so 600 g of flour and 3 eggs.
    [1 mark]
11) Work out the price per carton for each multi-pack:
    Multi-pack of 4: £6.88 ÷ 4 = £1.72 per carton
    Multi-pack of 6: £9.90 ÷ 6 = £1.65 per carton
    So, the multi-pack of 6 is better value. *[3 marks]*

Page 18 (Revision Summary for Unit 1 — 1)

4) £17.33
9) (a) 9.7×10^5 (b) 6.83×10^6 (c) 3.56×10^9
10) 0.00000275
15) £3710 *(£5300 × 0.70)*
16) £58.75 *(£50 × 1.175)*
17) No — the top would cost £36
18) £140.26
19) £1.41 *(Divide by 5 and multiply by 3.)*
20) 250 g for 52p *(Divide by the price in pence and compare.)*

Page 22 (Warm-up and Exam Questions)

1) Stratified sampling.
2) The population is all residential addresses in Birmingham.
   The sample is made up of 600 residential addresses in
   Birmingham. We are not told how the sample is chosen.
   The results obtained are likely to be biased as the interview
   timing will exclude households where the occupants are at
   work during normal working hours.
1) No. in sample for each group = no. of people in age group
   ÷ total pop. (720) × sample size (80)
   0-5: 38 ÷ 720 × 80 = 4 (nearest whole number);
   6-12: 82 ÷ 720 × 80 = 9 (nearest whole number);
   13-21: 108 ÷ 720 × 80 = 12;
   22-35: 204 ÷ 720 × 80 = 23 (nearest whole number);
   36-50: 180 ÷ 720 × 80 = 20;
   51+: 108 ÷ 720 × 80 = 12.
   Total = 80. *[3 marks]*

Page 30 (Warm-up Questions)

1) Mode = most common.
   Median = middle value.
   Mean = total of items ÷ number of items.
   Range = how far from the biggest to the smallest.
2)

Number of cars	Frequency	No. of cars × F
0	1	0
1	24	24
2	36	72
3	31	93
4	22	88
5	9	45
6	1	6
	= 124	= 328

(a) Mean = 328 ÷ 124 = 2.645
(b) Median = 124 ÷ 2 = 62ⁿᵈ value = 3
(c) Mode = 2
(d) Range = 6 − 0 = 6
(e) Probability = 36 ÷ 124 = 0.29 (to 2 d.p.)

Height (cm)	Frequency	Midpoint	Midpoint × F
$145 \leq x < 155$	18	150	2700
$155 \leq x < 165$	22	160	3520
$165 \leq x < 175$	24	170	4080
$175 \leq x < 185$	15	180	2700

= 79   = 13 000

(a) Mean = 13 000 ÷ 79 = 164.56 cm.

(b) Median = 40th value,
which is in the group 155 cm $\leq x <$ 165 cm.

(c) Modal Group = 165 cm $\leq x <$ 175 cm.

age 31 (Exam Questions)

(a)

Time (t mins)	Frequency	Mid-point	Midpoint × F
$0 < t \leq 1$	77	0.5	38.5
$1 < t \leq 2$	142	1.5	213
$2 < t \leq 3$	143	2.5	357.5
$3 < t \leq 4$	60	3.5	210
$4 < t \leq 5$	49	4.5	220.5
$5 < t \leq 6$	29	5.5	159.5

= 500   = 1199

Mean = 1199 ÷ 500 = 2.398 minutes.

[4 marks]

(b)

Time (≤ mins)	Cumulative Frequency
1	77
2	219
3	362
4	422
5	471
6	500

[3 marks]

(c)

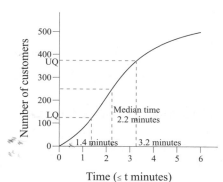

[4 marks]

(d) (i) 2.2 minutes (see graph). *[1 mark]*
(ii) IQ range = UQ – LQ = 3.2 mins – 1.4 mins
= 1.8 mins *[2 marks]*

Page 37 (Warm-up Questions)

1)

```
0 | 2 4 9
1 | 2 2 7 9
2 | 3 5 9
3 | 1 9          1 | 7 represents 17
```

2) Graph 1 — Moderate positive correlation.
Graph 2 — Weak negative correlation.

3)

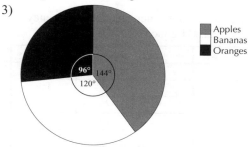

Apples
Bananas
Oranges

Your pie chart should have a radius of 3 cm.
(Angles: Apples: 12/30 × 360 =144°
Bananas: 10/30 × 360 = 120°
Oranges: 8/30 × 360 = 96°)

Pages 39-40 (Exam Questions)

3) (a)

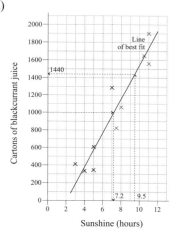

[1 mark]

(b) As the number of hours of sunshine increases, so does
the number of cartons sold. This shows a positive
correlation between the two quantities.
[1 mark]

(c) See graph above. Any suitable line of best fit similar to
the one shown would receive one mark. *[1 mark]*

(d) (i) Dependent on the line of best fit, answer in range of
7 to 7½ hours. *[1 mark]*
(ii) Dependent on the line of best fit, answer in range of
1400 to 1500. *[1 mark]*

4) (a) Work out the products of the midpoint of each category and its frequency. Then add them all up to get an estimate of the total length of all the songs:
$(125 \times 1) + (165 \times 9) + (190 \times 15) + (210 \times 17) + (235 \times 12) + (280 \times 6) = 12\,530$.
Now divide this by the total number of songs, which is 60: $12\,530 \div 60 = 208.833...$
$= 208.8$ seconds (1 d.p.). *[2 marks]*

This is the same as producing the third and fourth columns in a grouped frequency table (see page 27).

(b) Work out the class widths. Then calculate frequency density for each class (frequency ÷ class width).

Song length in seconds (x)	No. of songs	Class width	Freq. Density
$100 \le x < 150$	1	50	0.02
$150 \le x < 180$	9	30	0.3
$180 \le x < 200$	15	20	0.75
$200 \le x < 220$	17	20	0.85
$220 \le x < 250$	12	30	0.4
$250 \le x < 310$	6	60	0.1

Finally, plot the frequency density histogram.

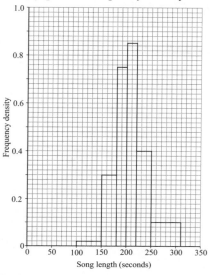

[2 marks]

5) (a) Total number of cyclists = $15 + 3 + 2 = 20$
Percentage taking Medium route = $3 \div 20 \times 100\% = 15\%$
[1 mark]

(b) Long bar: $12 \div 30 \times 100 = 40\%$
Medium bar: $15 \div 30 \times 100 = 50\%$
Short bar: $3 \div 30 \times 100 = 10\%$

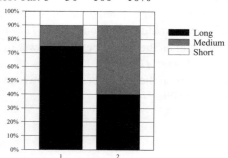

[2 marks]

(c) The same proportion (10%) chose the Short Route in both weeks or fewest people chose the Short Route each week. *[1 mark]*

Page 46 (Warm-up Questions)

1) 1/216 or 0.0046. *(1/6 × 1/6 × 1/6)*
2) 16/49 or 0.33. *(4/7 × 4/7)*
3) 1/8 or 0.125. *(1/2 × 1/2 × 1/2)*
4) 6/7 or 0.86. *(prob at least one of each colour*
= 1 – prob all blue – prob all red
= 1 – (3/7 × 2/6 × 1/5) – (4/7 × 3/6 × 2/5) = 6/7.)

In a question like this, there are lots of ways of getting at least one of each colour, but there are only two ways that it can't happen, i.e. if all balls are red, or all blue. So work out those probabilities and subtract them from 1.

Page 47 (Exam Questions)

2) P (grey, grey) + P (black, black) + P (red, red)
$$= \left(\frac{12}{24} \times \frac{11}{23}\right) + \left(\frac{8}{24} \times \frac{7}{23}\right) + \left(\frac{4}{24} \times \frac{3}{23}\right)$$
$$= \frac{132}{552} + \frac{56}{552} + \frac{12}{552} = \frac{200}{552} = \frac{25}{69}$$
OR 0.3623. *[5 marks]*

3) (a)

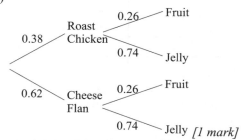

[1 mark]

(b) $0.38 \times 0.74 = 0.2812$. *[2 marks]*

4)

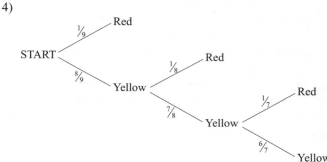

$$\left(\frac{1}{9}\right) + \left(\frac{8}{9} \times \frac{1}{8}\right) + \left(\frac{8}{9} \times \frac{7}{8} \times \frac{1}{7}\right) = \frac{1}{3}. \quad \textit{[3 marks]}$$

You should begin to see that all these questions boil down to drawing a tree diagram and then multiplying down the branches.

Page 48 (Revision Summary for Unit 1 — 2)

3) (a) Mode and mean.
(b) Mode = size 6, Mean = 20 pairs
((21 + 35 + 7 + 16) ÷ 4)
5) $1 < m \le 5$.
6) 161 min
9) (a) 170 cm   (b) 10%
14)(a) Both things increase or decrease together and they're closely related.
(b) No
16) Yes *(chance = 1/6 × 1/6 = 1/36)*

Page 53 (Warm-up Questions)

(a) 1, 4, 9   (b) 1, 8
(c) 2, 4, 8   (d) 2, 3, 5, 7
(a) 36   (b) There aren't any
(c) 32   (d) 31, 37
(a) 4^3 (b) 6^3 (c) 3^8
(a) 2   (b) $1\frac{32}{49}$ (c) 9
$\sqrt{30}$
$\sqrt{36} = 6$

Page 54 (Exam Questions)

These are the square numbers, so the 15th number is
$15 \times 15 = 225$. *[1 mark]*
(a) $\sqrt{16} = 4$ (rational) *[1 mark]*
(b) $\sqrt{2.5}$ (irrational) *[1 mark]*
(a) p^7 *[1 mark]*
(b) $2t^3$ *[1 mark]*
(c) $36a^6d^4$ *[1 mark]*
(d) $10a$ *[1 mark]*

$\dfrac{16}{\sqrt[5]{81}} = \dfrac{16}{\sqrt[5]{3^4}} = \dfrac{16}{3^{4/5}} = 16 \times 3^{-4/5} = 2^4 \times 3^{-4/5}$ *[3 marks]*

$\dfrac{2}{\sqrt{7}} = \dfrac{2\sqrt{7}}{\sqrt{7} \times \sqrt{7}} = \dfrac{2\sqrt{7}}{7}$ *[2 marks]*

Page 62 (Warm-up Questions)

$231 \div 3 = 77$, or $231 \div 7 = 33$, or $231 \div 11 = 21$.
So 231 has more than 2 factors.
1, 2, 4, 5, 8, 10, 20, 40
$2 \times 2 \times 2 \times 5$ (or $2^3 \times 5$)
40% *(one-fifth of 100% is 20%, so two-fifths is 40%)*
66.66666…%
(a) $\dfrac{4}{10}$ or $\dfrac{2}{5}$ (b) $\dfrac{4}{9}$ (c) $\dfrac{5}{11}$
(a) 0.7
(b) 0.7777777…
(a) $\dfrac{4}{15}$ (b) $\dfrac{2}{5} \times \dfrac{3}{2} = \dfrac{6}{10} = \dfrac{3}{5}$
(c) $\dfrac{6}{15} + \dfrac{10}{15} = \dfrac{16}{15} = 1\dfrac{1}{15}$ (d) $\dfrac{10}{15} - \dfrac{6}{15} = \dfrac{4}{15}$
45, 60, 75 *(3 + 4 + 5 = 12 parts, so 180 ÷ 12 = 15 per part.)*

Page 63 (Exam Questions)

(a)

So $168 = 2 \times 2 \times 2 \times 3 \times 7$ *[1 mark]*

(b)
```
        210
      10    21
     / \   / \
    ②  ⑤ ③  ⑦
```
So $210 = 2 \times 3 \times 5 \times 7$.
The common factors are 2, 3 and 7.
So HCF of 168 and 210 $= 2 \times 3 \times 7 = 42$ *[2 marks]*

(a) $\dfrac{37}{7} - \dfrac{13}{5} = \dfrac{185}{35} - \dfrac{91}{35} = \dfrac{94}{35} = 2\dfrac{24}{35}$ *[2 marks]*

(b) $\dfrac{8}{3} \times \dfrac{15}{4} = \dfrac{120}{12} = \dfrac{10}{1} = 10$ *[2 marks]*

---

4) Fraction she didn't spend $= \dfrac{1}{10} + \dfrac{1}{3} = \dfrac{3}{30} + \dfrac{10}{30} = \dfrac{13}{30}$
So fraction to spend $= 1 - \dfrac{13}{30} = \dfrac{17}{30}$
So amount to spend $= \dfrac{17}{30} \times 60 = £34$ *[3 marks]*

5) $\dfrac{27}{99} = \dfrac{3}{11}$ *[2 marks]*

6) (a) Let A = Andersons, B = Brents, C = Campbells.
A : B : C = 1.5 : 3 : 1 = 3 : 6 : 2 *[2 marks]*
(b) Total number of parts = 3 + 6 + 2 = 11
£187 ÷ 11 = £17
So Andersons owe 3 × £17 = £51
Brents owe 6 × £17 = £102
Campbells owe 2 × £17 = £34 *[3 marks]*

Page 71 (Warm-up Questions)

1) (a) 2   (b) 2   (c) 6   (d) 2
   (e) 3   (f) $\dfrac{1}{3}$ (g) -8   (h) -2
2) (a) $2a - 5c$ (b) $7r^2 - 5r - 1$
3) (a) $8p + 28$ (b) $8x^2 - 2$ (c) $5a^2 - 3a$
4) (a) $2(3p - 6q + 2)$ (b) $2cd(2d - 1 + 5cd^2)$
5) $(x + 2y)(x - 2y)$
6) (a) $\dfrac{11x}{10}$
   (b) $\dfrac{ac^2}{b}$ *(turn 2nd fraction upside down and multiply)*
7) (a) $x = 3$ (b) $x = -3$ (c) $x = 5$
8) (a) p (b) t

Pages 73-74 (Exam Questions)

5) (a) Collect like terms together:
$(3x^2y + x^2y) + (-2xy^2 - 4y^2x)$;
$4x^2y - 6xy^2$ *[2 marks]*
(b) Collect together the r terms and k terms:
$(4k - 3k - 2k) + (8r - 2r)$;
$6r - k$ *[2 marks]*
6) (a) $8x - 12 - 12 - 9x$;   (b) $6c^2 - 2c + 18c - 6$;
$-x - 24$ $6c^2 + 16c - 6$
[2 marks]   *[2 marks]*
7) (a) $\dfrac{8 + 6x}{3x}$ *[1 mark]*
(b) $\dfrac{x^2y}{z} + \dfrac{xy^3}{3z} = \dfrac{3x^2y + xy^3}{3z} = \dfrac{xy(3x + y^2)}{3z}$ *[2 marks]*
8) (a) $6cd^2 (2cd + 3 - 5c^2d^2) = 6cd^2 (1 - cd)(3 + 5cd)$
[2 marks]
(b) (i) $8b^3cd$ *[2 marks]*
(ii) $2t - t^2$ *[2 marks]*
9) (a) This one is tricky — there are no factors common to all
the terms. But two terms have $2c$ in and the other two
have y in them, so try taking these out:
$2cx + xy + 2ac + ay = 2c(x + a) + y(x + a)$
Now both of these terms have $(x + a)$, so you can take
that out as a common factor to get $(x + a)(2c + y)$.
[3 marks]
On this one, it's easy to get stuck and give up at the start, but if you just play with it a bit, the answer will suddenly pop out of nowhere…
(b) You've got a squared term minus another squared term,
so use the "difference of 2 squares":
$(4x - 2p)(4x + 2p)$. *[2 marks]*
Look back to page 67 if you've forgotten what the difference of 2 squares is all about.

10)(a) $7x - 3x = 7 + 3$;
$4x = 10$;
$x = 2.5$ *[2 marks]*

(b) First of all, multiply by 20 to get rid of the numbers on the bottom.
$4(3x - 1) = 5x + 10$;
$12x - 4 = 5x + 10$;
$7x = 14$;
$x = 2$ *[3 marks]*

11)(a) $x^2 - 6x + 9$ *[2 marks]*

(b) $(x^2 - 6x + 9) - x^2 + 4x$;
$-2x + 9$ *[2 marks]*

(c) Use your answer to part b) to get:
$-2x + 9 = 7x + 18$;
$-9x = 9$;
$x = -1$ *[2 marks]*

12)(a) The cost of buying, copying and posting n CDs is:
c = cost of n blank CDs + admin charge for n CDs + postage for n CDs.
E.g. $c = 0.33n + 0.05n + (p/100)n$
$c = 0.38n + \dfrac{pn}{100} = n\left(0.38 + \dfrac{p}{100}\right)$ *[2 marks]*

(b) Just put $n = 150$ and $p = 32$ into the formula:
$c = 150(0.38 + (32 / 100)) = 150 \times (0.38 + 0.32)$
$= 150 \times 0.7 = £105$ *[2 marks]*

It's easy to get confused between pounds and pence on this one — in the formula you need to divide p by 100 because c is in pounds.
In part b), you put in p = 32, not p = 0.32 because p is in pence.
Just think carefully about what you're doing and you should be alright...

Page 75 (Revision Summary for Unit 2 — 1)

4) (a) Approximately 2^9 (b) Approximately 2^{12}

14) 240 *(150 × 8 ÷ 5)*

16) Jill £18, Heather £15 and Susie £9 *(3 + 2.5 + 1.5 = 7 parts, so one part = £42 ÷ 7 = £6)*

Page 79 (Warm-up Questions)

1) Answer is (b) *((x + 6) (x − 2) = x² + 4x − 12)*

2) Answer is (b) *((3x + 1) (x − 2) = 3x² − 5x − 2)*

3) (a) $(x + 4)(x + 7)$.
(b) $(x + 14)(x + 2)$.
(c) $(x + 14)(x - 2)$.

4) (a) $x = -3$ or $x = -5$ *(it factorises to (x + 3) (x + 5) = 0)*
(b) $x = 2$ or $x = -7$ *(it factorises to (x − 2) (x + 7) = 0)*
(c) $x = 3$ or $x = 4$
(Rearrange to give x² − 7x + 12 = 0, then factorise to give (x − 3) (x − 4) = 0, so x = 3 or x = 4.)

5) $(x + 4)^2 + 4$ *((x + 4)² gives x² + 8x + 16, so complete the square by adding 4.)*

6) $x = 9$ or $x = 1$ *((x − 5)² gives x² − 10x + 25 so complete the square by subtracting 16;*
(x − 5)² − 16 = 0
(x − 5)² = 16
(x − 5) = √16
(x − 5) = 4 or (x − 5) = −4
x = 9 or x = 1.)

Pages 80 (Exam Questions)

3) (a) $(x + 4)(x - 5)$. *[1 mark]*
(b) $(3x - 4)(2x + 3)$. *[2 marks]*
This one's a tricky one — there's lots of different possible combinations of number — just keep trying and you'll get there sooner or later.

4) Factorise to give $(2x + 2)(x - 4) = 0$,
so $x = -1$ or $x = 4$. *[3 marks]*

5) Rearrange to give $x^2 - 7x + 12 = 0$, then factorise to give
$(x - 3)(x - 4) = 0$. So $x = 3$ or $x = 4$. *[3 marks]*

6) Rearrange to give $x^2 + 9x + 18 = 0$, then factorise to give
$(x + 3)(x + 6) = 0$. So $x = -3$ or $x = -6$. *[3 marks]*

7) $(x + 5)^2$ gives $x^2 + 10x + 25$, so complete the square by
subtracting 15; so the answer is $(x + 5)^2 - 15$. *[2 marks]*

8) $(x - 3)^2$ gives $x^2 - 6x + 9$, so complete the square by
subtracting 49.
So $(x - 3)^2 - 49 = 0$
$(x - 3)^2 = 49$
$(x - 3) = \sqrt{49}$
$x - 3 = 7$ or $x - 3 = -7$
$x = 10$ or $x = -4$ *[3 marks]*

Page 84 (Warm-up Questions)

1) $x = 2, y = 5$
(Subtract the equations to give 2y = 10, therefore y = 5.
Substitute the y = 5 into the second equation to give
2x + 5 = 9, therefore x = 2.)

2) $x = 4, y = 4$
(Add the equations to give 4x = 16, therefore x = 4.
Substitute x = 4 into the first equation to give 12 + 2y = 20
giving y = 4.)

3) (a) 8, 13, 18, 23, 28, 33
(b) 8, 11, 14, 17, 20, 23

4) (a) $5n$ (b) $3n + 4$

5) There is always one cross in the centre, and the number of other crosses is 4 times the pattern number (because there are 4 "arms" coming from the centre). So in the nth pattern there will be a total of $4n + 1$ crosses.
This method is a kind of 'common sense method'. You can get the same result by finding 'a' and 'd' and then using dn + (a − d).

Page 85 (Exam Questions)

2) $5x + 4y = 75$ — (1) $2x + 4y = 54$ — (2).
Subtract to give $3x = 21$, therefore $x = 7$.
Substitute $x = 7$ into first equation to give $35 + 4y = 75$,
so $4y = 40$, therefore $y = 10$.
Answer: $x = 7$ and $y = 10$. *[3 marks]*

3) $3x - 2y = 7$ — (1) $4x - 4y = 8$ — (2).
Double the first equation to give: $6x - 4y = 14$ — (3).
Subtract equation (2) from equation (3) to give $2x = 6$,
therefore $x = 3$.
Substitute $x = 3$ into the first equation to give $9 - 2y = 7$,
therefore $y = 1$.
Answer: $x = 3$ and $y = 1$. *[3 marks]*

$x = 4y + 3$ — (1) $3x^2 = y + 1$ — (2)

The second equation is a quadratic — you need to rearrange this to get y on its own, then substitute that into the first equation:

Rearranging (2) gives: $y = 3x^2 - 1$ — (3)

Now substitute equation (3) into equation (1):

$x = 4(3x^2 - 1) + 3$

$x = 12x^2 - 4 + 3$

$12x^2 - x - 1 = 0$

Factorise to solve for x:

$(4x + 1)(3x - 1) = 0$

So $x = -1/4$ or $x = 1/3$.

Now substitute these into equation (1) to find values for y:

$x = -1/4$ in (1): $-1/4 = 4y + 3$; $4y = -13/4$; $y = -13/16$.

$x = 1/3$ in (1): $1/3 = 4y + 3$; $4y = -8/3$; $y = -2/3$.

So the answers are: $x = -1/4$ and $y = -13/16$

OR $x = 1/3$ and $y = -2/3$. *[5 marks]*

These simultaneous equation questions involving quadratics might seem quite tricky, but it's just a set method, so once you've learnt it it's not hard at all. (Remember — if there's a quadratic in it, you're going to get 2 sets of values.)

(a)

[1 mark]

(b) The missing numbers from the table are:
10, 13, 16. *[1 mark]*

(c) $3 \times 20 + 1 = 61$ *[1 mark]*

(d) $3 \times n + 1 = 3n + 1$ *[2 marks]*

(a) x x x x x
   x x x x x
   x x x x x
   x x x x x
   x x x x x
   ● ● ● ● ● *[1 mark]*

(b) n dots. *[1 mark]*

(c) n^2 crosses. *[1 mark]*

Page 94 (Warm-up Questions)

(a) $y = x$.   (b) Horizontal line, $y = 4$.

(c) Vertical line, $x = -1$.   (d) $y = -x$.

Positive: C, E. Negative: A, D. Gradient of zero: B.

(a)

x	0	2	3
y	-4	2	5

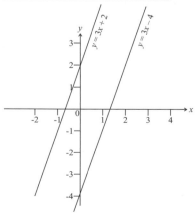

(b) See diagram above.

$y = 3x + 2$ will be parallel to $y = 3x - 4$ and will pass through the point (0, 2) on the y axis.

Page 95 (Exam Questions)

2) (a) A and D. *[1 mark]*
Have to find two lines with the same gradient, or in other words two with the same coefficient of x. This is not immediately obvious but by dividing D by two on both sides we see A & D both have the form y = 3x + c, and thus both have a gradient of three. Therefore A and D are parallel.

(b) B and E. *[1 mark]*
Because they both have negative coef. of x in the format y = mx + c. NB. for E you need to move the x to the other side to get it in this form.

(c) A and E. *[1 mark]*
Put in x = 4 and see which give a y value of 10 :
A: y = 3x – 2, when x = 4, y = (3 × 4) – 2 = 10, so A has point (4, 10).
E: y = 14 – x, when x = 4, y = 14 – 4 = 10, so E has point (4, 10).

3)

x	-3	-1	1	3
y	-10	-5	0	5

[1 mark]

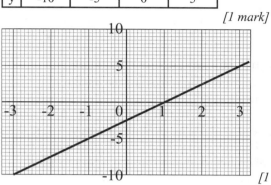

[1 mark]

4) (a) 4 km *[1 mark]*

(b) The points where the graph is horizontal are where Dominic has stopped.
So the answers are D and F. *[2 marks]*

(c) The fastest leg of his journey was stage E (the slope is greatest here).
The speed on a distance-time graph is the gradient, so work out the gradient at this point.
Gradient = change in y / change in x
Read the values off the graph:
the change in y is $17 - 9 = 8$ km
the change in x is 30 minutes = 0.5 hours.
So the gradient is $8 / 0.5 = 16$ km/h.
So his speed is 16 km/h. *[3 marks]*

(d) To work out his average speed for the total journey, draw a straight line on the graph from his start point to finish point and work out the slope of this line, like above:
the change in y is 24 km,
the change in x is 9:40 am to 1:40 pm = 4 hours.
So the gradient is $24 / 4 = 6$ km/h.
[3 marks]

Page 99 (Warm-up Questions)

1) $x = 13, 14, 15, 16$.

2) $n = -3, -2, -1, 0, 1, 2, 3$.

3) Dividing by 4 gives $2 < x < 5$,
but x must be an integer so $x = 3, 4$.

4) $2q + 2 \le 12 \Rightarrow 2q \le 10 \Rightarrow q \le 5$.

5) $4p + 12 > 30 \Rightarrow 4p > 18 \Rightarrow p > 4\frac{1}{2}$.

6)

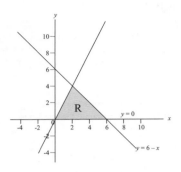

Page 100 (Exam Questions)

4) $x = -3, -2, -1, 0, 1, 2$. *[2 marks]*

5)

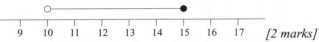

| | | | | | | | | |
| 9 | 10 | 11 | 12 | 13 | 14 | 15 | 16 | 17 |

[2 marks]

Remember — a filled-in circle means "includes the value", an empty one means it doesn't...

6) $5a - 10 > 50$; $5a > 60$; $a > 12$. *[2 marks]*

7) Subtract 3 from both sides and the middle, then divide by 4:
$13 < 4t + 3 < 27$; $10 < 4t < 24$; $2.5 < t < 6$. *[3 marks]*

8) You need to divide by -3, which means you need to flip the inequality sign around (dividing or multiplying by a negative number always flips the inequality sign):
$-3x > 12$; $x < -4$. *[2 marks]*

9)

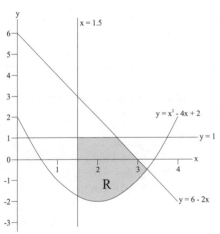

[4 marks]

Page 101 (Revision Summary for Unit 2 — 2)

6) (a) $3.00 = 5x + 3y$, $4.00 = 10x + 2y$
   (b) £4.50

11) (a) A straight line.
    (b) E.g.

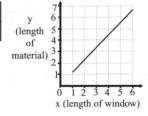

Page 105 (Warm-up Questions)

1) (a)

x	-2	-1	0	1	2	3	4	5
x^2	4	1	0	1	4	9	16	25
$-2x$	4	2	0	-2	-4	-6	-8	-10
-1	-1	-1	-1	-1	-1	-1	-1	-1
$y = x^2 - 2x - 1$	7	2	-1	-2	-1	2	7	14

(b)

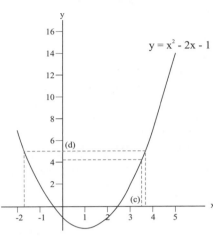

(c) See graph. 4.25 (a value between 4.2 and 4.3 is acceptable).

(d) See graph. $x = -1.65$ and 3.65 (values between -1.6 and -1.7 and between 3.6 and 3.7 are acceptable).

2)

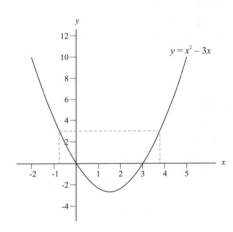

(a) $x = 0$ and 3.
(b) $x = -0.8$ and 3.8.

Pages 106 (Exam Questions)

2) (a) C *[1 mark]*
   (b) B *[1 mark]*
   (c) D *[1 mark]*
   (d) A *[1 mark]*

(a)

t	0	1	2	3	4	5	6
$h = 4.2t - 0.7t^2$	0	3.5	5.6	6.3	5.6	3.5	0

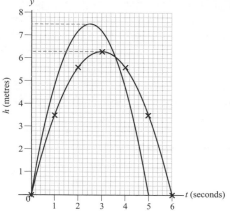

[4 marks]

(b) Nick (Nick's graph has a higher max pt). *[1 mark]*

(c) Read off the max values from the graph:
7.5 – 6.3 = 1.2 m. *[2 marks]*

(d) Just read down from the point where the graphs intersect:
Answer: 3.6 s (values between 3.5 - 3.7 s are acceptable).
[1 mark]

Once you've drawn the graph (and made sure you've done it accurately), all you need to do is read off the points, like the maximum height, and the point where they cross, showing they are at the same height.

ge 113 (Warm-up Questions)

(a) $x = 6, y = 6$.   (b) $x = 2, y = 4$.   (c) $x = 3.1, y = 1.7$.
Just read off the points where the lines cross... erm, that's it.

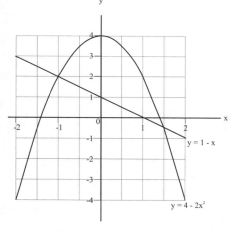

$x = -1$ and 1.5.
(The solution is just where the two graphs cross.)
$y = 5 - x$.
(This is like the reverse process of question 2. You need to think which equation you can combine with the one given to get to the one you want.
$y = 5 - x$ *meets* $y = x^2 - 3x + 2$ *when* $5 - x = x^2 - 3x + 2$,
i.e. $x^2 - 2x - 3 = 0$ *as required.)*

(a) $x = 0.39$ or -10.39

(b) $x = 1.46$ or -0.46

(c) $x = 0.44$ or -3.44

$x = 2.5$ *(2.4 is too small, 2.5 is too big. So try 2.45 — as that is too small, $x = 2.5$ to 1 d.p.)*

(a) $A = kr^2$.

(b) $D = k/R$.

(c) $H = k/D^3$.

(d) $V = kS^3$.

Pages 116-117 (Exam Questions)

5) (a) 5, 3, 2, 1.4. *[2 marks]*

(b)

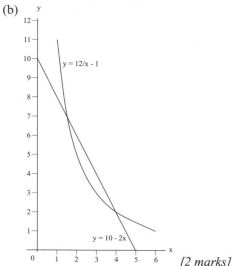

[2 marks]

(c) $x = 4$ and $x = 1.5$
(values between $x = 3.9$ to 4.1 and $x = 1.4$ to 1.6
are acceptable). *[2 marks]*

6) Plot each graph. You will have 2 crossing points, so two sets of answers.

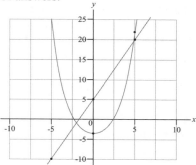

Approximate answers (cannot be exact because we are reading from a graph) are: $x = 4.8$ and $y = 19.5$ AND ALSO $x = -1.7$ and $y = -0.5$. *[3 marks]*

7) Substitute $a = 1, b = 8, c = -4$:

$$x = \frac{-8 \pm \sqrt{8^2 - (4 \times 1 \times -4)}}{2 \times 1} = \frac{-8 \pm \sqrt{64 + 16}}{2}$$

$$= \frac{-8 \pm \sqrt{80}}{2} = \frac{-8 \pm 8.94}{2}$$

so $x = \dfrac{-8 + 8.94}{2}$ or $x = \dfrac{-8 - 8.94}{2}$

so $x = 0.5$ or $x = -8.5$ (both to 1 d.p.) *[3 marks]*

8) Since there are no hints about completing the square or trial and improvement, you should use the formula
(the expression won't factorise, because the question asks for "2 decimal places").
Substitute $a = 2, b = 3, c = -4$:

$$x = \frac{-3 \pm \sqrt{3^2 - (4 \times 2 \times -4)}}{2 \times 2} = \frac{-3 \pm \sqrt{9 + 32}}{4}$$

$$= \frac{-3 \pm \sqrt{41}}{4} = \frac{-3 \pm 6.40}{4}$$

so $x = \dfrac{-3 + 6.40}{4}$ or $x = \dfrac{-3 - 6.40}{4}$

so $x = 0.85$ or $x = -2.35$ (both to 2 d.p.) *[3 marks]*

9) Rearrange to give $3x^2 - 5x - 12 = 0$.
Substitute $a = 3$, $b = -5$, $c = -12$:

$$x = \frac{-(-5) \pm \sqrt{(-5)^2 - (4 \times 3 \times -12)}}{2 \times 3}$$

$$= \frac{5 \pm \sqrt{25 + 144}}{6} = \frac{5 \pm \sqrt{169}}{6} = \frac{5 \pm 13}{6}$$

so $x = \dfrac{5 + 13}{6}$ or $x = \dfrac{5 - 13}{6}$

So $x = 3.00$ or $x = -1.33$ (both to 2 d.p.) *[3 marks]*

In this question, you need to give the first value of x to 2 decimal places ("3.00"), and not just "x = 3", because the question specifically asks for this level of accuracy. Always be careful to give your answer to the right number of decimal places, otherwise you'll lose marks needlessly.

10)

x	$x^3 - 3x^2$
4.5	30.375
4.3	24.037
4.4	27.104
4.45	28.713625
4.46	29.041736
4.455	28.87742137

You can see that x lies between 4.455 and 4.46. So to 2 decimal places, $x = 4.46$ (because x is definitely more than 4.455, it must round up to 4.46 not down to 4.45). *[4 marks]*

11)(a) Start with the equation $C = kd^3$, where k is a constant to be found.
Now substitute in $C = 270$, $d = 1.5$ to find k:
$270 = k \times 1.5^3$; $k = 80$.
So the equation is $C = 80d^3$. *[3 marks]*

(b) Just put $d = 1.8$ into the equation and find C:
$C = 80 \times 1.8^3 = 466.56$ litres. *[2 marks]*

(c) Put $C = 140$ into the equation and solve for d:
$140 = 80d^3$; $d^3 = 1.75$; $d = 1.21$ metres. *[2 marks]*

Don't forget the units in your answer, otherwise it's more easy marks down the drain...

12)(a) Start with the general equation:
$F = k/t^2$
Now put in $F = 40$, $t = 5$ to find k:
$40 = k / 5^2$; $k = 1000$.
So equation is $F = 1000/t^2$. *[3 marks]*

(b) (i) $F = 1000 / 200^2 = 0.025$. *[1 mark]*

(ii) $50 = 1000 / t^2$; $t^2 = 20$; $t = \pm 4.47$ (3 s.f.).
[2 marks]

Page 130 (Warm-up Questions)

1) 672 cm³ *(area of triangle × length = ½ × 12 × 8 × 14)*

2) (a)

side elevation   side elevation   (b) front elevation   (c)   plan view

3) (a) 1963.5 mm² *($\pi r^2 = 25^2 \times \pi$)*

(b) 37 146 mm² *(area of rectangle minus area of four circles)*

(c) 148 584 mm³ *(volume = area × thickness)*

Page 131 (Exam Questions)

2) (a) exterior angle = 360° ÷ number of sides
so for octagon, 360° ÷ 8 = 45° *[2 marks]*

(b) interior angle = 180° − 45° = 135° *[1 mark]*

3) (a) Area of metal = area of whole circle − area of segment.
Area of whole circle = $\pi r^2 = 15^2 \times \pi = 706.9$ mm²
Area of segment = $(\theta \div 360) \times$ area of circle
$= (70 \div 360) \times 706.9 = 137.5$ mm²
Area of metal = 706.9 − 137.5 = 569.4 mm². *[3 marks]*

(b) Perimeter of fastener = perimeter of circle
− perimeter of arc segment + edges of segment.
Perimeter of circle = $\pi \times$ diameter $= 30\pi = 94.2$ mm
Perimeter of arc segment = $(\theta \div 360) \times$ perim of circle
$= (70 \div 360) \times 94.2 = 18.3$ mm.
Perimeter of fastener = 94.2 − 18.3 + (2 × 15)
= 105.9 mm *[3 marks]*

4) (a) volume $= \dfrac{4}{3}\pi r^3 = [(4 \times 3^2)/3] \times \pi = 12\pi$ *[2 marks]*

(b) volume of cone $= \dfrac{1}{3}\pi r^2 h$
so $12\pi = \dfrac{1}{3}\pi r^2 h$
The πs cancel: $12 = \dfrac{1}{3}r^2 h$
so $r^2 = (12 \times 3) \div h$
Putting the numbers in: $r^2 = (12 \times 3) \div 4 = 9$
$r = 3$ cm *[3 marks]*

Page 138 (Warm-up Questions)

1) $a = 115°$, angles on a line add to 180°, so $a = 180 - 65$.
$b = 115°$, a and b are corresponding angles, so $a = b$.
$c = 65°$, c and 65° are also corresponding angles.
$d = 115°$, angles on a line add to 180°, so $d = 180 - c$.
There are often different ways of going about angle questions. Just keep scribbling down angles as you find them. It can make it easier to get the angle you want.

2) $M = N = 64°$
(Angles M and N are equal to the 64° angle given, using the theorem that angles in opposite segments are equal.)
$L = 52°$
(Angles in a triangle add to 180°, so 180 − 64 − 64 = 52°.)

Page 140 (Exam Questions)

3) (a) Angle OAT is 90°. OAB = 90 − 60 = 30°.
Triangle OBA is isosceles so X = 180 − 30 − 30 = 120°
[3 marks]

(b) Angle subtended at the centre is twice the angle subtended at the circumference. i.e. X = 2Y.
Y = X ÷ 2 = 120 ÷ 2 = 60°. *[2 marks]*

(c) Triangle BAT is isosceles by "equality of tangents" rule
Angle TAB = angle ABT = 60°.
Therefore, Z = 180 − 60 − 60 = 60°
(so in fact triangle BAT is equilateral.) *[2 marks]*

4) Angles on a straight line add up to 180°.
so angle CAB = 180° − α
and angle CBA = 180° − β
Angles in a triangle add to 180°.
180° = 110° + (180° − α) + (180° − β)
180° = 470° − α − β
α + β = 290° as required. *[3 marks]*

Page 148 (Warm-up Questions)

1) (a) a and e   (b) b and f

2) C→D, reflection in the y-axis, and an enlargement SF 2, centre the origin. D→C, reflection in the y-axis, and an enlargement SF ½, centre the origin.

3) $\begin{pmatrix} -3 \\ 3 \end{pmatrix}$

(a) $\dfrac{1}{4.5}$ or 0.222 or $\dfrac{2}{9}$

Note that the enlargement scale factor is less than one — so the 'enlargement' actually makes the shape smaller.

(b) 2.6 cm

64 m²

(a) 230 000 cm²

(b) 3.45 m²

(a) 5 200 000 cm³

(b) 0.1 m³

Pages 149-150 (Exam Questions)

$4.2 \div 2.5 = 1.68$. $9.24 \div 1.68 = 5.5$ cm *[2 marks]*

$12 \times 2.5 = 30$ cm

$8.5 \times 2.5 = 21.25$ cm

So dimensions are 30 cm × 21.25 cm *[2 marks]*

(a) + (b)

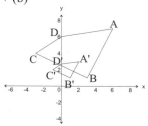

[1 mark] + [2 marks]

(c) B' is the point (1, 1) *[1 mark]*

(a) Reflection in the line y = 0 (the x-axis) *[2 marks]*

(b)

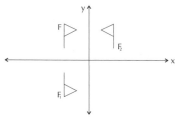

[1 mark]

(c) Rotation 180° centre (0, 0)

OR Enlargement SF -1 centre (0, 0) *[2 marks]*

$20 \times 6 \times 1.2 = 144$ m³.

$144 \times 1\,000\,000 = 144\,000\,000$ cm³ *[2 marks]*

Page 151 (Revision Summary for Unit 3 — 1)

1) £1008

2) 213.628 cm²

4) (a)   (b)   (c)

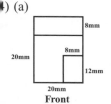 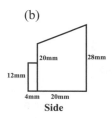 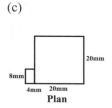

Front   Side   Plan

5) 125

6) 150 cm wide, 300 cm long, 250 cm high

Page 159 (Warm-up Questions)

(a) 13.1 cm *(by Pythagoras)*

(b) 40° *(tan x = 8.4 ÷ 10)*

AC = 9.6 cm *(by sin rule :* $\dfrac{AC}{\sin 52} = \dfrac{12}{\sin 80}$ *)*

104.5° *(by cos rule :* $\cos A = \dfrac{6^2 + 4^2 - 8^2}{2 \times 6 \times 4}$ *)*

Pages 160-161 (Exam Questions)

3) (a) BD² = 6.4² – 5.5² by Pythagoras.
   Therefore BD = √(6.4² – 5.5²) = 3.27 m. *[3 marks]*

   (b) AB = AD + DB = 8.7 + 3.27 = 11.97
   = 12.0 m to 3 s.f. *[1 mark]*

   (c) AC² = AB² + BC² = 12² + 5.5². AC = √174.25
   = 13.2 m. *[3 marks]*

4) (a) Call the height of the tower h.
   tan 52.1 = h ÷ 24.
   So h = 24 tan 52.1 = 30.8 m high. *[3 marks]*

   (b) Call the angle of elevation x.
   tan x = 30.8 ÷ 31.
   x = 44.8°. *[3 marks]*

5) (a) Call height x.
   Angle opposite x = 180 – (41 + 85) = 54°.
   Using the sine rule:
   $$\frac{x}{\sin 54} = \frac{3.1}{\sin 41} \text{ so } x = \frac{3.1}{\sin 41} \times \sin 54$$
   = 3.82 m. *[4 marks]*

   (b) area = ½ab sinC = ½ × 3.1 m × 3.82 m × sin 85
   = 5.90 m². *[3 marks]*

Page 165 (Warm-up and Exam Questions)

1) Choose from:
   similarities: they both have the same shape /
   same range (-1 and 1)
   differences: they cross the x-axis at different places /
   translating the sine graph by 90° horizontally gives the
   cosine graph.

2)

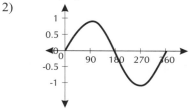

3) Both graphs have the same shape, but the second is shifted
   up the y-axis by 2 units.

1) (a) This is an x-shift to the right (in the positive x-direction)
   Minimum point: (6, 1) *[1 mark]*

   (b) This is an x-stretch — the graph is scrunched up along
   the x-axis. Minimum point: (1, 1) *[1 mark]*

   (c) This is a y-shift upwards. Minimum point: (4, 4)
   [1 mark]

Page 168 (Warm-up Questions)

1)   2)

                    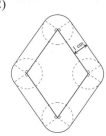

(Not to scale.)

3) Check your answer by measuring the sides with a ruler and
   the angles with a protractor.

228

4)

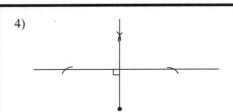

Page 169 (Exam Questions)

2)

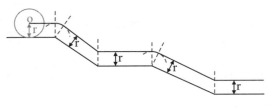

[3 marks]

3)

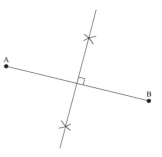

[3 marks]

4)

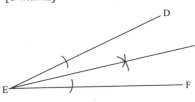

[3 marks]

Page 175 (Warm-up Questions)

1) $12.7 \times 1000 = 12\ 700$ g

2) $1430 \div 100 = 14.3$ m

3) 2.2 lbs $\approx$ 1 kg, so 10 lbs $\approx 10 \div 2.2 = 4\frac{1}{2}$ kg.

4) 11.3 g/cm³ *(density = mass ÷ volume)*

5) 96 g *(volume = 5 × 4 × 6 = 120 cm³.*
   Then use mass = density × volume.)

6) 90 km/h *(Speed in m/s = 100 ÷ 4 = 25 m/s. Multiply by 3600 to get m/h, then divide by 1000 to get km/h)*

7) 9 km *(distance = speed × time)*

8) $\dfrac{94 \times 1.9}{0.328 + 0.201} \approx \dfrac{90 \times 2}{0.3 + 0.2} = \dfrac{180}{0.5} = 360$

Page 176 (Exam Questions)

4) $295.25 \div 250 = 1.181$
   Exchange rate is £1 : €1.181 *[1 mark]*

5) 8 km is about 5 miles, so 24 km is about 3 × 5 = 15 miles.
   [1 mark]

6) 1 kg is about 2.2 lbs, so 5 lbs ÷ 2.2 is just over 2 kg.
   [1 mark]

7) There are approximately 4.5 litres per gallon,
   so 36.5 miles per gallon = 36.5 ÷ 4.5 ≈ 8 miles per litre
   So 120 miles will use about 120 ÷ 8 = 15 litres
   15 litres costs 15 × £1.12 = £16.80 ≈ £17 *[3 marks]*

8) Volume is 4 × 4 × 4 = 64 cm³
   Mass = Density × Volume = 13.55 × 64 = 867.2 g *[3 marks]*

9) $495 \div 4 = 123.75 = 120$ km/h (2 sig. fig.) *[2 marks]*

10) Takes 2 hours 40 mins = $2\frac{2}{3}$ hours.
    Average speed = Distance ÷ Time = $30 \div 2\frac{2}{3} = 11.25$ km/h
    [2 marks]

11) $\dfrac{29 \times 2.9}{9.1 - 6.9} \approx \dfrac{30 \times 3}{9 - 7} = \dfrac{90}{2} = 45$ *[2 marks]*

Page 180 (Warm-up Questions)

1) (a) $\vec{AB} = \begin{pmatrix} 7 \\ 2 \end{pmatrix}$ (b) $\vec{BC} = \begin{pmatrix} 6 \\ -3 \end{pmatrix}$ (c) $\vec{ED} = \begin{pmatrix} 8 \\ 0 \end{pmatrix}$

   (d) $\vec{CD} = \begin{pmatrix} -2 \\ -4 \end{pmatrix}$ (e) $\vec{AM} = \begin{pmatrix} 12 \\ -3 \end{pmatrix}$

2) (a) $\begin{pmatrix} 4 \\ 9 \end{pmatrix}$ (b) $\begin{pmatrix} -1 \\ 2 \end{pmatrix}$ (c) $\begin{pmatrix} 5 \\ 7 \end{pmatrix}$ (d) $\begin{pmatrix} -1 \\ -6 \end{pmatrix}$ (e) $\begin{pmatrix} 1 \\ 10 \end{pmatrix}$
   These are straightforward — just deal with the top and bottom numbers separately, then it's a simple matter of addition and subtraction.

3) 6 m/s *(using Pythagoras)*

4) Speed = 9.43 m/s (3 sig.fig.). Direction = 58.0° east of due north, or a bearing of 058° (3 sig.fig.).
   (finding the speed by Pythagoras and using tan to get the direction)

Page 182 (Exam Questions)

2) (a) (i) a + 2b. *[1 mark]* (ii) ½ a + 2b. *[1 mark]*
   (b) (i) and (ii) both = a + b. *[1 mark each]*
      (this is most easily done by drawing a quick sketch)
   (c) The lines are parallel and of equal length. *[2 marks]*
      (they have the same vector)

3) (a) This is basically a triangle question.
      Use Pythagoras to get the resultant speed:
      $\sqrt{6^2 + 5^2} = 7.81$ km/h (3 s.f.).
      Then use tan $x = 5 \div 6$, which gives $x = 39.8°$.
      So 50.2° to the bank (3 s.f.) (accept 180 − 50.2 = 129.8°)
      [2 marks]
   (b) Start by drawing a sketch:

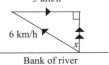

   This time, the hypotenuse of the triangle is 6 km/h.
   So use sin $x = 5 \div 6$.
   This gives $x = 56.44°$ which means an angle of
   90 − 56.44 = 33.6° to the bank (3 s.f.)
   (accept 180 − 33.6 = 146.4°). *[2 marks]*
   (c) Start with a sketch again:

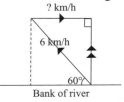

   From the sketch, you can see that the river speed you want is the same (though in the opposite direction) as the horizontal component of the boat's speed vector.
   So the river's speed is 6 cos 60° = 3 km/h. *[2 marks]*
   For these vector questions, a quick labelled sketch will nearly always make your life a lot easier.

Page 183 (Revision Summary for Unit 3 — 2)

3) 4.72 m

7) 41°

19) £20.63

21) 65 kg

EXAM PAPER ANSWERS

Unit 1

(a)

	1	2	3	4	5	6
Heads	H1	H2	H3	H4	H5	H6
Tails	T1	T2	T3	T4	T5	T6

[1 mark for correct table.]

(b) 2/12 = 1/6
[1 mark for 2/12; 1 mark for correct final answer.]

(c) 4 out of 12 combinations win a prize, so probability of lucky dip prize = 4/12 = 1/3. 60 × 1/3 = 20 lucky dip prizes
[3 marks available — 1 mark for calculating the probability of getting a lucky dip prize; 1 mark for 60 × P(lucky dip prize) or equivalent calculation; 1 mark for correct final answer.]

(a) E.g. the data does not support the hypothesis as there is a strong positive correlation between weight and head circumference.
[1 mark]

(b) E.g. it is an unreliable assumption. Although this value would fit the pattern, the new data point falls outside the range of the original data and it cannot be assumed that the pattern would continue.
[1 mark]

(a) Midpoints of height categories: 135, 145, 155, 165, 175.
(135 × 5) + (145 × 10) + (155 × 14) + (165 × 8) + (175 × 3) = 6140
6140 ÷ 40 = 153.5 cm
[3 marks available — 1 mark for finding the midpoints of the height categories; 1 mark for showing the value 6140; 1 mark for correct final answer.]

(b) E.g. the modal class for Class A is 150 ≤ h < 160 and the modal class for Class B is 160 ≤ h < 170. So the modal class is taller for Class B. For Class A the median is in the class 150 ≤ h < 160 and for Class B the median is in the class 160 ≤ h < 170. So the median height is taller for Class B. The mean height for Class B is 158.8 cm (5400/34 = 158.8 cm) and the mean height for Class A is 153.5 cm. So the mean height of Class B is taller than the mean height of Class A.
[3 marks available — 2 marks for showing any two measures of average (modal class, median, mean) for both classes; 1 communication mark for making two correct comparisons following on from working.]

(a) If the house sells for 10% below the asking price then it would sell for 0.9 × £190 000 = £171 000.
Shirleys fees = £3700 regardless of selling price.
Tibbersons fees = 0.0195 × £171 000 = £3334.50.
Therefore Tibbersons will be cheaper.
[3 marks available — 1 mark for correct value of house after 10% drop, 1 mark for calculating Tibbersons' fees; 1 mark for stating that Tibbersons will be cheaper.]

(b) Original asking price = 100%
Asking price now 100% − 15% = 85% of original price.
Original price = £212 500 ÷ 0.85 = £250 000
[3 marks available — 1 mark for showing that £212 500 = 85%; 2 marks for correct original price, or 1 mark for partially correct calculation e.g. £212 500/85 = 1%]

(a) (i) E.g. This is a leading question which suggests what the reply should be.
[1 mark for a suitable problem with the question.]

(ii) E.g. Does Digton need a new supermarket?
[1 mark for suitable suggestion.]

(b) E.g. No, the data will be biased. It will not include the opinions of people who shop in the evenings or at weekends, e.g. because they are at work or school during the day.
[2 marks available — 1 mark for concluding that the data will be biased or unreliable; 1 mark for a suitable reason.]

6 (a) $\dfrac{1.7 \times 10^{11}}{840\ 520\ 000} = 202.2557464$
= 200 trees/acre (nearest 10 trees/acre)
[2 marks available — 1 mark for the correct calculation; 1 mark for correct final answer]

(b) 840 520 000 × 0.993 = 834 636 360 = 835 000 000 to nearest million = 8.35×10^8 acres
[3 marks available — 1 mark for the multiplier 0.993 or finding 0.7% and subtracting; 1 mark for 834 636 360; 1 mark for the correct final answer.]

7 Account 1 = £4500 + (10 × 0.05 × £4500) = £6750
Account 2 = £4500 × 1.035^{10} = £6347.69 (2 d.p.)
The savings will grow the most in Account 1.
[3 marks available — 1 mark for showing a correct calculation that would enable the value of the money in Account 1 or Account 2 after 10 years to be calculated; 1 mark for showing 1 correct amount; 1 mark for showing both correct amounts and for stating that Account 1 would be the best.]

8 (a)

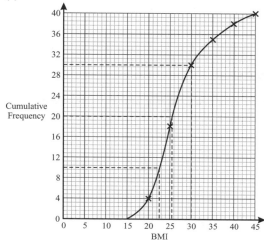

See graph — median = 25.5 (±1)
[1 mark]

(b) See graph — UQ = 30, LQ = 22.5, IQR = 30 − 22.5 = 7.5 (±1)
[2 marks available — 1 mark for the correct value for either the lower or upper quartile; 1 mark for correct final answer.]

(c) The median BMI for the men is 28 compared to 22.5 for the women, so the men have on average a higher BMI. The interquartile range of BMI for the men is 12 compared to 7.5 for the women, so BMI is more variable in the men than it is in the women.
[2 marks available — 1 mark for showing the figures for either the medians or interquartile ranges for both men and women; 1 communication mark for a correct comparison of average or spread.]

9 (a) Stratified sampling or Quota sampling
[1 mark]

(b) 16 to 24 age range: 0.21 × 38 = 7.98 → 8 people
25 to 44 age range: 0.63 × 38 = 23.94 → 24 people
45 to 65 age range: 0.16 × 38 = 6.08 → 6 people
[3 marks available — 1 mark for showing at least one correct calculation or giving the correct values but not rounded to the nearest whole number; 1 mark for giving at least 2 correct answers; 1 mark for giving all 3 correct answers.]

10 (a) Frequency density = frequency/class width.
So e.g. for 1st bar, 24/20 = 1.2; for 2nd bar, 24/10 = 2.4.

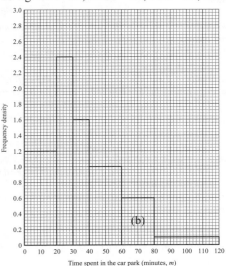

Time spent in the car park (minutes, m)

[2 marks available — 1 mark for calculating at least one correct frequency density; 1 mark for putting correct values on the y axis.]

(b) See graph above. Frequency density = frequency/ class width.
12/20 = 0.6.
[1 mark for a bar with a height of 0.6 in the correct place.]

11 (a) See diagram.

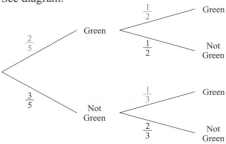

[2 marks available — 1 mark for finding one of the missing probabilities; 1 mark for finding all three missing probabilities.]

(b) P(one Green, one Not Green)
= (2/5 × 1/2) + (3/5 × 1/3) = 2/10 + 3/15 = 2/5
[2 marks available — 1 mark for a calculation to find P(Green, Not Green) + P(Not Green, Green); 1 mark for correct final answer.]

(c) P(Green, Green) = P(1st Green) × P(2nd Green if 1st Green)
so P(2nd Green if 1st Green) = P(Green, Green) ÷ P(1st Green)
$= \dfrac{3}{10} \div \dfrac{2}{5} = \dfrac{3}{4}$
[2 marks available — 1 mark for showing 3/10 and 2/5; 1 mark for correct final answer.]

12 The maximum safe load could be as low as 1895 kg.
The maximum each rod could weigh is 82.5 kg. So a full pallet with 10 rods on weighs a maximum of (82.5 × 10) + 20 = 845 kg. The truck can therefore take up to 1895/845 = 2.24..., which rounds down to 2 full pallets (20 rods) weighing 845 × 2 = 1690 kg. This leaves 1895 − 1690 = 205 kg, which allows 1 more pallet and (205 − 20) ÷ 82.5 = 2.24... ⇒ 2 more rods to be transported.
So the greatest number of rods is 20 + 2 = 22.
[4 marks available — 1 mark for giving the maximum rod weight of 82.5 kg and the safe load of 1895 kg; 1 mark dividing 1895 kg by the weight of rods and proportional number of pallets; 1 mark for '22 rods'; 1 communication mark for a clear and logical explanation.]

Unit Two

1 75 × 5 = 375 miles a week.
375 × 24 = 9000p
9000 ÷ 100 = £90
[3 marks available — 1 mark for multiplying 75 by 5; 1 mark for number of miles multiplied by 24; 1 mark for correct final answer.
Or 3 marks for any other correct calculation giving £90.]

2 (a) £45.25 ÷ 5 = £9.05
3 × £9.05 = £27.15
[2 marks available — 1 mark for dividing £45.25 by 5 and multiplying by 3 or equivalent calculation; 1 mark for the correct final answer.]

(b) £30 − £17.40 = £12.60 spent on drinks
£12.60 ÷ 30 = (£12.60 ÷ 3) ÷ 10 = 4.20 ÷ 10 = 0.42
0.42 × 100 = 42%
[3 marks available — 1 mark for £30 − £17.40 = £12.60; 1 mark for dividing £12.60 by £30 or equivalent calculation; 1 mark for the correct final answer.]

3 (a) 2 — subtract 11 each time.
[2 marks available — 1 mark for correctly finding next number in sequence; 1 mark for explaining the rule.]

(b) 2n + 2 = 65
2n = 63
n = 31.5
No, 65 is not in the sequence because for 2n + 2 = 65, n is not a whole number.
OR 2n will be an even number for all values of n, so 2n + 2 will also be even. 65 is not an even number, so cannot be in the sequence.
[2 marks available — 1 mark for a valid method of showing that 65 is not in the sequence; 1 communication mark for stating 'no' linked to a correct explanation.]

4 For the Youth Centre to cover its costs exactly, costs must equal the amount of money they get back, i.e:
100 + 15n = 23n, where n = number of people
100 = 8n
n = 12.5.
So the number of people must be 13 for the trip to go ahead.
[4 marks available — 1 mark for attempting to form an equation with total costs on one side and money they'd get back on the other side; 1 mark for showing 100 + 15n = 23n (or equivalent); 1 mark for showing the value 12.5; 1 communication mark for '13' following on from a correct method of working.]

5 $\dfrac{5z}{4} \leq 2z - 3$
so 5z ≤ 8z − 12
so -3z ≤ -12
so z ≥ 4
[2 marks available — 1 mark for multiplying both sides by 4 and forming an inequality with z on one side; 1 mark for correct final answer.]

6 m is the cost per mile and t is the cost per minute.
For Amelia   10m + 29t = 20.8   (Equation 1)
For Bert   2m + 7t = 4.4   (Equation 2)
(Equation 2) × 5   10m + 35t = 22   (Equation 3)
(Equation 3 − Equation 1)   6t = 1.2, so t = 1.2/6 = 0.2
So the fixed cost per minute is £0.20
Substitute this value, t, to find the cost per mile:
2m + (7 × 0.2) = 4.4
2m + 1.4 = 4.4
2m = 4.4 − 1.4 = 3
m = 3/2 = 1.5
So the fixed cost per mile is £1.50
[5 marks available — 1 mark for writing a correct equation to represent the cost of Amelia's journey; 1 mark for writing a correct equation to represent the cost of Bert's journey; 1 mark for either writing a 3rd equation so that the elimination method could be used to solve the equations or for rearranging one of the equations so that the substitution method could be used; 1 mark for finding the fixed cost per minute; 1 mark for finding the fixed cost per mile.]

$c = (r \times v/5) + 10\,000$

so $c \approx (20 \times 20\,000/5) + 10\,000$

$= (20 \times 4000) + 10\,000$

$= 80\,000 + 10\,000$

$= 90\,000$ capes

[3 marks available — 1 mark for correctly rounding to 20 and 20 000; 1 mark for correctly substituting the values into the formula; 1 mark for correct final answer.]

8 $3(2y + 8) = 5(4y - 40)$

$6y + 24 = 20y - 200$

$6y + 224 = 20y$

$224 = 14y$

$112 = 7y$

$y = 16$

[3 marks available — 1 mark for multiplying the right hand side by 3 and the left hand side by 5; 1 mark for either correctly adding 200 to both sides or subtracting 6y from both sides; 1 mark for correct final answer.]

9 (a) $\dfrac{\sqrt{r}\,s^2 t}{r^{\frac{3}{2}} st^3} = \dfrac{r^{\frac{1}{2}} s^2 t}{r^{\frac{3}{2}} st^3} = \dfrac{s}{rt^2}$

[3 marks available — 1 mark for each of two variables to the correct power; 1 mark for correct final answer.]

(b) $8xy(3x - 2 + 4y)$

[1 mark]

(c) $8x^2 - 18y^2 = 2(4x^2 - 9y^2) = 2((2x)^2 - (3y)^2) = 2(2x + 3y)(2x - 3y)$

[2 marks available — 1 mark for 2(4x² – 9y²); 1 mark for correct final answer.]

10 (a) See graph below.

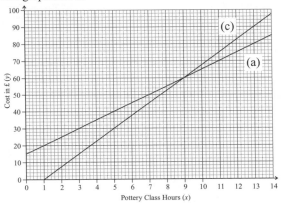

[2 marks available — 1 mark for a line with a y-intercept of 15 or a gradient of 5; 1 mark for correct final answer.]

(b) cost $(y) = 7.5$(hours $(x)) - 1$)

so $y = 7.5(x - 1)$

so $y = 7.5x - 7.5$

[1 mark]

(c) See graph above.

The cost is the same for 9 hours, so 10 hours or more.

[2 marks available — 1 mark for a correctly plotted line; 1 mark for 10 hours or more.]

11 $x^2 - 2x = 15$

so $x^2 - 2x - 15 = 0$

so $(x + 3)(x - 5) = 0$

so $x = -3$ or $x = 5$

[3 marks available — 1 mark for x² – 2x – 15 = 0; 1 mark for (x + 3)(x – 5) = 0; 1 mark for correct final answer.]

12 (a) $\sqrt{6}(\sqrt{2} + \sqrt{3}) = \sqrt{6}\sqrt{2} + \sqrt{6}\sqrt{3} = \sqrt{3}\sqrt{2}\sqrt{2} + \sqrt{2}\sqrt{3}\sqrt{3}$

$= 2\sqrt{3} + 3\sqrt{2}$ cm²

[3 marks available — 1 mark for (√6√2 + √6√3); 1 mark for multiplying out surds; 1 mark for correct final answer.]

(b) $(\sqrt{2} + 3)(\sqrt{2} + 2)$

$= \sqrt{2}\sqrt{2} + 2\sqrt{2} + 3\sqrt{2} + 6$

$= 2 + 5\sqrt{2} + 6$

$= 5\sqrt{2} + 8$

[2 marks available — 1 mark for correctly multiplying out the brackets; 1 mark for correct final answer.]

13 (a) $2a = bc^2$

$b = 2a/c^2$

[2 marks available — 1 mark for taking a first correct step in rearranging the equation to make 'b' the subject; 1 mark for correct final answer.]

(b) $12(by - 4) = bx + 8$

$12by - 48 = bx + 8$

$12by - bx = 56$

$b(12y - x) = 56$

$b = \dfrac{56}{12y - x}$

[3 marks available — 1 mark for the top line of working above; 1 mark for correctly rearranging so both of the 'b' terms are on one side of the equation, 1 mark for correct final answer.]

(c) $abc\left(\dfrac{1}{a}\right) + abc\left(\dfrac{1}{b}\right) = abc\left(\dfrac{1}{c}\right)$

$bc + ac = ab$

$ab - bc = ac$

$b = \dfrac{ac}{a - c}$

[3 marks available — 1 mark for multiplying all terms by 'abc'; 1 mark for correctly rearranging so both of the 'b' terms are on one side of the equation, 1 mark for correct final answer.]

14 (a) $\dfrac{2(2x + 5)}{2(3x + 7)} = \dfrac{2x + 5}{3x + 7}$

[2 marks available — 1 mark for taking out 2 as a common factor in both the numerator and the denominator; 1 mark for correct final answer.]

(b) $\dfrac{(x - 4)(x + 3)}{(x + 7)(x + 3)} = \dfrac{x - 4}{x + 7}$

[3 marks available — 1 mark each for factorising the numerator and the denominator correctly; 1 mark for correct final answer.]

15 Multiples of 3 have the nth term $3n$. So two consecutive multiples of 3 could be represented by $3n$ and $3n + 3$.

Consider the sum of the squares of two consecutive multiples of 3:

$(3n)^2 + (3n + 3)^2$

$= 9n^2 + 9n^2 + 9n + 9n + 9$

$= 18n^2 + 18n + 9$

$= 9(2n^2 + 2n + 1)$

Therefore the sum of the squares of any two consecutive multiples of 3 must always be a multiple of 9.

[5 marks available — 1 mark for writing down a general expression for a multiple of 3 and the next consecutive multiple of 3; 1 mark for deriving the expression (3n)² + (3n + 3)² or equivalent to represent the given situation; 1 mark for simplifying the expression to give 18n² + 18n + 9; 1 mark for showing that all terms in the expression are divisible by 9; 1 communication mark for a clear conclusion backed up by a logical sequence of algebraic statements.]

Unit Three

1 (a) Substitute $x = 1$ and $x = 2$ into the equation.
When $x = 1$, $x^3 - x - 4 = 1^3 - 1 - 4 = 1 - 5 = -4$ (too low).
When $x = 2$, $x^3 - x - 4 = 2^3 - 2 - 4 = 8 - 6 = 2$ (too high).
Therefore the solution must lie between $x = 1$ and $x = 2$.
[2 marks available — 1 mark for x = 1 answer = -4;
1 mark for x = 2 answer = 2.]

(b) Try $x = 1.5$, $x^3 - x - 4 = 1.5^3 - 1.5 - 4 = -2.125$ (too low).
Try $x = 1.8$, $x^3 - x - 4 = 1.8^3 - 1.8 - 4 = 0.032$ (too high).
Try $x = 1.7$, $x^3 - x - 4 = 1.7^3 - 1.7 - 4 = -0.787$ (too low).
So try $x = 1.75$:
$x^3 - x - 4 = 1.75^3 - 1.75 - 4 = -0.390...$ (too low).
So the solution must lie between $x = 1.75$ and $x = 1.8$.
Therefore $x = 1.8$, correct to 1 d.p.
[4 marks available — 1 mark for trying a value of x between 1 and 2
and giving the outcome; 1 mark for trying x = 1.7 and
x = 1.8 and giving the outcomes; 1 mark for a trial between 1.75 and
1.79 inclusive, 1 mark for correct final answer.]

2 (a) Alternate angles: $a = 80°$
[1 mark for correct answer.]

(b) Remaining angle on top line = $180 - 70 - 80 = 30°$
Corresponding angles: $b = 30°$
[2 marks available — 1 mark for showing working to calculate
additional angle; 1 mark for correct final answer.]

(c) Angles on a straight line add up to 180°
So, $c = 180 - b = 180 - 30 = 150°$
[1 mark for correct answer.]

3 First, find the total area of the warehouse walls:
$15 \times 3 = 45$ m²
$12 \times 3 = 36$ m²
$45 + 45 + 36 + 36 = 162$ m²
Area of the windows and door:
$(1 \times 2 \times 5) + (3 \times 2.5) = 10 + 7.5 = 17.5$ m²
Area to be painted:
$162 - 17.5 = 144.5$ m²
Number of litres needed:
$144.5 \div 13 = 11.1154$ litres
The painter will need to buy two 5 litre tins and one
2.5 litre tin.
Cost = $(2 \times 20.99) + 12.99 = £54.97$
[6 marks available — 1 mark for calculating the total area of all four
walls; 1 mark for calculating the area of 5 windows and the door;
1 mark for calculating the area to be painted; 1 mark for calculating
the litres of paint needed; 1 mark for correct final answer;
1 communication mark for a clear and logical explanation.]

4 (a) Surface area = total area of all five faces:
Area of triangle = ½ × base × height
Splitting the isosceles triangle into 2 right-angled triangles,
and using Pythagoras' theorem gives:
Height = $\sqrt{5^2 - 3^2} = \sqrt{25 - 9} = \sqrt{16} = 4$
Area of triangular end = ½ × 6 cm × 4 cm = 12 cm²
Area of side face = 5 cm × 12 cm = 60 cm²
Area of base = 6 cm × 12 cm = 72 cm²
Total area = 12 + 12 + 60 + 60 + 72 = 216 cm²
[3 marks available — 1 mark for using Pythagoras to work out the
height of the triangular ends; 1 mark for giving the value of '60' or
'72'; 1 mark for the correct final answer, including units.]

(b) Volume = area of cross-section × length
= 12 cm² *[from part (a)]* × 12 cm = 144 cm³
[2 marks available — 1 mark for multiplying cross-sectional area by
length; 1 mark for correct final answer.]

5 (a) 3.5 miles
[1 mark]

(b) From the graph, it takes her 1 hour 20 minutes to walk to the
garage. 3.5 miles $\div 1\frac{1}{3}$ hours = 2.625 miles per hour.
[2 marks available — 1 mark for correctly reading time from the
graph; 1 mark for '2.625'.]

(c) s = d/t, so t = d/s. 3.5 miles ÷ 21 mph = 0.1666... hours.
0.1666... × 60 minutes = 10 minutes.

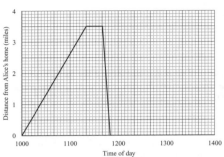

[2 marks available — 1 mark for calculating time taken; 1 mark for
correctly completing the graph.]

(d) 1000 until 1150 = 1 hour 50 minutes
[1 mark for '1 hour 50 minutes' or '110 minutes'.]

6 (a) Using Pythagoras' theorem:
distance = $\sqrt{12^2 + 5^2} = \sqrt{144 + 25} = \sqrt{169} = 13$ km
[2 marks available — 1 mark for using Pythagoras' theorem with two
short sides of 12 km and 5 km; 1 mark for the correct final answer.]

(b) See diagram below:

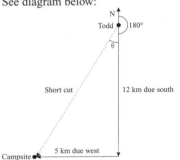

$\tan \theta = 5/12$
so $\theta = \tan^{-1} 5/12 = 22.6198...°$
bearing = $180° + \theta = 180° + 22.6198...° = 203°$ (3 s.f.)
[2 marks available — 1 mark for deriving θ = tan⁻¹ 5/12 or correct
alternative calculation; 1 mark for correct final answer.]

(c) Walking along original route = 5 km/h = 12 minutes per km
Time taken to walk along original route
= 12 minutes per km × (12 km + 5 km) = 12 × 17
= 204 minutes
Walking short cut = 4 km/h = 15 minutes per km
Time taken to walk short cut
= 15 minutes per km × 13 km = 195 minutes
204 minutes – 195 minutes = a saving of 9 minutes.
OR: $s = d/t$, so $t = d/s$:
Time for original route = 17/5 × 60 mins = 17 × 12 = 204 mins
Time for short cut = 13/4 × 60 mins = 13 × 15 = 195 mins
204 – 195 = 9 minutes
[4 marks available — 1 mark for a correct calculation to find time for
original route; 1 mark for a correct calculation to find time for short
cut; 1 mark for the correct time for one route; 1 mark for the correct
final answer.]

7 (a) 90° clockwise rotation about the centre of rotation (-1, -1).
[3 marks available — 1 mark for 'rotation' and correct angle; 1 mark
for giving the direction of rotation; 1 mark for giving the centre
of rotation.]

(b)

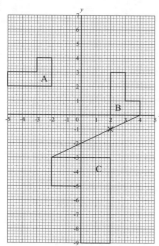

[2 marks available — 1 mark if 'C' is the correct size and shape; 1 mark for putting 'C' in the correct position.]

(a) $2e(2 - 3f)$
[1 mark for correct answer]

(b) $g^2 - 16 = g^2 - 4^2 = (g - 4)(g + 4)$
[2 marks available — 1 mark for $g^2 - 4^2$; 1 mark for correct final answer.]

(a) Split the trapezium into a rectangle and a right-angled triangle with sides GH, 4.8 cm and $(15.5 - 10) = 5.5$ cm.
$GH^2 = 5.5^2 + 4.8^2 = 30.25 + 23.04 = 53.29$
$GH = \sqrt{53.29} = 7.3$ cm
[3 marks available — 1 mark for splitting up the shape to give a right-angled triangle; 1 mark for correct use of Pythagoras' theorem; 1 mark for correct final answer.]

(b) Call angle EHG θ:
$\tan\theta = \dfrac{\text{opp}}{\text{adj}} = \dfrac{4.8}{5.5}$
$\theta = \tan^{-1}\dfrac{4.8}{5.5} = 41.1°\,(1\,\text{d.p.})$
[3 marks available — 1 mark for stating $\tan\theta = \text{opp/adj}$; 1 mark for deriving $\theta = \tan^{-1} 4.8/5.5$; 1 mark for correct final answer.]

0 (a) ½ab sin$C$ = area of a triangle
Since the area of the triangle is 35 cm²,
½ × 8.5 × 10 × sin$S$ = 35
42.5 sin$S$ = 35
sin$S$ = 35/42.5
S = sin⁻¹ 35/42.5 = 55.43967822
S = 55.4° (1 d.p.)
[3 marks available — 1 mark for substituting correct values into the formula for the area of a triangle, 1 mark for deriving 42.5sin$S$ = 35, 1 mark for correct final answer.]

(b) Using the cosine rule $a^2 = b^2 + c^2 - 2bc\cos A$
$(RT)^2 = 8.5^2 + 10^2 - (2 × 8.5 × 10 \cos 55.43967822)$
$(RT)^2 = 75.81349239$
$RT = \sqrt{75.81349239}$
$RT = 8.71$ cm (3 s.f.)
[3 marks available — 1 mark for substituting correct values into the cosine rule; 1 mark for deriving $(RT)^2 = 75.81349239$; 1 mark for correct final answer.]

1 From the given equation $a = 1$, $b = -8$ and $c = 3$
$x = \dfrac{-b \pm \sqrt{b^2 - 4ac}}{2a}$
$= \dfrac{8 \pm \sqrt{(-8)^2 - 4 × 1 × 3}}{2 × 1}$
$= \dfrac{8 \pm \sqrt{64 - 12}}{2} = \dfrac{8 \pm \sqrt{52}}{2}$
$= \dfrac{8 \pm \sqrt{4} × \sqrt{13}}{2} = \dfrac{8}{2} \pm \dfrac{2\sqrt{13}}{2} = 4 \pm \sqrt{13}$
[3 marks available — 1 mark for successfully identifying the values of a, b, and c and substituting them into the quadratic formula; 1 mark for simplifying the working to give '$x = (8 \pm \sqrt{52})/2$'; 1 mark for correct final answer.]

12 p is inversely proportional to the cube of d, so $p = \dfrac{k}{d^3}$
When $p = 60$, $d = 2$, so $60 = \dfrac{k}{2^3}$
$k = 60 × 2^3$
$k = 480$
Therefore the required formula is $p = \dfrac{480}{d^3}$
[3 marks available — 1 mark for writing an expression to show p inversely proportional to the cube of d, i.e. $p = k/d^3$, 1 mark for finding k to be 480, 1 mark for giving the required formula.]

13 (a)

d	0	20	40	50	60	80	100
h	0	32	48	50	48	32	0

[1 mark]

(b)

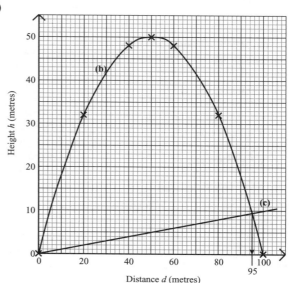

[2 marks available — 1 mark for correctly plotting all the given points; 1 mark for correctly plotting the point from part (a) and joining them all with a curve.]

(c) 95 m (See graph above).
[3 marks available — 1 mark for drawing the correct straight line intercepting the origin with gradient 0.1; 1 mark for reading off the solution where the two lines cross; 1 mark for the correct solution of 95 m, within 1 m.]

14 (a) $\overrightarrow{DC}$ = -2$\mathbf{x}$
[1 mark]

(b) $\overrightarrow{CA}$ = 2 × $\overrightarrow{SP}$ = 2$\mathbf{y}$
[1 mark]

(c) $\overrightarrow{QB}$ = -$\overrightarrow{SD}$ = -$\mathbf{x}$
[2 marks available — 1 mark for '-'; 1 mark for 'x'.]

(d) $\overrightarrow{DB}$ = $\overrightarrow{DC}$ + $\overrightarrow{CA}$ + $\overrightarrow{AB}$ = -2$\mathbf{x}$ + 2$\mathbf{y}$ - 2$\mathbf{x}$ = -4$\mathbf{x}$ + 2$\mathbf{y}$
[2 marks available — 1 mark for '-4x'; 1 mark for '+2y'.]

15 (a) Using 'angle at the centre is twice the angle at the circumference',
$b = a ÷ 2 = 36 ÷ 2 = 18°$
[1 mark]

(b) Area of the whole circle is πr^2, so $\pi × 3^2 = 9\pi$.
Proportion of minor segment = 36/360 = 1/10.
$9\pi × 1/10 = 9\pi/10$ cm².
[3 marks available — 1 mark for calculating the area of the whole circle; 1 mark for calculating the proportion of the minor segment; 1 mark for correct final answer in terms of π.]

(c) Circumference of the whole circle is πd, so $\pi × 6 = 6\pi$.
Proportion of minor segment = 36/360 = 1/10.
$6\pi × 1/10 = 6\pi/10$ cm = $3\pi/5$ cm.
[3 marks available — 1 mark for calculating the circumference of the whole circle; 1 mark for '$6\pi/10$'; 1 mark for correct final answer.]

Index

Index

CGP

Make sure you're not missing out on another superb CGP revision book that might just save your life...

...order your **free** catalogue today.